W9-CMZ-669

❖❖❖❖❖❖

PATHETIC SYMPHONY
A Novel About Tchaikovsky

❖❖❖❖❖❖

Pathetic Symphony

A NOVEL ABOUT TCHAIKOVSKY
By KLAUS MANN

ALLEN, TOWNE & HEATH, *INC.*

NEW YORK

c. 6

TO CHRISTOPHER ISHERWOOD

◆◇◆◇◆◇

FIRST MOVEMENT
Allegro non troppo

◆◇◆◇◆◇

◇◇◇◇◇◇◇◇◇◇◇◇◇

ANATOL WAS worried. The message he had received
from his brother made it only too clear that the situation in
Moscow was becoming untenable. Why else should Peter
have asked for a telegram summoning him to St. Petersburg on account of "urgent musical business"? According to
his brother's instructions, Anatol was to sign the wire with the
name of one of Peter's old friends in the capital, Napravnik—
an innocuous forgery that seemed permissible under the circumstances. Obviously, Peter Ilych could not stand his present
life any longer and had recourse to this "white lie" lest his wife
prevent him from leaving.

What a mess! What an absurd, embarrassing fiasco!

Not that it came as a complete surprise to Anatol. He had
felt anxious and apprehensive ever since the day of his brother's
wedding, two and a half months ago. The ceremony had taken
place on July 18, 1877, at the Church of St. George in Moscow,
with Anatol and the violinist Kotek as the only witnesses. And
what a weird affair it had been! Even while watching the som-
ber bridegroom and the sheepishly grinning bride as they approached the altar, Anatol had been struck by the at once far-
cical and tragic character of the whole situation. What had this
wonderful, problematical man, Peter Ilych Tchaikovsky, to do
with that gauche, watery-eyed girl, Antonina Miliukova? Why
was he making her his wife?

Of course, Anatol was not unaware of the motives behind
his brother's decision. To begin with, Peter felt that it would
have been cruel and unfair on his part to disappoint an honest
girl whose love he had "thoughtlessly encouraged," as he put
it himself. Besides, there were certain other considerations which
Peter did not like to discuss—not even with Anatol. The only

[3]

member of the family who enjoyed his full confidence was Anatol's twin brother, Modest. But as there were no secrets between the twins, Anatol knew all about Peter Ilych.

Clearly, Peter had married poor, sentimental Antonina for the definite purpose of silencing certain rumors—malicious, venomous talk about the emotional weakness Peter and Modest had in common, and to which they were wont to refer mysteriously as "THIS." Anatol had first tried to convince himself that there was nothing wrong with such a diplomatic maneuver. People were so given to gossiping, and Peter Ilych could not afford to have a bad reputation—especially in his present status of a teacher at the Moscow Conservatory. Why should he not marry a devoted girl student if it would help to solidify his social and professional position? After all, it was nobody's business whether the marriage was ever to be consummated—nobody's except Antonina's. And as for her, she must surely have known what she was in for when accepting Peter Ilych's proposal, or rather, when forcing him to propose in spite of his reluctance. No, he was not the man to lie or to pretend to his future wife. He told her the truth; and he offered her what might be even more precious than love—his friendship. Why should they not be happy together—Antonina and Peter, a pair of comrades? Why should not the experiment of their unemotional, sober ménage work out successfully?

Thus Anatol had first been reasoning. It is true he found it difficult to keep up his forced optimism after having witnessed the dismal ceremony at St. George's. But even then he tried to belittle or ignore his misgivings. If Peter had appeared morose on the occasion of his own wedding—well, might not that have been just one of his curious whims, a pose meant to conceal his self-consciousness and excitement? . . .

But the next time Anatol saw his older brother, he seemed even more nervous and downhearted. The meeting occurred in Kamenka, near Kiev, at the country estate of their sister, Alexandra Davidov. Peter Ilych arrived there in August, just about four weeks after the wedding—alone; Antonina had been left behind, in Moscow. The whole family was alarmed to find him in such poor shape—tired, irritable, and gloomy. As the weeks passed by, however, he began to recover.

He did not go to the Caucasus as he had been planning, but prolonged his stay in Kamenka. The quiet, congenial atmosphere of the place soothed his tormented nerves. Alexandra Davidov was an ideal hostess—considerate, unobtrusive. Alexandra made him drink the healing Yessentuki waters for the sake of which he had intended to visit Yessentuki in the Caucasus. He would take extensive, very pleasant walks with her, and once in a while would spend an evening with Davidov and his friends. Most of the time, however, he preferred the solitude of his room. No one disturbed him there; they knew he was occupied—working on his new symphony, the Fourth, or writing letters.

He wrote endless letters to his new friend and admirer, a wealthy widow by the name of Nadezhda von Meck. He never wrote to his wife, who was waiting for him back in Moscow. He never even mentioned her.

In September he had to return to his job at the Conservatory —and to Antonina. He was sorry to leave but did not seem too upset or dejected in bidding farewell to his brothers and the Davidovs. They thought he had resigned himself to his new condition and was now facing the prospect of his married life with comparative calm.

The first letters Anatol received from Moscow rather confirmed this optimistic impression. Of course, there were occasional complaints ("Kotek and wine are my two only comforts," the young husband observed bitterly); but the general tenor by no means suggested that a crisis was imminent. In one of his letters Peter described a party his publisher, Jürgenson, had given for him and his wife. It was not without a certain ironical pride that he dwelt on the "favorable impression" Antonina had made.

But then Peter stopped writing; during the past few weeks there had been an ominous silence. And now that strange, intriguing telegram! WIRE ME AT ONCE, SIGNING NAPRAVNIK'S NAME, TO THE EFFECT THAT MY IMMEDIATE PRESENCE IN ST. PETERSBURG IS INDISPENSABLE.

Yes, Anatol was positively worried as he walked to the Nikolayevsky Station in St. Petersburg to meet his brother. It was a beautiful morning in early October—not yet very cold, just pleasantly fresh and breezy. The sky was a little misty but the sun would soon be powerful enough to penetrate the delicate silver veil.

"Let's hope poor Peter will be in a frame of mind to enjoy this splendid panorama," Anatol was thinking. "If I had to live in Moscow, I'd get cranky too! In Moscow, everything is dark, heavy, oppressive. Petersburg is much more civilized, much more *European*. Why, it looks almost like a Scandinavian city, like Christiania or Stockholm, with its broad, elegant avenues and the noble façades of its eighteenth-century palaces. There is nothing Asiatic about our capital—which is why Peter, that old 'westerner,' should be happy here, if anywhere. . . . Poor Peter!"

Poor Peter! Poor old boy. . . . Was it not curious—indeed absurd and paradoxical—that one had to think in such patronizing terms of one's famous, wonderful brother? The two "little ones," Anatol and Modest, had always loved and admired Peter. He was their hero, their idol, and—even though ten years older than the twins—he was also their best friend and playmate. What a good sport Peter was! And how kind, how generous! Too kind, too gentle, perhaps, for this ruthless, cynical world.

Really, one could not help feeling sorry for him at times. For all his genius and intelligence, he seemed somehow incapable of coping with the realities of life. Any contact, however casual, with human meanness and brutality would shock and hurt his vulnerable heart; any precarious situation or disturbing problem would upset his labile equilibrium. Unable as he was to face even minor difficulties, how would he react to a more serious predicament? Presuming that his present trouble was indeed of a serious nature, how would he take it? In what kind of state would he be?

"I'll know in a minute or so," Anatol thought as the train pulled in; the engine, a panting giant, stopped almost in front of him. It was with a strange mixture of relief and growing apprehension that the young man watched the arrival of the Moscow express. Yes, it would be good to see dear old Peter again and hear what had really happened. . . . Or should he rather expect an unpleasant, painful scene? Was it to be a melancholy reunion?

"If only Modest were here! He knows how to handle him. Of what help can I be?—particularly if his troubles have to do with 'THIS'!"

While thus wondering and speculating, Anatol kept an eye on the passengers getting out of the sleeping-cars and first-class compartments. There were slim, bespectacled officials carrying brief cases, dashing young lieutenants, a couple of priests with enormous beards and small, wily eyes, a grim-looking general, his breast covered with decorations, an English tourist in an aggressively checkered top coat—all kinds of people. One of the few women was exceedingly beautiful, with passionate eyes in a pale, haughty face: just what Anatol liked, the Anna Karenina type. He watched her as she allowed her ageing husband to kiss her gloved hands and her immaculate marble forehead. How unspeakably bored she seemed by his all too eager attentions! Her proud, sensual mouth curled as though with disgust as she accepted his flowers.

So absorbed was Anatol in the sight of her voluptuous gestures that he forgot all about Peter Ilych; it was only when the regal lady was gone that he remembered his brother. Where was he? The platform was almost empty!

Anatol felt a sudden pang of dismay and alarm. What had happened? Had Antonina discovered her husband's plan and interfered at the last moment? Or was it something worse? Peter was ill, perhaps, or he had. . . . All those close to him knew that at times he toyed with the idea of suicide. Anatol shuddered.

Then he noticed the motionless, stooping figure at the other end of the platform—an old man, as Anatol thought at first, a stranger he had never seen before. But as he looked at him a second time, he recognized the man.

Peter seemed to be fifteen or twenty years older than he had been at their last meeting only five or six weeks before. What an appalling change! His face was uncannily white and tense under the round fur cap—a tragic mask with sightless, deep-blue eyes. The unkempt beard and the shadows under his eyes—very dark, extensive semicircles—added a certain savage and depraved note to his appearance. There were streaks of gray in his wild, bristly beard—Anatol's heart contracted with pity as he noticed them. How old was his brother? Just thirty-seven. . . . What had they done to him that he was now looking like a patriarch gone mad over some tragic news?

"Hello, Peter," Anatol said, and his voice quivered slightly. "Had a pleasant trip?" As there was no answer, he added with somewhat forced humor, "Good old Napravnik is already waiting for you."

The tragic patriarch did not smile or move; he was just standing there, next to the sleeping-car from which he had alighted —a tall, broad, massive figure standing as if petrified by a blow of destiny.

"You seem to be rather tired, old boy," Anatol said a bit nervously. "Let's have some breakfast, and then you go to bed. I've a very handsome suite reserved for you at the Dagmar Hotel."

He took his brother's arm—how dead and heavy the arm was, like a piece of iron hanging in the sleeve of the fur coat—and led Peter with gentle force along the deserted platform, through the hall of the railroad station, to the open square outside. The old man of thirty-seven groaned and gasped a little as he walked slowly and toilsomely as though in a painful trance. His labo-

rious gait, his fixed, unseeing eyes, the tension of his features—
everything about him suggested pain, suffering. Anatol, glanc-
ing shyly at him, felt that he had never before seen any human
face expressing such inordinate affliction.

The younger man hailed a droshky—an elegantly shaped, low
carriage drawn by two handsome horses. "You must admit our
cars here in Petersburg are much smarter than yours in Moscow," Anatol observed as they seated themselves on the narrow,
leather-covered bench. But his companion remained silent—his
lips sealed as if by unspeakable grief.

What could Anatol say to help his dumb, desperate brother?
How could he make him speak? The young man tried very
hard to find the adequate word—an affectionate phrase, warm
enough to melt the ice of this silence. Finally he merely put his
arm on Peter's shoulder, smiled at him, and said, "The Dagmar
isn't very far, you know. We'll be there in a few minutes."

And for the first time Peter reacted! He made an attempt to
return the brotherly smile—an unsuccessful attempt, to be sure;
but the effort as such was moving and reassuring. At the same
time his shoulders began to tremble under the touch of Anatol's
caressing hand.

Peter Ilych cried. The tears came copiously from his wide-
open, blinded eyes, over his chalk-white face, into the savage,
grayish beard which absorbed them as a dried-out sponge would
absorb rain water. He did not raise his hand to wipe the tears
off his cheeks. He remained motionless, except for a soft shaking
of his massive body—due in part to the vibrations of the moving
carriage, in part to the convulsive sobs that seemed to come from
the very depths of his being.

"I'm so sorry, Tolya," he managed to stammer after a little
while. "Forgive me, please. . . . It's awful—my behavior. I'm
so ashamed . . . so *terribly* ashamed of myself!"

And Anatol, with his arm more firmly around these trembling
shoulders: "That's quite all right, Petrushka, that's quite all
right. . . ."

The arrival at the hotel was a little embarrassing as Peter, still in tears, was unable to acknowledge the flowery compliments offered to him by a servile and eager staff. The manager, addressing him as "Your Excellency," asked whether he expected to have a new work produced at the Imperial Opera—whereupon Peter Ilych, the collar of his fur coat turned up and the round cap pressed well down over the forehead, only snorted and groaned, while trying to hide his tearful face from the glances of the curious employees.

Up in his second-floor apartment—which turned out to be at least as comfortable as Anatol had promised—Peter abandoned himself with a kind of masochistic enthusiasm to the throes of a violent nervous attack.

If his weeping had at first been comparatively quiet and moderate, now it became excessive, frightening. The shower of tears submerging his twisted face was too much for the thirsty beard to absorb; it was as though his inconsolable eyes, tired of beholding the images of this accursed creation, wanted to dissolve into salty liquid.

But even worse than this inordinate fit of crying was the next stage of the nervous crisis—an outburst of fury of truly demoniac vehemence. Foaming at the mouth, his face turned a dark bluish red, Peter Ilych—usually so gentle and soft-spoken—hurled abusive words and frantic maledictions. Anatol, terrified, heard a strange, bellowing voice repeat inarticulate sounds, fragments of sentences, bits of senseless, puerile obscenities.

"*I hate her!*" These three words returned like an evil refrain throughout his delirious accusations. "She's as much in love with me as a cat! I hate her. . . . She's stupid, she's an idiot, she bites her nails, bites them all the time, to the quick. . . . Once she sent me a letter stained with blood—imagine! Stained with blood from her nails. I hate her. . . . The Jürgensons may find her attractive, but I don't! She's repulsive to me. I can't stand her foolish, vapid grin. I can't stand her smell—that cheap perfume she uses! I can't stand her stupid voice, her stupid nose, her stupid little hats: I hate her. . . . She calls me 'Peter the Great—isn't that outrageous? 'Peter the Great'— what a hideous, distasteful nickname to give anyone! The other day she went so far as to ask me, grinning sheepishly: 'Are you happy, Peter the Great? Are you happy with me?'—Happy! Happy, indeed!"

He burst out laughing—a terrible, insane laugh—while repeating with fierce obstinacy: "Happy! She asks me if I'm happy! Isn't that quite the funniest thing you've ever heard in your life, Tolya? Happy! Yes, I am so happy with her that I'd kill her, rather than stand it another day! Rather kill myself than stand it another hour. . . . That's how happy I am! That's how I hate her!"

As far as Anatol could make out from Peter's incoherent report, his brother had in fact tried to commit suicide—a few days before sending his message to Anatol in St. Petersburg. It seemed, according to his wildly muddled confession, that one night he had hurried down to the river Moskva and stepped fully clothed into the icy water till it reached his chest. It had been extremely unpleasant, as he now pointed out angrily; but he had stayed for quite some time in the cold water—hoping that he would contract pneumonia and unobtrusively die of it. The inflammation of the lungs did not materialize, however; his suicidal adventure resulted merely in a nasty cold.

He went on fuming and raving, denouncing by turns Antonina's vicious stupidity and his own moral weakness and lack of resolution. "It's my fault!" he insisted. "I should never have listened to her fatuous love declarations! Why didn't I have the courage to turn her down? Oh, what a fool I was—what a pitiful imbecile! If I have to suffer now, it serves me right; I've actually asked for it! Why did I have to be so damned clever and calculating? To delude the world, to cover up 'THIS,' by marrying a half-wit—wasn't that the idea? Wasn't that my cunning little scheme? Well, it didn't work: one doesn't get away with such cheap, sordid tricks. It doesn't pay to be diplomatic.

. . . The scandal I've been trying to avoid—I'll get it now! A bigger and better scandal than I'd have had without my so-called marriage! A devastating scandal! A deadly scandal. . . . Oh, why don't you let me die? I want to die, Tolya. . . . I want to be dead . . . dead . . . dead. . . ."

Then he cried again—weakened by his outburst and, as Tolya suspected, also by the nasty cold he had caught in the chilly river. His state was becoming more and more alarming, with spasmodic shivers added to the crying fit. The next moment, Anatol had to run for a hand-basin: his poor brother was vomiting. "So sorry," Peter groaned—sullied all over, looking more wretched, more deplorable than ever. ". . . Perfectly awful of me to behave like that . . . unforgivable . . . so ashamed of myself . . ."

Anatol, holding the patient's head, felt the feverish heat of this tormented brow. There could be no doubt that Peter Ilych was running a temperature, that he was ill—dangerously so, per-haps. The nervous strain, the terrific tension of the past few days had been too much for his sensitive organism. Obviously, he was going all to pieces.

A doctor—that's what he needed! Anatol, now rather shaky himself, rushed out to the corridor, called the waiter, the cham-bermaid. "A doctor!" he cried. "A physician! My brother—he's in a bad way. . . . I don't know what it is . . . some kind of fever . . . a breakdown. . . .Hurry up! What are you waiting for!"

When he returned to the room, he found Peter frothing, stammering, gesticulating; the delirium had reached its most virulent, most terrifying stage.

"Peter the Great!" he kept shouting in a hoarse, angry voice. "Peter the Great is happy . . . Happy Peter the Great had to rush to his capital; he was needed there—urgent business, you know, musical affairs of the greatest importance. . . . Good-bye, my dear wife—I hate you. What a cute little hat! . . .

While the Emperor is in Petersburg, Empress Antonina will cry from the roofs of Moscow what she knows about him—and she knows everything about him: she knows 'THIS.' . . . She'll cry 'THIS' from the roof tops. . . . What a scandal! What a great, fat, imperial scandal! . . . Her stupid voice is going to tell the world the Emperor's little secret. . . . A charming Empress, isn't she though? . . . 'But my dear Tchaikovsky, your little wife is *charming!*'—'So pleased you like her, my dear Jürgenson.'—Her watery eyes in particular—Jürgenson is quite right: they couldn't be more attractive. . . . How icy the water was! How my teeth chattered! Why didst Thou not let me die? I bit my nails to the quick—my blood dropped on the paper—but Thou didst not let me die. . . . A nasty cold —that's all I got out of it . . . a nasty, nasty cold. . . . Oh, how cold it was in the river! How cold her eyes are—her hateful cold-water eyes!"

His teeth chattered again, while at the same time he managed to gnash them—a most unpleasant effect. Anatol was horrified. If only the doctor would come!

When he showed up at last, the fury of the attack had already spent itself. The patient, much calmer now, was resting on a couch, while Anatol, sitting next to him, applied compresses to his burning forehead. Even though he seemed completely apathetic, Peter noticed immediately the presence of the physician. "So kind of you to come, doctor," he murmured with a strangely vague, weary smile. "My behavior—inexcusable. . . . The Empress will cry it from the roof tops. . . . See these stains on my coat? It's blood from her bitten nails. . . . Will you protect me, doctor? She's as much in love with me as a cat. Got me all dirty, the catty thing, the bloody nail-biter. But now I am safe . . . protected. . . ."

And, still smiling, he fell unconscious.

The doctor—a dapper little gentleman with a pince-nez and a curiously pointed black beard—had the patient undressed and carried to the bedroom. Having examined him, he gave Anatol a sympathetic look through the thick, shining lenses of his pince-nez.

"Your brother . . . ," the physician began warily. "May I ask if he is very close to you, Mr. Tchaikovsky?"

"Very close," Anatol said. "Very close indeed."

"Be prepared for the worst," the doctor said in an unctuous, velvety voice, while caressing his pointed beard. "He is in grave condition. Maybe he will never awake from his present coma. Or he may awake in a few hours—only to start raving and fuming again. I cannot promise you that your brother is going to live, or that he will recover sanity, if he survives the crisis."

The thick lenses of his pince-nez flashed triumphantly as he watched Anatol, whose eyes were now full of tears.

*   *   *

The diagnosis of the dapper little physician proved erroneous. The vitality and power of resistance of this unusual patient gave the lie to the doctor's professional pessimism. What a scientifically trained eye had taken for a deadly coma turned out to be a tonic, healing sleep.

Peter Ilych remained unconscious for two days and nights—forty-eight hours full of anxiety and suspense for Anatol, who hardly left his brother's bedside. He had notified their father, old Ilya Petrovich, and some other members of the family—Modest, the Davidovs—of Peter's nervous breakdown, not without quoting the doctor's ominous warning to be "prepared for the worst." In the beginning there had been no reason, alas, to doubt that distressing prognosis. The patient—groaning, struggling, writhing in his sleep—had obviously been under an all but unbearable strain. His bloated, distorted face had reflected the agonies through which he was passing.

But after a few hours, his sleep had become more peaceful, and by now his heavy body appeared completely relaxed. At times he would sigh a little, but there was nothing convulsive or frightening about these discreet, almost toneless moans. Then even the sighing ceased. The sleeper rested comfortably, breathing without pain or effort. Thank God, he was through the worst!

Anatol thought: "I thank you, my God, for having spared his precious life!"

He had not had the strength to pray while the crisis was on; but now, with his brother clearly out of danger, he appealed to Heaven, expressing his gratitude and begging Providence to protect Peter Ilych henceforth. "He needs protection," young Anatol informed God. "He needs guidance and help. Practical-minded fellows like myself always manage, always muddle along. But not Peter—he's different. He's such a problem child, so naïve and absent-minded, that he'll perish unless we look after him—you, my God, and his dear ones here below. Do not let him perish, God! Think of all the lovely melodies that would remain unsung if You failed to take care of him. Let him live! Let him wake up and be all right again!"

And after forty-eight hours, Peter Ilych woke up.

"Welcome!" Anatol cried enthusiastically. "Welcome to our world, Petrushka! You've been away for quite some time, you know."

Peter yawned, stretched, and smiled. "Hello, Tolya," he said. "It is good to see you again."

Anatol had the samovar ready. Would Peter have a glass of tea with rum? He would indeed; nor did he refuse the crackers with preserved cherries his brother offered him. As soon as the little snack was over, he asked, somewhat abruptly, "Well, and what's going to happen next? How do I get out of the mess I left behind, in Moscow? Frankly, I don't know what to do; all I know is that I cannot live with Antonina any more. I have to get rid of her. It's a matter of life or death."

Having pondered over the situation from all possible angles,

the two brothers finally made a decision. Anatol was to go to
Moscow immediately and persuade Antonina to consent to a
divorce.

"It's not going to be easy," Peter said. "You know how stub-
born she is. But I suppose she'll give in if you tell her in what
kind of a state I am. Of course, she must also be warned against
stirring up a scandal. It's to her own interest, after all, to spare
my reputation and avoid unnecessary gossip."

They agreed to give out the story that Peter Ilych was ill
("a minor liver condition," Tolya suggested cheerfully) and had
to go to a famous spa abroad. His dear wife would follow him
shortly.

"How clever we are!" Anatol laughed. "How cunning!"

And Peter, laughing with him, thought, "Clever? Yes. . . .
But what for? I wanted to die—why did He not let me? Why
did it not please Him to take up my challenge? The water was
cold but clean. Death is clean. Life is dirty. It compels you to
do dirty things, to be clever and calculating. I hate life as I hate
her. . . . I want to die. Maybe I will commit suicide while
Tolya is in Moscow."

"Won't you be lonely without me?" Anatol asked. "I hate
to leave you all by yourself in this strange hotel room."

But Peter smiled at him, reassuringly. "I won't be lonely,
my boy," he said. "And I won't get bored. I'll try to do some
thinking while you're away. There are so many things I have
to straighten out in my mind."

*   *   *

Anatol is on his way to Moscow. Peter Ilych, alone in a
strange hotel room, tries to straighten out a few things in his
mind. But, finding certain problems discouragingly, hopelessly
entangled, he addresses his questions directly to a more competent, better-informed authority.

"Why didst Thou not let me die? I am not fit to live, I do
not enjoy living—so why should I be forced to go on? It's unfair,

unreasonable. . . . The grotesque debacle of my so-called marriage would have warranted even an open, spectacular suicide, with poison or revolver. But I pefered to handle the matter tactfully and discreetly—the way my mother did. . . . There is nothing scandalous about dying of pneumonia as long as nobody knows how you contracted it. Nobody would have known. Nobody watched me when I stepped into the icy-cold water, nobody heard the little noise produced by my chattering teeth. It was the most unpleasant experience I ever had in my life; but I took it bravely, hoping that it would be my last ordeal. Why didst Thou not let me die?"

No answer—only the vast, overpowering stillness which always follows our appeals to Him. He listens but does not talk back.

"I know quite well He's hearing me," Peter Ilych thinks, "alone, or not really alone, in His impersonal, elegant shelter. However remote He may be, He overhears my thoughts and the mutterings of my lips. He Who understands what is incomprehensible to us, Who remains terribly serious about what to us seems laughable, and Whose inscrutable countenance, behind its sevenfold veil, remains undisturbed by our earthly woes and by the tears which start from mortal eyes. But He holds His peace and waits. It is true, I cannot help wondering why He prevented me from dying; but even while questioning His wisdom, I am convinced, at the bottom of my heart, that there is a purpose in all He does to us and in all He exacts from us. Yes, I believe in Him and in His terrible justice. I know that He is the sublime and untouched witness of my trifling battles and defeats. He does not laugh at us, nor does He weep over us. He is just, and waits. He desires to wring the true purpose of our life out of us by means of terrible penalties and unending castigation.

"As we do not know His aim, it is only natural that we should also be unaware of the significance of His punishments. Often we are disconcerted by them, particularly when they come upon us unexpectedly—a practice frequently employed by the Inscrutable One. But we must take all penalties willingly upon ourselves for the sake of the true purpose of our lives. Do we, by thus suffering, draw nearer to Him? Scarcely—no, certainly not. . . . He will not allow any of the veils to drop from His brow, as long as we, in our earthly garb, conduct ourselves so unwisely. So we, in our anguish, invent a little name for the Remote One, a foolish syllable with which our cry of helplessness may disturb His ear. We call on *God* and, because no answer comes, we are inclined to suspect that our cry has gone out into the void and that He on Whom we called does really not exist, that He is just a fraud and a baseless hope. But how could He answer, since we do not even know His name, and our brains are so feeble and can convey no message to our lips beyond a foolish stammer? Our foolish lips go on stammering: *God— God—God*, and He is expected to answer, He Whose name is as great a mystery as His countenance, His voice, and all that He plans and decrees! The wisest and most learned among men have not yet discovered a single one of the letters that compose His name. If a single letter of His real name—His awe-inspiring, overwhelming Name—became known to the ears of mankind, then the earth would split into fragments like a piece of the most fragile glass dashed to the ground. Yes, some day it will all be splintered like glass, but not until the Law has been fulfilled —not until the Inscrutable One has brought about His whole purpose, by means of inconceivable, long-drawn-out, and painful penalties. Then, and then only, above our annihilated planet, will be uttered the first letter of His Name as the first sign of redemption.

"But I will no longer stammer *God, God, God*. I will leave behind all these inadequate thoughts of Him and return to the narrow world of my own life and my own insignificant problems—which, after all, are not unconnected with Him and are indeed a part of Him, for they are a part of the great and onerous scheme by means of which He will extort from me the true purpose of my life.

"*Why didst Thou not let me die?*

"What is the true purpose of my life He has decided to wring out of me?

"What is my life? Why has it been such a failure?"

And Peter Ilych, sitting on the edge of his bed, leans over the table and fumbles among the objects on it, knowing from long experience that they have the power to evoke certain memories: they are the talismans of memory. Between the valerian drops and the bicarbonate of soda lie the beautiful platinum watch ornamented with gold figures of Apollo and the Maid of Orleans, and the two faded photographs—his most cherished possessions, accompanying him wherever he goes, even on this hectic and painful journey.

The larger one of the pictures—a daguerreotype of the year 1848—shows the whole Tchaikovsky family. On the right sits Ilya Petrovich Tchaikovsky in a carved chair—a vigorous, jolly man, his hair already gray, but the thick moustache still black (quite possibly dyed); on his lap we see the little Hippolyte, then four years of age, in a white frock; the left wing of the group takes in Peter Ilych himself, wearing a little checked coat; the eight-year-old boy looks seriously over the stiff white collar, his lips a little apart. He is leaning tenderly against his mother, who is sitting next to him in an armchair. The beautiful Alexandra Andreyevna, in an attitude of dreaminess and brooding, supports her chin on the back of her long, noble, white hand; her dark, smoothly dressed hair frames attractively the delicate oval of her pale face; her soft, sensitive mouth, with its beautiful upper lip and a lower lip that is perhaps a trifle too heavy, recalls the mouth of her favorite son, Peter. Her dark, veiled glance—distrait and saturnine under thick black eyebrows—passes with proud indifference beyond her family, beyond her son Peter who would like to retain it, and into space.

Little Alexandra Ilyinisha, two years younger than Peter, two years older than Hippolyte, supports herself against the richly embroidered dress of her mother; her petite lace drawers descend below the stiff, white, tightly sashed frock. Under her smoothly brushed hair, the small girl reveals a defiant, resolute face. Behind, stands a grown-up young lady, with her arm on Alexandra Andreyevna's shoulder; this is Zinaïde, Peter's half-sister, daughter of the enterprising Ilya Petrovich by his first wife, the German Marie Karlovna Keiser. Between Zinaïde and the father stands, finally, Nikolay; he, too, is well-brushed in a black suit with a white lace shirt, in the dignified and self-assured pose of the eldest son. He was born in 1830, ten years before Peter.

Such was the Tchaikovsky family in the year 1848: the jolly papa with little Hippolyte; the half-grown Nikolay; the grown-up Zinaïde; the sad-eyed mother; Peter in his pretty checked suit, and a defiant little Alexandra in lace drawers. The youngest ones, the twin boys Anatol and Modest, had not yet been born at that time: they were to come two years later, and the mother would not long survive them. In or about the year 1848 the father had retired with a pension; he was fifty-three years of age and had an important mining career behind him—and, moreover, various other callings and adventures in front of him, as befitted his enterprising nature.

The second photograph dates from 1855—a year after Alexandra Andreyevna's death. It shows Ilya Petrovich with the twin boys, Anatol and Modest, who at this time were five years old. They wear Russian shirts, knickerbockers, and top-boots; their hair is arranged in a flat fringe over their blank, innocent foreheads. One of them, Anatol, clings to his father's arm with both of his little hands; the other, Modest, has projecting ears but a more soulful and at the same time more determined expression than his brother's. The father's moustache is now white like his hair, for he has lost his dear wife. Sad, lovely Alexandra died very suddenly, under rather curious circumstances. . . . But Ilya Petrovich, although he has grown white, still holds himself remarkably well, the clean-shaven chin propped on the rim of his stiff collar; he is still enterprising and vital in his elegant indoor coat. Sitting there in his chair, a worthy and in no sense a broken man, he still gives the impression of being the head of the family; the two little twin boys, Anatol and Modest, look at him with confidence and respect. To tell the truth, he cannot be regarded as a very reliable prop, the hearty old Ilya Petrovich. White moustache or not, he still is somewhat easy-going and cannot break himself of a certain venture—some predilection for games of chance—which explains the unfortunate fiascos and collapses that occurred during his long and eventful life. All of this Peter Ilych has learned in the meantime; but the tender twin boys, pressed up against their father's chair, naturally know nothing about it.

With emotion, and not without dismay, Peter Ilych contemplates the faded photograph. The emotion stems from his almost too keen attachment to his own past and the past of his family; but the dismay has to do with the painful effort to establish the identity between these two top-booted lads and his two friends and brothers of the present, Tolya and Mody.

Yes, these two boys are dead, and today there are two other persons living—two pleasant, loyal young men whom Peter Ilych calls his friends and brothers. However likable and helpful they may be, they bear no resemblance to that couple of youngsters whose faces, voices, and laughter Peter Ilych so well remembers. Every moment, as it has passed, has changed something in them; Time has transformed the faces, voices, laughter. For Time is a murderer, and every moment is a little death, a killer of life; but Time is also life, its very substance and essence, as life consists of such fleeting moments, slipping away, irrevocably. . . . Only memories remain—sweet, saddening, beloved memories.

"Isn't it curious, though?" Peter Ilych muses. (There are so many things he has to straighten out in his memory-laden mind!) "Not a single minute of my life would I wish to live again, and yet I am disconsolate over the loss of every single minute. The only consolation we can get out of this life, the only thing indeed that makes it bearable, is its transitoriness, its ghostly unreality, the evasive impermanence of its very nature —and still we cherish our memories which embalm and preserve the suffering we passed through. Out of the sea of the past rise faces—behold, they are of tenderer and yet more enduring substance than the lost things whose shadows they are!"

Peter Ilych does not have to look at the photographs any more; the faces present themselves, are there, behind his eyelids, smile at him, are alive, real, and tangible. There is *Maman* (the children always used the French word when addressing her, for Alexandra Andreyevna, *née* Assier, was partly of French stock and never brought herself to like the Russian language); and there are Tolya and Mody, and little Alexandra—look, and Fanny, the beloved governess! It is she, more than any of the others, who symbolizes the world of childhood—the vanished world, a world obliterated by the passage of time.

Fanny Dürbach of Montbéliard near Belfort was full of tales and songs; but much the most marvelous was when she talked about the Maid of Orleans. She had some fine pictures of her to show, too. The boy was allowed to look at them when he was very good: she could have offered him no greater reward, for there was nothing so dazzling, so graceful and slender, so proud and delicate as the boy-girl in armor, with the shining look in her eyes. Young Peter knew why her eyes shone: it was because she had heard heavenly voices. No knight could have donned armor and buckler more eagerly than she, but of course she did not do anybody any harm; when she lunged with her lance it was a sort of chivalrous game—the way she smiled showed that. It was a sweeter smile even than that of the Virgin Mother.

The enthusiastic child wrote verses to the slim, boyish, heroic figure, and these he would recite to his beloved Fanny:

On t'aime, on ne t'oublie pas,
Héroïne si belle!

Tu as sauvée la France,
Fille d'un berger.
Mais qui fait ces actions si belles!
Barbares anglais vous ont tuée!
Toute la France vous admire.
Tes cheveux blonds jusqu'à tes genoux,
Ils sont très beaux.
Tu étais si célèbre
Que l'ange Michel t'apparut.
Les célèbres, on pense à eux,
Les méchants, on les oublie!

"I'll have to write an opera about the Maid," Peter Ilych is now thinking. "But of course it will be much less sincere and original than my funny little poem."

He recalls having produced still more French "verses" during that vanished period; but these are the only ones he has kept, and it was about these that Fanny said, when he read them to her of an evening: *"C'est vraiment très joli, mon petit Pierre!"*

Fanny was kind. She had brought a music box with her from France and kept it in her little room; on this she played all sorts of charming melodies, the most charming of all being one that Peter later discovered was from Mozart's *Don Giovanni*. He thinks now: "And really, nothing could be more enchanting than that little tune; it seemed quite outside material considerations and stood high above Time which was slipping by. Ah, one would never be able to raise oneself as high as that; one is a prisoner, bound fast."

He loved Fanny with all his heart. When fears assailed him in the night, her voice soothed him. There were great fears which he was never to overcome; for every noise in the room can be terrifying, the tick of the clock is terrifying, it is terrifying the way the seconds glide away and drop into the abyss of eternity. At such times he would cry out, and Fanny would at once sit up in her bed and say in her reassuring voice: "You must go to sleep, *mon petit Pierre*." And then you felt her hand on your forehead, and you fell asleep.

Mother never appeared at such critical moments. She was not to be counted on, as Fanny was, and she was much farther away: one realized this in the hours of danger and darkness. He loved his mother, too, with all his heart, but not without a certain shy humility. Perhaps it was this very shyness, a bitter-sweet ingredient of love, which made the love itself so exciting and so painfully strong.

Everything about Fanny was familiar; everything about *Maman* was strange. Her face often seemed strained and sad; it was long since she had been talkative and affectionate. Sometimes she would not speak for hours, but would stare in front of her with lowering brows. Her lovely, long white hands, from which the bluish veins stood out rather too prominently, lay like dead things in her lap; and her ebony-black hair, as severely dressed as a widow's, framed a pale, tragic face. But when *Maman* was in a merry mood she was full of the most delightful pranks. When she was merry she spoke only French. *"Tu veux voler un peu, mon petit Pierre?"* she would cry, lifting the boy high in the air, although he was already quite heavy. But a few minutes later, she was likely to become depressed and distrait again.

It was from Fanny that he had discovered that his mother's family came from France—from that very France which was also the homeland of the Maid of Orleans and that of Fanny as well. What a splendid country it must be! *Le petit Pierre* liked to murmur *Maman's* maiden name over to himself: Assier, Assier, Assier—it sounded so sweet to his ears.

And it was Fanny again who told him that his mother was very much younger than his father—"which is bad," as the governess added with a certain asperity. "It bodes no good luck." These words frightened little Peter. He brooded over some dark connection between the somewhat disturbing and frequently gloomy character of his mother and the disparity between her age and that of his father. Of an evening he would pray for his beloved *Maman*. He had often heard Fanny say: "You must always obey your mother and follow her in all things." Little Peter prayed: "Dear God, please let me always obey my mother and follow her in all things"—as if faith and implicit obedience for which he prayed to God would be useful to his mother and comfort her in her mysterious affliction. "Let me always follow my mother. I wish always to obey her. Always!"

Fanny Dürbach went back to Montbéliard in faraway, lovely France. Why did she have to do that? Pierre thought he would die of grief. For days his weeping, shouting, and fuming would not be calmed down; for months he was upset and bad-tempered. A new governess made her appearance; Pierre hated her. He became refractory and lazy. Even the pianoforte lessons he was now taking gave him no pleasure; nobody had the impression that he was particularly musical. She who might have helped him was gone, to another land. And the other person whose encouragement he so much longed for—his mother—did not trouble herself much about the difficult, over-sensitive boy.

It was about this time that the family moved from the provincial town of Votinsk, where Ilya Petrovich had been active as a mining official, to a new home in Moscow. The time of childhood, the time for which one feels homesick, was past and gone—slipped away, lost in the abyss. "Votinsk and Fanny, Fanny and Votinsk," this was the incantation that would conjure up the deepest sense of homesickness.

"Fanny is no doubt long since dead," Peter Ilych thinks. "I wonder if she had a good death? I wonder how long she has been dead?"

Two years later his mother brought the two eldest boys, Nikolay and Peter, to St. Petersburg. Nikolay was installed in the State Institute of Mining; Peter, in the law school, where boys were prepared for careers as officials. Nikolay lived with a friendly family, but Peter shared his room with strange boys in the boarding-school. How he clung to his mother when she, with the appalling intention of leaving him there alone, wished to get back into the carriage! But with her cool and lovely hands

Maman removed his hot arms from her shoulders. "You must be reasonable, Pierre!" He sprang once more onto the splashboard after the carriage had already started. A teacher from the Law School pulled him back.

How much had happened between that bitter day and the even more bitter one when he was called to his mother's deathbed! He found her no longer conscious—already terribly changed. There had been an interval of four years between these two doleful days, Peter Ilych now reckons; for he remembers that he was enrolled at the Law School in the year 1850, and 1854 was the year in which his beautiful mother died of cholera.

There was a strange mystery about this sudden and cruel death. A rumor spread among the members of the household and among their acquaintance that Alexandra Andreyevna had actually *wanted* to die. She had challenged Death, provoked him; she had beckoned to Death with her own hand, as she lifted to her mouth the glass of water which she knew was tainted. For it was thus that she had behaved in her sorrow.

The rumor could not be hushed up; it was of uncanny strength and persistence. People had seen the beautiful woman grow more and more melancholy. Her far too enterprising husband—he also contracted cholera but recovered from it and lived for another twenty-five years—had lost his estate; owing to the influence of reckless companions he had plunged deeper and deeper into frivolous and risky undertakings. Now poverty! Alexandra Andreyevna had had enough. What caused cholera? A couple of mouthfuls of water were sufficient.

She had not decided unequivocally to commit suicide, for she was religious. But God had never forbidden one to drink a glass of water. It was His concern if the water was poisoned or not— one had put nothing evil into the water oneself. The decision rested entirely in His hands. And He decided. He brought convulsions and violent pains upon Alexandra Andreyevna; He discolored her cheeks and lips a blackish hue; but finally He colored them waxen and beautified them with a strange and forbidding beauty. And then her suffering was over.

His mother had died on purpose. *"God, let me follow my mother! I will follow her. I wish to follow her in all things."*

*   *   *

Young Peter had to go back to Law School; but he no longer lived at the boarding-school. His father had once more taken a house in St. Petersburg, where there was plenty of room for his sons. The cheerful noise of the little twin boys, Anatol and Modest, could be heard all over the place, and altogether it could not be said that life had become less pleasant after Mother's departure. But sometimes, in the midst of his merriment, a heavy and sorrowful feeling came over Peter's heart—a sense of guilt, as though his merriment were unseemly and a forbidden thing. (*"I ought to follow my mother. . . ."*)

It almost looked as if the Tchaikovsky family were once more on the upward grade. The position of the indestructible papa improved to some extent. In the summer they rented a small house in the country; the Tchaikovskys were having fun. There were lots of girls around: Zinaïde, Peter's grown-up half-sister; his cousins Lydia and Anna—two of the innumerable daughters of Uncle Peter Petrovich, in whose house they all settled later on; and the little sister Alexandra whom they called Sasha. Peter loved to make friends with the girls. He felt more at home with them than with the boisterous young men who turned up in order to flirt with the young ladies. Peter consorted with the girls as though he were one of them and helped them with their handicrafts. He became very intimate with his sister Sasha, loving her because she had eyes like *Maman's* and hands that were almost as cool and delicate. He was also fond of his cousin Anna, with whom he particularly enjoyed playing hide-and-seek. Girls were pleasant company—much pleasanter indeed than the law school boys who always tended to get rough and start a fight. As for Peter, he couldn't stand fighting; he was by nature gentle and conciliatory.

But he lost interest in the girls when he became acquainted with that fabulous boy, Apukhtin.

If Peter Ilych was fairly popular with his classmates and was thought of as a nice enough fellow, easy to get along with, Apukhtin enjoyed a much more sensational reputation. Wonderful things were whispered about the abundance of his talent and depravity. He had read all the modern philosophers, and believed in neither God nor the Devil. He knew all of Pushkin's works by heart, and he himself wrote such fine poetry that the famous Turgeniev ventured to predict: "The boy Alexey Nikolayevich Apukhtin will one day be the greatest poet of Russia!"

The boy Apukhtin, the pride of the law school, the diffidently admired and much courted idol of his class, was of small build—considerably shorter than Peter Ilych, who was of the same age as he; but he was dynamic, wiry, nimble, a brilliant athlete. Whereas Peter Ilych behaved with the same bashful kindliness towards everybody, Apukhtin was hard, repellently cold, or sarcastically aggressive in his attitude towards most people but employed all the clever arts of his self-assured charm upon those who appealed to him. For some reason or other, he took to Peter Ilych. He approached his gentle, inexperienced comrade seductively, like a bad angel. Peter yielded himself up to the hard glance of his dark, lustrous eyes, was disconcerted, enchanted by his somewhat hoarse, mocking, or tender laugh and by the provocative, irreverent talk of this strange, fascinating youth with the mobile red mouth.

Peter Ilych was under Apukhtin's spell. The years that now followed—the decisive years of growth and development—were controlled by the dark angel and evil genius, by his charm, his malice, his recklessness, his callow skepticism. What wonderful evenings they spent in Apukhtin's untidy room, smoking endless cigarettes and endlessly arguing, or going for walks together! But it did not stop at discussions or walks. It was most delightful, and yet most disturbing of all, when Apukhtin broke off the conversation with a coarse, gently mocking laugh and raised his thin, supple, always slightly dirty hands to caress Peter's hair, or his blushing face, or his trembling body. Then Peter would close his eyes, and the bad angel would whisper: "Do you like that? Do you find it pleasant? But of course you do. . . . We will never fall in love with women—promise me that, Petrushka! It's silly to love women—it's wrong for people like us. Let's leave that sort of thing to the Philistines who want to have children and lead a regular life. A regular life would be a bore to us; nor do we want to have children. How hideous —to turn love into a business transaction! We prefer to love without ulterior motive; we must love for love's sake only. . . . Don't you agree, little Pierre?"

And little Pierre agreed.

Sometimes it was he who would start the bitter-sweet, extremely pleasant and—as little Pierre suspected—somehow reprehensible game. When the bad angel failed to take the initiative, the enchanted victim whispered: "Let's do THIS!" And they did it.

They went on doing it, even after they had become young men. Their friendship lasted eight years. It started a year before the death of Peter Ilych's mother; he began to extricate himself from it when he was twenty-five. Then he was suddenly alarmed by the situation in which he found himself. There was, he felt, something degrading, sordid about THIS.

The law school was already two years behind him and he was nineteen years old when, as "Titular Counselor"—that is, secretary of the Administration—he entered the Ministry of Justice. The young civil servant was even lazier and more pleasure-seeking than the student had been. The short office hours were sheer boredom to him, and he did his best to sleep them away. Only the nights were worth living, with their unending thrills ingeniously arranged by Apukhtin. The evil genius was not content with the simple games at which only two can play;

rich in inventiveness, he discovered ever new combinations. All this cost money. Moreover, the eccentric dandified clothes which Peter Ilych liked to wear at that period were expensive. He fell into debt and went about borrowing money wherever he could; his father, who lived on a modest pension, could not be responsible. The situation became decidedly disagreeable, and nobody knew where it would lead.

In the year 1861 Peter Ilych's first journey abroad marked a natural division in his life. He traveled through Berlin, Hamburg, Brussels, and London to Paris, as the companion and interpreter of a gentleman who had been a business friend of his father's. The trip did not turn out to be very successful: in Paris, he came into conflict, and finally to a break, with his employer, who expected from his companion other services than those of an interpreter—services which, in this particular case and in these circumstances, disgusted Peter Ilych. He made the return journey alone. On the outward journey he had written to his sister Sasha: "What can I hope from the future? It is dreadful to think of it." But in the meantime he had—suddenly, quietly—developed a new idea about his future career.

He began to interest himself in music. Had he never done this before? Had he never had a vague presentiment, during all those empty, dissolute years, that Reality had not yet even begun for him? It may be that presentiments had come to him; it is possible that there had even been moments when they attained a strength as inspiring as it was puzzling and disquieting. But no decision, no intention had grown out of such transient moods. Now he overcame his inertia, his sluggishness. He pulled himself together; took lessons; he worked—at first while he was still going to the Ministry and even during his office hours. But some years later he quit his government job. Anton Rubinstein had opened a conservatory in St. Petersburg, and thither Peter Ilych went as a student.

This came as the greatest surprise to his family and to his circle of friends. Peter Ilych wanted to be a musician? The lazy,

slipshod, kindly, absent-minded Tchaikovsky wanted to *work?*
It sounded incredible!

But, as though a Voice had told him, the lazy Peter knew
perfectly well now what it was he wanted and needed. His life
underwent a change. He became almost an ascetic. Yes, he
worked! He occupied a little room in his father's modest house.
Evenings he remained at home or taught private students,
whom Anton Rubinstein procured for him in order to improve
his pupil's miserable financial position. Anton Rubinstein was
an exacting teacher and very hard to please, but he could also
be helpful and generous. Peter Ilych feared him and admired
him.

There was so much to learn. For the suffering—all the suffering with which one was already familiar—had to be transmuted
into rhythm and melody. *That* was the Task. The naturally lazy
Tchaikovsky, suddenly become industrious, had merely to carry
it out. It was fatiguing; this delicate process of transformation
did not by any means accomplish itself, simply and like some
game. The reformed Peter Ilych, however, having discovered
unsuspected energies in himself, did not give way. He came to
realize that the laws of sounds and harmony possessed a certain
strange resemblance to those rules of mathematics which at
school he had found so detestable. Accumulated emotions did
not transform and resolve themselves without sustained effort;
indeed, music was a strict, intricate formula that one mastered
only after one had acquired considerable technique and had
remained conscientiously true to the Task. The lyrical outpouring of feeling was not enough. The harder Peter Ilych worked,
the more he realized what knowledge and what experiences
were necessary to enable the composer to transmute his personal
drama into art. He despised those ignoramuses who made things
easy for themselves by their wonderful "originality." He did not
wish to be an ignoramus. He preferred to study and to struggle.
The hard work of preparation which preceded the actual process of transmutation proved to be inspiring in itself—a solace

that lightened his heart and ministered to his general well-being.

When one of his first scores was finished—it was a short overture to Ostrovky's play, *The Storm,* which he had composed in the summer of 1864—he could not bring himself to show it to Rubinstein but decided to get a fellow-pupil, Herman Laroche, to do so in his behalf. Laroche was some five years younger than Tchaikovsky, very gifted, very lazy, and very pleasant. His nerves were not very tender, and he took on the task of going with his friend's score to the master. Rubinstein fumed; he considered the instrumentation almost wildly extravagant. A dogged conservative in all questions of musical taste, Anton Rubinstein resented any signs of "modernisms" *à la* Berlioz, Liszt, and Wagner in his disciples' compositions.

It was in the following summer—1865—that a work of Tchaikovsky was performed publicly for the first time. At that period his sister Sasha was already married; Peter Ilych passed the summer with her in Kamenka. It so happened that Johann Strauss, the Vienna Waltz King, was giving concerts in that area. Laroche and a few other Petersburg friends had sent him one of young Tchaikovsky's compositions, *The Dance of the Serving Maidens.* The Waltz King liked the piece and included it on his program. Peter Ilych always regarded it as particularly fitting and significant that he had made his first bow to the Russian public through the mediation of Johann Strauss. The Vienna Waltz King had introduced him in Russia; but it was he, Peter Ilych, who later introduced the waltz into great Russian music. He loved the waltz—its at once nostalgic and serene rhythm—and always remained faithful to this predilection.

In the fall of the same year Peter Ilych took his final examinations at the Conservatory, without, however, especially distinguishing himself. The task that Anton Rubinstein had set was a composition for chorus and orchestra on Schiller's *Ode to Joy* —the same poem Beethoven had used in his Ninth Symphony.

Peter Ilych hated the idea of competing with the great German master; he considered his *Ode* a complete failure and was so ashamed of it that he did not appear at the public performance. The silver medal and a grudging report were sent to him at home. César Cui, the leading composer and spokesman of the young Russian nationalist school of musicians, now for the first time took notice of Tchaikovsky, with whom he was later on to come into frequent and furious conflict. His succinct verdict read: "The Conservatory composer, Mr. Tchaikovsky, is quite incompetent." But Herman Laroche assured him quietly and positively: "You are the greatest musical talent of presentday Russia."

*   *   *

Peter Ilych has grown sleepy. He opens the case of his handsome watch. It is nearly four o'clock in the morning.

"Now one ought to sleep. Better to think about Nothingness and Silence, which will come when the heart ceases to beat, rather than about all that has passed and gone but that still has the power to wound."

Nevertheless, whether he desires it or not, his eyes, under their heavy half-closed lids, cannot refrain from building up pictures of the past—saddening, enchanting images that are of tenderer and yet more lasting substance than the living things.

True, they now seem less distinct and somewhat baffling. Events become confused and repeat themselves. Work, travel, good companionship with a few colleagues, and the more emotional friendships with young people—friendships which brought unrest and disappointment, but also short and rapidly passing hours of bitter-sweet happiness.

A couple of months after his final examinations at the Petersburg Conservatory, Peter Ilych went to Moscow. He had been invited by Nikolay Rubinstein, Anton's brother, to become a teacher of theory at the newly established Moscow Conservatory. All at once the young composer found himself past the worst; his income, although modest, was now regular. He took up the position in the autumn of 1866.

Nikolay looked after his protégé as a father might. He took him into his house and presented him with some clothes—a heavy fur coat, and a suit that a violin virtuoso had once left behind by mistake. The suit was rather too large for Peter Ilych (the virtuoso must have been a giant!), but everybody seemed to think he looked quite presentable in it. Nikolay was good-natured and helpful; in contrast to his morose, haughty brother, who had been spoiled by too much fame and success, he was one of simplest and warmest-hearted of men. True, he also had certain characteristics that could get on one's nerves: he was blustering and dogmatic, and he liked to meddle in matters that concerned his "problem child," Peter Ilych. The young man, even though gratefully devoted to him, breathed a great sigh of relief when—though this was not until a year later—he was able to rent a little home of his own and take his leave of Nikolay, his benefactor and "nursery governess."

There was a circle of good fellows in Moscow. Peter Ilych, who feared loneliness—and yet recognized that loneliness was a part of his predestined lot—was rarely alone. In addition to Nikolay and the loyal Herman Laroche, there were Peter Jürgenson, who at that time had just opened a small music shop, an energetic and indefatigable worker who was to become Russia's most important music publisher and Tchaikovsky's most faithful propagandist; Nikolay Kashkin, a professor at the Conservatory, equally meritorious as pianist and as critic, who had a pleasant young wife and kept open house; and finally, Constantine Karlovich Albrecht, inspector at the Conservatory and Nikolay Rubinstein's right-hand man—a quiet, modest, and somewhat whimsical fellow. Peter Ilych arranged to take his meals with this last friend, for Albrecht was even poorer than he, and this was a tactful way of helping him out a little. Constantine Karlovich was interested in everything between earth and heaven:

geology, biology, astronomy, and politics. He collected beetles
and invented little things; unfortunately, nobody ever found a
use for any of his gadgets. In musical matters his views were on
the radical side; in his opinion, music had come into existence
only with the later Beethoven, Wagner, and Liszt. Politically,
however, he was as reactionary as the best of them, and at least
once a day lamented the abolition of serfdom and the forbear-
ance shown by the Government toward the Nihilists. Peter
Ilych—though by no means much of a liberal himself—felt that
at times his friend went rather too far in his rabid denunciations
of Socialism and other subversive tendencies. Great discussions
took place during the modest meals consumed in Albrecht's
home, which always smelled of dusty old books and cabbage.

More worldly and elegant was the home of Vladimir Petrovich Begichev, Intendant of the Moscow Imperial Opera. Peter
Ilych befriended this ageing Casanova and *homme du monde*
not so much for Begichev's dashing charm or potential useful-
ness as for his two stepsons, Constantine and Vladimir Shilovsky. The two boys were delightful, particularly Vladimir, the
younger, who was only fourteen when Tchaikovsky made his
acquaintance. The handsome, delicate youth, who adored music,
became Peter Ilych's pupil; the relationship between the youthful teacher and the adolescent disciple was affectionate, har-
monious, most rewarding for both.

"Yes," thinks Peter Ilych (he cannot fall asleep; out of the
sea of the past rise the faces), "yes, I was almost happy with little
Vladimir, for some time we were almost happy together."

But of course, there was always the fear that THIS might be
discovered by the family, always the compulsion to love fur-
tively. And later on, there was the anxiety about the boy's precarious state of health. The trip to western Europe, in the early
summer of 1868, was darkened by the specter of Vladimir's
illness. The doctor in Berlin said the youth was showing in-
cipient signs of tuberculosis, whereupon Begichev, who was
traveling with them, insisted on rushing to Paris and consulting

the most famous specialist there. The specialist sent Vladimir
to a sanatorium—which meant separation, if only for the time
being.

There was always suffering; suffering was the most faithful of
companions. The short romance with Désirée Artôt resulted in
nothing but suffering and frustration.

This must have been just a few months after the trip to Paris
—yes, it was in the fall of 1868 that the Italian impresario Merelli had come to Moscow with his opera company. Désirée was
the great attraction—not so much on account of her looks (the
celebrated songstress was in fact only moderately handsome) as
by virtue of her sparkling personality and artistic talent. Moscow society raved about her performance as Desdemona in
Rossini's *Otello*—the opera in which Peter Ilych saw her for the
first time.

"Was I in love with Désirée Artôt?" the lonely man in the
hotel room asks himself. "I told her, '*Je t'aime!*' But was I really
in love? I proposed to her. But did I actually want her to accept
my proposal? I made conditions. I told her that she would have
to renounce her profession as I did not care for the pitiful role
of a famous wife's husband. I knew she would not give up her
career. But if she had renounced her fame for my sake, if she
had made the great sacrifice, would I then have loved her?

"Oh, you whom I might have loved!" the sleepless dreamer
addresses Désirée's shadow—one of the many shadows emerging from the past. "*Ô toi que j'eusse aimée!*

"What resignation," he muses, "what hopelessness may be
contained even in the words *Je t'aime*—words used a million
times every day, and every time with fresh conviction—a cry of
lamentation sent into the unanswering void. And now this *je
t'aime* is changed into the qualified *ô toi que j'eus aimée*,
which is practically a confession of defeat, of resignation. It
should have been you for whom I sought if—*if* . . . But beyond this "if" opens an abyss."

Peter Ilych had been quite upset when told, shortly after

Désirée's departure from Moscow, that his "fiancée" had married another man—the Spanish baritone, Mariano Padilla y Ramos. What a beautiful name! Nikolay Rubinstein, who broke the news to Tchaikovsky, had an almost triumphant way of pronouncing the exotic syllables: *Mariano Padilla y Ramos!* Good old Nikolay had always been against the liaison between his protégé and the foreign star. Clearly, he enjoyed informing Peter Ilych of Désirée's faithlessness. She had married the baritone in Warsaw, the next stop of the Merelli troupe after their Moscow season. "Padilla seems to be just the right kind of man for her," Nikolay said. "A bull with a splendid voice. That's what she needs—not a romantic dreamer like you. But you, Peter Ilych, you're needed too—by us, by Russia! Not as the pet and servant of a French prima donna!"

Peter Ilych turned very pale. Without saying a word, he left the theater.

The painful conversation had taken place at the Bolshoi Theater where Nikolay Rubinstein was then rehearsing Tchaikovsky's first opera, *The Voyevode.* The work, based on a libretto by the popular playwright Ostrovsky, was quite a success when first presented, on February 11, 1869. And a couple of weeks later Nikolay Rubinstein conducted Tchaikovsky's symphonic poem, *Fate,* at a concert under the auspices of the Russian Musical Society. No doubt, Peter Ilych's situation was picking up from a professional point of view, however unsatisfactory and confused it remained in other respects.

He fled from suffering to work; but the work itself involved suffering, a dubious solace indeed! While writing his first symphony, *Winter Day Dreams,* (this was before the meeting with Désirée) he thought he would die of torment. He scarcely slept at all, spent endless nights racked by anxiety, haunted by hallucinations; to his terrified mind the darkness seemed alive with noises, circling colors, hideous grimaces. A doctor whom the frightened family called in declared that Peter Ilych was "just one step away from madness." When the symphony was at last finished—born of what diabolical anguish!—it did not turn out to be particularly good. Anton Rubinstein, before whom it was laid, regarded it as a failure. At first only the two middle movements were performed—not too successfully.

The Artôt affair, with its unprecedented torments and agonies, proved musically stimulating. Even while the problematical flirtation was going on, in November 1868, Peter Ilych invented one of his most catching melodies—the sweet, nostalgic Romance in F minor (dedicated to Désirée). It was of no particular weight or significance, to be sure; a little too pleasing, perhaps, and somewhat on the vulgar side; but charming— "une vraie trouvaille," as the grateful Artôt put it. Nikolay Rubinstein used the delightful piece as his favorite encore at all his piano recitals. Audiences all over the world were to applaud Peter Ilych's melancholy little confession.

He went on pursuing his strange alchemistic task of transforming pain into beauty. *Fate* and *The Voyevode* were followed in quick succession by the overture-fantasy, *Romeo and Juliet* ("one of my more successful efforts!" the lonely dreamer decides, not without a certain melancholy pride), by the Quartet No. 1, a second opera, *The Oprichnik*, and the Second Symphony. Then came the symphonic fantasia, *The Tempest*; another opera, *Vakula the Smith*; the Third Symphony; two more quartets; the Concerto for pianoforte and orchestra in B-flat minor; and the *Swan Lake* ballet—not to mention a considerable number of songs and other minor composition.

Quite an impressive output!—the convalescent in his strange hotel bed cannot help admitting it to himself. "Of course," he thinks, sorrowfully, "most of these works were certainly not very good: indeed, were rather unsuccessful, and could not be rightly measured against the high and exacting Task one had before one. But perhaps, after all, there were a few things of a certain value—in the second quartet, for instance, and in the piano concerto, two achievements that seem to enjoy some popularity abroad."

The concerto, curiously enough, had been played for the first time in Boston, in the faraway United States, by the German pianist-conductor, Hans von Bülow. It was to him that Peter Ilych had dedicated the work—not to Nikolay Rubinstein, as originally intended. What an unforgettably unpleasant hour *that* had been—that chilly afternoon hour when Peter Ilych played the concerto for his friend Nikolay in an empty classroom at the Moscow Conservatory! Throughout the whole performance the teacher had maintained an ominous, hostile silence, only to break out with the violence of an angry god as soon as the recital was over. The concerto was impossible, Rubinstein shouted, a bad, trivial, vulgar piece of music, altogether unperformable. Perhaps one or two pages were worth saving; as for the rest. . . .

"Well, it isn't so bad as all that," the sleepless dreamer thinks, smiling now at Nikolay's blusterous rudeness which had once hurt him so. "It contains indeed a few passages that may endure. For how long? Before whom? Before Him, perhaps, Who does not weep over my clever little *trouvailles,* nor laugh over them, but Who observes them, listens to them with awe-inspiring patience—realizing that all those poor, humble efforts have but one objective: to fulfill the true purpose of my poor, humble life."

How trying it often was! How strenuous! First the suffering, then the painful process of transmutation, finally the disillusioning hour of the first public performance. And then the whole thing over and over again! Sometimes Peter Ilych felt that the concerts and opening nights were the most agonizing part of the bitter cycle—worse than any of the preceding ordeals. The work, once it was handed over to the world, always seemed to fall short of what it had been meant to be; the realization never lived up to the ideal. It was particularly after those frustrating first nights that Peter Ilych was overcome by the desire to hide and to escape, that he most ardently wished himself elsewhere—anywhere but here, anywhere; best of all, nowhere.

With the income from his work increasing, he was able to allow himself these hunted, erratic flights. In the company of friends and (if he could afford it) of a manservant, he traveled all over Europe—Berlin, Paris, Nice, Vienna, Switzerland, Italy, the Bohemian watering places. For the most part he was scarcely happier abroad than he was at home; for when he was "here" he wished to be elsewhere, and when he was elsewhere he wished to be "here." The Law from which he tried to escape, the intrinsic law of his own life and character, remained inexorably over him under whichsoever heaven he made his flight.

But how had he ever come to be so desperate that he fell into the miserable affair with poor Antonina? And how came he to handle that affair so weakly and clumsily?

The man who surveys his life and tries to clarify its true purpose feels incapable of facing this most absurd, most embrassassing chapter. He who has welcomed all the smiling or tearful faces emerging from the past refuses to look at this mediocre physiognomy—the narrow forehead and the watery eyes of the wretched Miliukova girl. Not to mention her bitten nails, her tinny voice ("Happy, Peter the Great?"), the vapid taste of her kisses! *She is as much in love with me as a cat . . . I hate her.* . . . The lonely man does not want to repeat these hideous words any more: they have nothing to do with the true purpose of his drama but are in fact incompatible with it. If the bitter-sweet pain of love is inspiring and stimulating, hate is sterile, evil, poisonous.

Or is suffering wholesome in itself—however petty and ugly its source? Will even this grotesque and sordid tribulation eventually reveal its beneficent impact? Can even this most loathsome experience be transformed into beauty?

Peter Ilych paces the room—suddenly restless, excited. He feels like rushing to a desk or to a pianoforte, like buckling down right now to the terrible, splendid job of creative alchemy. Yes, decidedly, he feels like working!

It is light outside—a typical Petersburg morning, with a delicate silver hue cast over the distinguished, somewhat frosty panorama of the imperial city.

What time is it? Consulting his platinum watch makes him pensive once more, sends his thoughts towards its donor, his good fairy and mysterious friend, Nadezhda Filaretovna von Meck.

"How clever He is, the Remote One!" Tchaikovsky reflects with a half-amused, half-awesome gratitude. "He wants me to carry on, insists on my finishing the heavy Task—which is why He has assigned a discreet and efficient guardian angel, Nadezhda Filaretovna, to make things easier, or a little less bitter, for me."

The whole relationship is indeed not without fantastic, fairy-tale-like elements. The wealthiest lady in town—the reserved, practically inaccessible widow of a Baltic nobleman, Georg Otto von Meck—falls in love with one's music. It so happens that Nikolay Rubinstein, hoping for money from her for his struggling Conservatory, plays his piano transcription of the *Tempest* fantasy—and the impressionable widow finds herself in a delirium of delight. She learns that the composer is constantly harassed by financial difficulties, and—using as a go-between young Kotek, with whom she practices music—the guardian angel commissions small compositions, paying abnormally high prices for them: a very discreet and efficient way of increasing her idol's inadequate income. He accepts the compensation—"too lavish for such a minor effort!"—without any squeamishness, and she continues supporting him on an ever more generous scale.

But however gratifying and significant the financial implications of this friendship may be, at least as valuable is the moral and psychological help that Peter Ilych owes to it. His correspondence with Madame von Meck, polite and formal at first, has already become an integral part of his life, the most reliable source of encouragement and comfort. There is an affinity between their souls, a mutual understanding which helps Peter Ilych to overcome his usual inhibitions. Addressing himself to this singular friend, he unburdens his heavy heart—if only through the medium of the written word. During the Antonina episode, it is she, Nadezhda Filaretovna, to whom Peter Ilych confides his most shameful and bitter experiences. At Kiev (Madame von Meck has financed his trip to the Caucasus which is to end in Kamenka) the unhappy husband composes his detailed confession to "my best, my most loved sweet friend"—dwelling on all "the spiritual tortures" he is undergoing as a result of his ill-starred matrimonial experiment.

Yes, she is his best, most beloved friend, even though he has never met her personally and does not expect to do so in the future. For this is the only condition imposed by the great-hearted and sensitive woman: she wishes never to become acquainted with the object of her dreams and benevolence. Should meetings take place accidentally, he is not to greet her, nor to look at her. A capricious idiosyncrasy, this—adding to the connection a pleasantly remote and romantic flavor.

Peter Ilych likes to think of his "soul friend" as the Great Unknown—a veiled, distant goddess residing in a vast mansion on the Boulevard Rozhdetsvensky. Surrounded by innumerable servants, pet animals, and children (Nadezhda has given birth to twelve little von Mecks!), the fabulous matron spends her days reveling in Tchaikovsky's music and sealing letters full of tender words and thousand-ruble bills. The addressee visualizes her as at once an ethereal and a sturdy figure, almost saintlike in her pure, ascetic fervor (Madame von Meck despises sex—which makes it ever so much more pleasant to think of her), but at the same time not without motherly features and a down-to-earth sense of realism. (It is she, the high-minded lover of Beauty, who talked the late Baron von Meck into certain business transactions to which the family fortune is due.)

"Our friendship will last," Peter Ilych decides, caressing the pretty watch, "for it is founded on the interchange of stimulating and intimate thoughts, rather than on any commonplace physical or emotional contact. I lost Désirée because I attempted to love her in a way inappropriate to my nature; I shall never see her again. I am through with pitiful Antonina whom I tried to use without loving her. But I will never lose Nadezhda and will never get tired of her; for she is my real wife, my Muse, the discreet and efficient angel assigned to help me in my hard, wonderful Task.

"It is clear, the Remote One did not want me to contract pneumonia because the greater part of the Task is still unfulfilled. The exacting Lord is not yet satisfied. He remains quiet, unsmiling, uncomplaining; only waiting. . . .

"I will try to live up to His expectations. I will try to live. I will try.

"Not that I know the use of it, really. To go on transmuting suffering into beauty—what a tedious and futile job! But it has to be done since He insists on it, in His unsmiling, uncomplaining fashion.

"I will try to write better music. The Fourth Symphony may turn out to be a little better than the Third. I will try to finish the Fourth Symphony according to His unspoken but clearly understandable order, and with the moral and financial support of my 'best friend' to whom the score is dedicated.

"And I will try to finish *Eugen Onegin* too—my *first* opera, since the previous ones do not count.

"So here I am, in the middle way, having spent fifteen years or so—fifteen years largely wasted—trying to learn to use rhythms and harmonies. Every attempt is a wholly new start, a new promise, and a different kind of failure. Here I am, trying to improve my transformative skill, my alchemistic technique. What for? What will be gained if I succeed? What would be lost in the case of my utter defeat?

"Never mind gain or loss. For us, there is only the trying. The rest is none of our business."

* * *

"Special emissary Tolya reporting back from Moscow," Anatol announced in his humorous manner. "Mission successfully completed."

Peter smiled, but his soft, brooding eyes remained serious, full of anxiety, as he embraced his brother. "Thank you, my boy," he said in a somewhat shaky voice. And, after a pause: "Tell me what happened, Tolya."

"First of all I want to hear your news, Petrushka," Anatol insisted cheerfully. "How have you been? You look better; still rather pale, though. Did you have a good rest?"

Peter Ilych (how old he seemed in his long dressing-gown of heavy, dark brocade!) waved the question off nervously. "I'm all right," he said. "Almost my old self again. Returning to life, little by little. . . . Now tell me, how was it in Moscow? Was it bad? Did she make a scene? Has she consented to a divorce? Why don't you tell me?"

Yes, Antonina was agreeable to a divorce. There had been no scene; on the contrary, she had listened to Anatol with what he described as "uncanny calmness."

"Really," he said, "there was something weird, almost frightening, about the way she took it. There seemed to be no emotion, no reaction at all—as if the whole matter didn't mean anything to her. 'He wants a divorce? He can have it.' That's about all she had to say to us. It was quite extraordinary; Rubinstein thought so too."

"She is mad," Peter Ilych whispered, as if divulging a sinister little secret. "Quite mad—I told you so. That's why she reacts in such an uncanny fashion, or doesn't react at all. She doesn't understand, she can't think, she isn't human." There was a short silence before he asked, as though with a sudden suspicion: "What was that you just said about Rubinstein? It almost sounded as if he had been with you when you went to see— that woman."

"He was," Anatol admitted. "Good old Nikolay—he insisted on coming along."

"That's just like him!" Peter was irritated. "Always meddling in other people's affairs!"

"He means well, though," Anatol reminded his brother. "Of course, if we had known how calm Antonina was going to be, I might as well have called on her by myself. But we expected protests, tears, a heated argument. So Nikolay volunteered to accompany me, thinking that I wouldn't be tough enough to weather the kind of storm we anticipated."

"That's all right," Peter said, still slightly annoyed. "I suppose it doesn't make much difference. But, frankly, I should have preferred to have as few people as possible involved in this sordid affair. Imagine—if Nikolay told the fellows at the Conservatory about the absurd conversation he witnessed!"

"But he wouldn't do such a thing," Anatol protested. "He's your friend—you know that."

Rubinstein and he, the younger brother explained, had decided to stick to the story about Peter's liver ailment. "You need that cure in Spa, or Baden-Baden, or wherever it may be," he laughed. "Need it in fact so badly that you can't even wait until your sweet little wife has finished her preparations—buying new clothes, or whatever she does in Moscow. But she'll follow us as soon as possible; in practically no time she'll join her loving husband!"

"Stop it," Peter demanded. "No jokes about that woman! I am *not* her loving husband. I hate her; but I will try to get over my hate. I will try to forget Antonina. May I ask you never to mention her name again. I wish to forget it."

*   *   *

It was understood that the two brothers would leave Petersburg and Russia almost immediately. The doctor—rather surprised by his patient's quick recovery—had suggested a complete change of surroundings. As if Peter Ilych needed such advice! Yes, he was willing to go—and the farther away, the better! His natural impulse to be "elsewhere"—*anywhere but here!*—

had assumed the character of a fixed idea, an obsession. The idea of returning to Moscow was literally sickening to him. Nor would he be able to face his relatives in Kamenka. He was afraid of everybody. He had to escape, to hide, to make himself invisible and let the world forget him.

Fortunately, Anatol never had anything to do and was available as a good-natured travel companion. There remained the financial question. By going abroad one would lose the Conservatory job and the regular salary; there was just enough money to last for a month or so. And then? What was going to happen when the last ruble was spent?

Peter, in general rather prone to a hypochondriac fear of sudden poverty, appeared this time surprisingly confident. "Don't you worry," he told Anatol. "There are special guardian angels to take care of people of my kind."

They went from St. Petersburg to Berlin, and from there on to Switzerland. The place where they decided to settle down, for the time being, was Clarens on the Lake of Geneva. As soon as the brothers had installed themselves in the fairly comfortable Pension Richelieu, Peter Ilych sat down and composed one of his long, eloquent letters to his good fairy and beloved friend.

"I need money again," he wrote, "and again I can ask no one but you. It is terrible, it is painful and lamentable, but I must do it."

He did it, and concluded: "When my brother came abroad with me, I realized I could not exist without your help and that again you would come forward as my savior. And now as I write this letter, tormented with shame before you, I still feel that you are my real friend, a friend that can read my very soul, in spite of the fact that we know each other only by letters."

It worked: the guardian angel functioned! The mysterious matron in the Moscow mansion functioned indeed beyond all expectation, on a grand scale, with truly astounding generosity. What Peter Ilych received from her this time was not just a check but the guarantee of regular, steady help—the promise of an annual allowance: six thousand rubles a year!

This was the miracle he had been waiting for—there it was, discreetly and efficiently performed by his invisible benefactress! Six thousand rubles a year meant security, independence, freedom! He was free to resign from Nikolay's Conservatory for good, free to travel, free to do as he pleased!

Was he really quite free? And what about the Task, the unspoken but inexorable demand of the austere Remote One? What about the senseless, unescapable compulsion to transmute suffering into beauty?

The slavery continued—not even the guardian angel on the Boulevard Rozhdetsvensky had the power to release him from it; in fact, the gesture of angelic generosity had only one sense and purpose: to compel the recipient to labor even harder than before.

"I doubt if the opportunity will ever come," Peter Ilych wrote to Madame von Meck (this was in November, and a cloudy sky hung over Lake Geneva), "for me to prove my readiness to make any sacrifice for you—you will never be able to ask me for a great enough service. And so I have no recourse but to serve you with my music. Nadezhda Filaretovna, from now on, every note that comes from my pen will be dedicated to you. When desire for work renews itself with redoubled strength, it will be owing to you, and when I am working, never, never for one second shall I forget that it was you who gave me the chance to go on with my career."

A few days before, he had concluded the orchestration of the first act of *Eugen Onegin*; but there were two more acts to be done. And the Fourth Symphony was not finished as yet.

If only there had not been so many disturbances! Among the worst were Antonina's letters. Clearly, "that woman" did not want to be forgotten by her ex-husband but reminded him persistently of her existence. Her first message was addressed to

Anatol, who found it exceedingly funny. She described how, on the train between Kursk and Kiev, "a real colonel" had made overtures to her. "And a very handsome gentleman he is, too," she pointed out proudly. "I gave him my address. He is in love with me."

Anatol roared with laughter as he read the letter to Peter Ilych. "A real colonel!" the younger brother cried. "A very handsome gentleman! It's quite the funniest thing I've ever heard in my life!"

But the ex-husband refused to join in his mirth. "Enough!" he interrupted the reading of the ludicrous letter. "Not another word! I'm about to get sick."

As for the address Antonina had disclosed to the gallant officer, it was Kamenka in the province of Kiev. The kind-hearted Davidovs had asked the former Madame Tchaikovsky to spend a few weeks with them: a terrible mistake on their part, as Peter realized immediately and as his poor sister Sasha was to find out before long. For "that woman," once she had established herself in the comfortable Davidov home, seemed determined to stay forever. If Alexandra had at first felt sorry for her, she soon began to see through her house guest's at once fickle and apathetic character, the gross vulgarity of her mind. And what objectionable habits she had! The hideous nail-biting! The hysterical giggles! The terrible penchant for lascivious anecdotes! And all this in front of the children!

Antonina, meanwhile, went on writing letters to Clarens, Switzerland. The more time passed since the day of her separation from Peter Ilych, the more bitter and aggressive became her communications. It was just a few months ago that the same woman had written to him: "My first kiss will be for you and for nobody else in the world. . . . Don't try to disillusion me about yourself, because you will only waste your time. I cannot live without you, and so perhaps I shall soon make an end of myself. Let me look at you and kiss you so I may carry that kiss into the other world." That had been in May. Now, in

November, her messages were full of disillusionment and self-pity. Peter Ilych, she wrote, had cheated her out of her youth, had abused her kindness, offended her womanhood, ruined her life. There were unpleasant undertones of blackmail in her illiterate lamentations. It sounded positively threatening when she spoke of the "general indignation" the story of her martyrdom would arouse all over the Continent. Who was going to reveal that melancholy story? Had Antonina decided to cry it from the roof-tops? She who had already violated one solemn agreement—the one obliging her to be content with a "sisterly" status—might be capable of another wanton and irresponsible breach.

With such obnoxious letters disturbing one's solitude, it was not easy to concentrate on the lofty and tedious Task. Besides there were other sources of irritation—for instance, the many Russians populating the hotels and villas of this idyllic resort. Peter Ilych was very annoyed indeed to find Clarens so heavily invaded by his compatriots: they were all over the place, the shores of Lake Geneva were teeming with bearded gentlemen and broad-faced ladies from Moscow and Petersburg.

Tchaikovsky was careful not to come in contact with those people; they were poison to him. For, to begin with, he was inclined to believe that all Russians, abroad as well as at home, knew all about his matrimonial scandal and were likely to make nasty remarks in his presence, referring to "THIS" and other disagreeable subjects. As for the particular type of Russians to be found in Switzerland—especially in this area—he disapproved of them also for other reasons.

Was it not known that thousands of Nihilists had found refuge in this hospitable little republic? Clarens seemed to be one of their favorite meeting-places. All those shabbily dressed, bespectacled professors and grim-looking matrons, those nervous students with their sallow, ascetic faces, and those cigarette-smoking young females in shapeless costumes (no corset!)—Peter Ilych distrusted the whole lot of them. Obviously, they were not harmless tourists but shady characters: political prisoners who had managed to escape from Siberia; bomb-throwing anarchists; conspirators, revolutionaries, enemies of the Tsar.

How stupid of them to hate his Majesty! His Majesty was charming—a fine monarch, graciously interested in concerts and operas. Peter Ilych's personal contacts with the Imperial Court had always been most pleasant and rewarding. One of his first compositions, the *Festival Overture* upon the Danish anthem, had been written on the occasion of the Tsarevich's marriage to Princess Dagmar of Denmark. Among his patrons and friends were various grand-dukes and princes. As for Alexander II himself, he was said to be very responsive to the civilized charm of Tchaikovsky's ballets and songs. So why should the composer, on his part, not be loyal to so understanding and appreciative a ruler?

Even though he would not go so far as his friend Albrecht, who defended serfdom, Peter Ilych was a conservative in the sense that he hated the idea of revolution. He knew nothing about the masses. If anybody tried to engage him in conversation on political or social topics, he remained detached, almost bewildered. This is not to say that he was callous or selfish; on the contrary, his sensitive, compassionate heart was easily and often painfully affected by the needs of others. He could never pass a beggar without putting his hand in his pocket, while to a friend or to a needy acquaintance who came with a request for help he would give his last coin. But he knew nothing about the destinies of classes or peoples. Entirely non-political by nature and conviction, he believed this lack of interest or partial blindness to be a logical and unalterable corollary of his being an artist. To his way of thinking, the artist was as much isolated from society as the criminal or the prince. Revolution, he thought, would brutally interfere with the splendid isolation the artist (in contrast to his degraded cousin, the criminal) enjoyed under the protection of his elevated brother, the prince.

By establishing the tyranny of the masses, revolution would inevitably spell the decline and ruin of Art.

That is why Tchaikovsky looked askance at his ever-disputing, ever-smoking, ever-unwashed compatriots on Lake Geneva. Subversive elements they were, fugitives, refugees! Curiously enough, the idea did not seem to occur to him that he, too, was an outcast seeking refuge abroad because he could not feel safe in his homeland; that he, too, belonged to a minority that was persecuted—if not exactly for political reasons. Or did the idea occur to him, after all? Was he aware, at bottom, of certain parallels between his predicament and the plight of those outlaws? And was it perhaps this secret awareness that really annoyed him so?

To be elsewhere! Anywhere but here! Best of all, nowhere; at any rate not here!

"I can't work here," he said to Anatol. "Too many Russian beards. And always those mountains, hiding their stupid peaks in the clouds! It's getting monotonous. . . . Besides, my stomach bothers me again—you know, the old nuisance: purely nervous, they say. I'd better consult my friend, *le docteur* Saligoux. How do you feel about a little trip to Paris?"

*   *   *

The weather turned out to be as unfriendly in Paris as on Lake Geneva. There were plenty of Russians here, too—those loathsome enemies of the "Little Father," Alexander II, infested the whole of Europe! *Le docteur* Saligoux, however, was out of town. The hotel manager recommended another physician, one Dr. Archambault, allegedly very famous.

Dr. Archambault, with stylish black whiskers and a shiny pince-nez, reminded Peter Ilych of the doctor who had treated him in Petersburg; though the Frenchman seemed to be more vicious.

"Your nationality?" he asked Peter Ilych sharply.

"Russian," Peter Ilych said with an apologetic smile.

Archambault shuddered a little—not in a jesting way but as though he had actually been touched by an icy wind. After a short pause he observed, *"Le climat y est bien rude"*—which sounded as if he were trying to explain to himself the chilling sensation he had just experienced.

The perplexed patient had barely begun his little case history when Archambault interrupted him with a curiously wry, Mephistophelian grin. *"Assez!"* he demanded, raising a long, elegant forefinger. "You needn't say another word, Monsieur. I know your story by heart." Then, always smiling in the same diabolical fashion, he went on enumerating the various symptoms of Tchaikovsky's ailment. His sneer became almost triumphantly offensive as he concluded his lecture with this ambiguous statement:

"Monsieur, votre maladie est inguérissable, mais on peut vivre avec elle jusqu'à cent ans."

He said it, and prescribed a laxative.

What a queer, puzzling diagnosis! "Sir, your disease is incurable, but even so you may live to be a hundred." Peter Ilych seemed to be still quite bewildered when repeating the doctor's oracle to his brother. Anatol laughed—half-amused, half-shocked. "Now really!" he exclaimed. "An incurable disease, of all things! Why, he must be out of his mind, your famous Monsieur Archambault!"

Was the doctor an irresponsible quack? Or had he just tried to be witty? Or had his peculiar remark meant to intimate that Peter Ilych was physically all right but an incurable hypochondriac, a *"malade imaginaire"* like the character in Molière's comedy? It was also possible, however, that the physician was indeed shrewder than he appeared to be, that he had recognized his patient as what Tchaikovsky actually was—an incurably stricken man—and that his equivocal prognosis was intended as an allusion to Tchaikovsky's innate anomaly, to his freakish disposition, to "THIS."

This last interpretation of the cryptic statement was of course by far the most disturbing one—the mere thought made Peter Ilych shiver. If Archambault really knew the true nature of that *"maladie inguérissable,"* how could he refer to it in so casual and cruel a fashion? What sadistic callousness on the part of a professional healer and helper!

Peter Ilych hated Archambault. Paris was getting on his nerves. "Let's leave!" he said to Anatol.

"Where do you want to go, Petrushka?"

"Anywhere."

"What about Italy?" Anatol suggested vaguely.

"Not a bad idea," said Peter Ilych. "If we start packing right now, we may make the night express."

They stopped at Florence, then went on to Rome—Anatol, cheerful and observant; Peter, gloomy and absent-minded. He did not seem to notice the artistic splendors, the charm and grandeur of the scenery. Everything was against him, he complained about everything: the hotels, the mail service (what had happened to the precious parcel containing his sketches of the Fourth Symphony?), the climate, the restaurants.

Should they go on to Naples? "I don't care," Peter Ilych said wearily. "To be quite frank, I'm tired of Italy. The climate doesn't seem to agree with me. Or is it the food? I don't know. In any case, I'd much rather be somewhere else."

"Where would you like to be, Petrushka?"

"Anywhere but here. Anywhere."

"Vienna, they say, is rather a pleasant city."

"Vienna? Why not? Let's leave tomorrow morning."

"Tomorrow? Isn't that a little sudden, Peter? You know, I have an appointment tomorrow night at the Hotel de la Russie, with that attractive countess."

"I hate to spoil your fun, Tolya, but I'm afraid I can't stand Rome any longer. Be a good boy and pour me another drink."

"Are you quite sure you want one? You've had plenty of brandy tonight."

"Just one more, little brother! Just one more little brandy! I need it. I really do."

*   *   *

From Vienna, Anatol returned to Russia.

"Don't you want to come with me?" he asked his brother, the day before his departure.

"I'd like to, in a sense . . ." Peter Ilych's face suddenly brightened; then he added, despondently, "But I can't—it's impossible, you know that. Think of the gossip spread by Antonina! Think of the scandal! It's more than I could face."

He cried bitterly when seeing his brother off at the Vienna station. "Remember me to Little Mother Russia," he said. "Tell her I am homesick. Take care of yourself, Tolya boy. Don't lose your luggage." (One of Anatol's suitcases contained a part of the *Eugen Onegin* score.) "See to it that Alexey comes soon. I'll be very lonely."

Alexey Sofronov, Peter Ilych's good-looking if somewhat boorish manservant, was to join his master in Vienna. Later on, there would be Modest, traveling with his boy pupil, and maybe Kotek who had quit his job with Madame von Meck (she no longer needed an intermediator now) and was studying with the great violinist Joseph Joachim in Berlin. Of course, one would be lonely—unalterably, incurably so, but at least not without cheering company.

Besides one had always things to depend upon, even in days of bitterness and despondency—the Task, and Nadezhda Filaretovna's friendship. The correspondence with the discreet and efficient matron continued steadily and assumed ever more impressive dimensions. The two kindred souls and prolific letter-writers, Madame von Meck and Peter Ilych Tchaikovsky, exchanged their ideas about everything between heaven and earth—Russian composers (Peter Ilych was rather blunt in his criticism of the noisy and pretentious nationalist school), landscapes, books, Mozart, Richard Wagner, architectural beauties,

God (the guardian angel, somewhat paradoxically, pretended not to believe in Him but only in Science and Reason), psychology, gossip, and Love. (Once the benefactress, less discreet than usual, asked her protégé whether he had ever experienced love "otherwise than in its Platonic form." Quite an embarrasing question, which Peter Ilych answered with an evasive "yes and no.") But the main subject of their written dialogues was of course Tchaikovsky's work—the music whose saturnine pathos and graceful urbanity had captivated, enchanted the widow's sensitive heart.

Surprisingly, almost incredibly, the haunted wanderer managed to work wherever he was. Vienna turned out to be almost as unbearable as Rome and Paris, so Peter Ilych—now accompanied by his loyal man, Alexey—rushed to Milan, and from there on to Genoa and San Remo. Of course, the Italian Riviera was an impossible place to stay—full of British tourists whom Peter Ilych considered almost as irritating, in their own way, as the Russian conspirators in Clarens. Prices in San Remo were outrageously high, and Alexey complained that nobody understood the only language—Russian—in which he was able to express himself more or less fluently. How many complications! What a difficult life! Yet it seemed advisable to settle down for a little while. The Task must not be neglected.

Would the most exacting listener, the unsmiling Remote One, be satisfied with the Fourth Symphony? If it was not good enough, it certainly was the best he had to give, at this stage of his pilgrimage. Certain parts of the ambitious enterprise were quite successful, no doubt. The third movement, for instance, the *"pizzicato ostinato"*—that was almost adequate, not far from the real thing, the fulfilment. Not that it quite commanded the otherworldly charm of masterpieces like the beloved tune from Mozart's *Don Giovanni*—the gem of Fanny Dürbach's music box—or the enthralling song Peter Ilych had heard in Florence the other day. (Unforgettable—the voice of the Italian boy singing in the street, that evening! Peter Ilych had cried and trembled, flooded with pure delight.) But if the *pizzicato* fell short of such celestial *"trouvailles,"* it was enjoyable enough in its own way, something to be proud of, a little triumph, almost a fulfilment. There were no traces of suffering left in that swift succession of winged rhythms and capricious melodies—a nearly flawless transmutation job. The awareness of one's own inexorable destiny seemed to dissolve in a whirl of iridescent images, the tragic consciousness gave way to a mood of playful enchantment and serene oblivion.

Of course, the sweet intoxication could not last; it was as fleeting as the blissful dreams it produced. "Fatum" had spoken in the first movement; the opening theme of the Symphony had echoed the imperative voice of Him Who neither smiles nor complains, the Inscrutable—the Remote One. The Fate theme will remain the leitmotiv of the whole composition. The second movement—a more brilliant achievement, from a technical point of view, than the somewhat oversized first—may try to forget the fatal verdict by indulging in nostalgic melodies and recollections. (The faces, the beloved faces, rising from the sea of the past!) But after the inspired interlude of the *pizzicato* and the somewhat less convincing joyfulness of the concluding movement, Fate will be heard again. The relentless force that prevents our hopes of happiness from being realized, that watches jealously lest our happiness should become full and unclouded, the sword of Damocles hanging over the head in unremitting torment—there it is once more, a rhythmic thunder from a darkened sky, a hammerlike blow from above.

Peter Ilych had ventured to imitate, to echo the voice of the Remote One. Would the musical audiences grasp the significance of his Fate theme, the fearfulness and grandeur of his vision? They did not, naturally. The symphony, for the first time performed in Moscow on February 22, 1878, failed to make any impression. The *pizzicato* was comparatively well received, but in general the audience did not show much enthusiasm.

Madame von Meck thought that "the composition was somewhat marred by a poor performance; the orchestra was worse than I ever heard it. Usually they give a good performance, but this time they surely did not rehearse enough." Clearly, the conductor, Nikolay Rubinstein, had not been at his best on that particular evening.

Nine days before the Moscow première of his Fourth Symphony, Peter Ilych in his Mediterranean exile had completed the score of *Eugen Onegin:* another part of the Task was done! The lyric scenes based on Pushkin's admirable poem were perhaps lacking in that dramatic verve so impressively commanded by such masters of the theatrical as Verdi and Richard Wagner. But Peter Ilych could not help feeling that his work had certain attractive and endearing qualities not to be found in any pompous *Musikdrama à la Siegfried* or in any spectacular grand opera *à la Aida.* If *Onegin* was not powerful, it was at least sincere and human; if it was not likely to appeal to the masses, it might delight many a responsive soul by virtue of its intimate and poetic charm, the persuasive elegance of its musical diction.

The job of orchestrating the last two acts had been almost uncannily easy and enjoyable; Modest, who joined his brother in San Remo, found him in a truly euphoric mood. "How well you look, Peter!" Modest cried, pleasantly surprised. "In fact, you look almost happy."

And Peter, with a smile: "Why shouldn't I look happy for a change, my boy? I have finished the opera, spring is coming, and this morning I had another delightful letter from Nadezhda Filaretovna—to say nothing of the equally delightful little check the good lady included. Why shouldn't I be in a rosy mood?"

They left San Remo for Florence—Peter Ilych, Modest, Peter's loyal and stolid man, Alexey, and Modest's deaf-mute pupil, little Kolya. The two brothers were so animated and talkative that they made Kolya chuckle—that is to say, he produced curiously gurgling sounds meant to express his amusement.

"What's so funny, young man?" Peter asked with mock-indignation. "I hope it's not *we* you're laughing at? **You** wouldn't go so far as to think *us* funny, Kolya?"

The deaf-mute boy gurgled with redoubled zest, while indicating by the way of eagerly fumbling gestures—the sign-language Modest had taught him with so much patience and diligence—"Yes, yes, it's *you* I think funny—you, Peter Ilych, and your brother Modest—because you keep chatting away and smoking cigarettes and drinking vodka. What a funny couple you are!"

Kolya was a tall, handsome boy of fourteen with bright, beautiful eyes and the innocent, slightly worried expression characteristic of those who are cut off from the outside world. Modest adored the boy, whose tutor he had been for some years, and Peter Ilych, too, was fond of the gentle and friendly deaf-mute. "Yes, he's wonderful, your smiling little Kolya," he would say to Modest, who could never hear enough compliments about his beloved pupil. "But then, I suppose all children are wonderful, once you get to know them. It's too bad that we can't have any children—you, Mody, and I. A great pity, isn't it?"

Another child whose voice and smile touched Peter Ilych's heart was the little Florentine street singer—the one who had made him tremble and weep with joy one night by singing an unforgettably celestial bit of melody. As soon as the Tchaikovsky party had established itself in a Florence *albergo*, Peter Ilych set out to locate the little musician. The other street singers, lavishly tipped by the bearded foreigner, were only too willing to produce the lad; and some ten minutes later a grimy youngster presented himself at the fashionable hotel.

Tchaikovsky looked him over—the unwashed little face, the greasy, unruly mop of black curls, the rickety body, the thievishly nimble hands—and he was disappointed. "You're not the right boy," the bearded foreigner said gloomily. "You can't be the one I heard singing, the other day.

"You just wait a little, Signor," the boy said with a disarming smile. "You just wait until I sing for you, and you'll see that I'm the one you're looking for. But first I want to be paid. Fifty centesimi."

Yes, it was he, all right—the sweet, velvety voice was unmistakably the same that had sung *"Perchè tradir mi, perchè lasciar mi,"* in the pale dusk of that winter evening, last December. Now he sang the simple little tune again, accompanying himself on his discolored, shaky guitar; then—having received some more fifty-centesimi pieces—he went on to more songs. All of them were enchanting, but the most enchanting one was a song called *Pimpinella*. The grimy youngster had to repeat it several times, while the insatiable stranger seemed to sit in some kind of blissful trance, his deep-blue eyes full of tears.

"There's something quite ravishing, something indescribably moving about the way that little urchin sings," Peter Ilych later said to Modest. "Of course, the songs are superb—but it's his voice that really got me: his voice more than anything else! It's too bad he won't have a chance to develop his natural gift. If his people had money, he'd probably become a great singer; but since his people are poor, his beautiful voice will soon be ruined forever: they make him sing from morning till evening! Even now the voice is a little cracked, compared with the first time I heard him. It adds a new charm to that slightly veiled, mellow timbre; but it won't be for long, alas! One should do something for the wretched, wonderful little fellow."

"Yes, one certainly should," Modest said. "Let's send some money to his family—something like fifty lire: that will mean quite a lot to them."

"Fifty lire won't do," Peter Ilych said. "Let's make it at least a hundred! I owe it to them, you know. For I'm going to do a song based on that charming *Pimpinella* tune—and the song I'm going to do will be almost as lovely as the original, almost as irresistibly sweet and simple and sad as the most precious pieces from Fanny Dürbach's precious little box!"

*   *   *

His feverishly active and euphoric mood continuing, he went on working with unprecedented swiftness and facility. Not that everything he produced in those vernal days was of great weight or lasting validity. It is true, the *Pimpinella* song (No. 6 of Opus 38, dedicated to Anatol) turned out to be a *trouvaille* almost as catching and likeable as the *Romance* written for Désirée. But as for the Twelve Pianoforte Pieces (dedicated to Modest) that he began to compose in Florence, Peter Ilych knew quite well, at the bottom of his heart, that these constituted only a minor contribution to the fulfilment of the heavy Task. Nor was he particularly proud of the long and ponderous Sonata for Pianoforte in G major.

"I am no good when I try to write for the piano without other instruments," he confessed to Modest. "I am not a Chopin—not light, not subtle enough. I'm afraid I am essentially a dramatic nature, whether I like it or not. And I am Russian, am I not? In other words, I like big noise, I need the contrabass, the drums, the horns, the harps—the whole rich, polyphonic, wonderful orchestra. . . . Don't you think, Mody, it would be a good idea for me to drop the piano sonata for the time being, and concentrate on the Violin Concerto?"

"But since when are you thinking of a violin concerto?" Modest asked, a trifle taken aback. "Really, I didn't have the faintest idea . . ."

"Oh, I thought I'd told you," Peter Ilych said apologetically and even blushed a little. "Yes, I've been sketching the first movement during the past few days. It was the obvious thing to do, in a sense—wasn't it?—with our master violinist Kotek here to advise me. . . ."

They were back at Clarens—revolutionaries or not, it was a picturesque, pleasant place, and now, with spring coming along, the weather, too, might be expected to be more coöperative. Early in March, the whole curious little Tchaikovsky caravan—Peter Ilych, always engrossed in work; Modest, flirting with every handsome boy on the train or in the hotel lobby;

Kolya, bright-eyed, silent, and smiling; Alexey, stolid, rough, and affectionate like a big, faithful dog—had proceeded from Florence to Lake Geneva. Yosif Yosifovich Kotek, coming from Berlin, had joined the party at the Pension Richelieu.

"It's wonderful to be here!" young Kotek exclaimed, at least once or twice a day. "Berlin was really a nightmare; but here one can breathe again. How refreshing the air is, and the lake —look, how beautiful!"

"I'm glad you don't dislike the place, Yosif," Peter Ilych said with an affectionate smile. "Because you'll have to stay here for quite some time whether you like it or not. We won't let you go, my boy, before you've gained some weight and stopped coughing. I don't like that cough of yours—I don't like it a bit."

Peter Ilych was truly worried about Kotek's health. The dry, rasping sound of his cough, the hectic glow of his eyes, the spotty flush of his sunken cheeks—it all reminded him of another youth he had seen in a similar condition, years before. There could be no doubt that Yosif Yosifovich, like little Vladimir Shilovsky, was suffering from virulent consumption.

"How curious!" Peter Ilych mused, gazing affectionately at the overtall and overthin young man with the lustrous eyes and the quick, nervous gestures. "How curious and how sad! It's always the same type that fascinates and attracts me—the phthisic type, the kind of youth destined to early doom. If only I could die and, by doing so, prolong the life of those fragile angels I love and desire so! But no such luck. . . . *Monsieur, votre maladie est inguérissable, mais on peut vivre avec elle jusq'à cents ans."*

But as soon as he sat down to work and concentrate on the Task, all gloomy thoughts were gone. The miracle of transmutation—it functioned! There was no strain or doubt, merely an elating awareness of one's own strength and competence, a great sense of joy and triumph and liberation.

Everything—the studio in which one worked, the scenery outside, the faces of one's companions—seemed to be transfigured, beautified as by magic, as the first movement of the Violin Concerto in D major was taking on its natural, predestined, unquestionably right and valid shape. How tonic and inspiring —the atmosphere of this cool, fragrant spring! As one wrote, one saw the water and the gleaming mountains—how moving, the sight of flowers growing among the remnants of last winter's snow! Forgotten, the dark November skies, the clouds, the storms, the dreary evenings! Forgotten, scandal and gossip, "that woman," Kotek's disease, one's own incurable affliction! Nothing remains, nothing has reality and relevance but those signs one is compelled to write down, those hieroglyphs which are the medium through which the process of transmutation manifests and fulfils itself.

Whenever a new movement, or a part of a movement, was ready, Peter Ilych would play it over with Modest and Kotek. "How is it?" the composer would ask eagerly. "Is it all right? Is it good? Better than the dull piano sonata? Is it good enough?"

"Why, it's splendid!" the two young men would cry, while Kolya produced one of his curiously gurgling laughs.

"But is it *violinistic?*" Peter Ilych insisted. "Tell me, Yosif! Tell me frankly and candidly! . . . Or, better still, play this passage for me! What are you waiting for? Go and get your fiddle! I want to hear the *Andante.*"

The *Andante* was not quite right? "Never mind," Peter Ilych said, moving his fists as if he were impatient to tackle ever new jobs and then do them all over again. "Never mind, boys. I'll write you another."

It took him just twenty-four hours to produce a brand new Andante. "It's perfect now," Kotek said. "It's fine, it's beautiful!"

"You played it beautifully," Peter Ilych said, with his arm around Kotek's shoulder. "You could play it in public at a moment's notice, my friend."

"Really, Peter Ilych? Do you really think so?" Kotek's young, sensitive face flushed almost scarlet with pride and gratitude. But presently he turned his face away. There was a silence before he said, in a strangely hoarse, strangled voice: "I'll never play your concerto, Peter Ilych."

"What a thing to say!" Peter Ilych tried to sound insulted, but his bluster did not quite come off. "Is my concerto not good enough for the great Yosif Yosifovich?"

But Kotek shook his head. His smile was sad but without bitterness as he said: "Your concerto is splendid, Peter; you know that. But I'll never play it. Don't you know that, too?"

Later in the evening—Modest and Kolya had already gone to bed—Kotek said to his host: "I envy you, Peter Ilych."

"What do you envy me, little Yosif? What's so enviable about my life?"

"Your strength," Kotek said. "Your endurance. Your genius. Your fame."

Peter Ilych sat silent and motionless, gazing into space. Finally he said, very softly: "I am a weak man—believe me, little Yosif. If I carry on all the same, it is because . . . well, just because I *have* to: there doesn't seem to be any choice. As for my genius, you'd better ask the critics: César Cui will give you the right answer. The guardians of Russian music in Moscow and St. Petersburg will not allow my fame to spread too far or to assume too impressive proportions."

"You will be very famous," Kotek insisted with bland obstinacy. "Famous all over the world. It must be wonderful to be a great man."

"But, Yosif, don't you see, fame doesn't really matter—" Peter Ilych began, then interrupted himself: "Well, what's the use? It's getting late, my boy—high time to go to bed. I want to start working early tomorrow morning. The second movement, you know . . ."

◇◇◇◇◇◇

SECOND MOVEMENT
Allegro con grazia

◇◇◇◇◇◇

◇◇◇◇◇◇◇◇◇◇◇◇◇

It was dark in the room except for the narrow shaft of light that came from the door. The light vanished as the waiter quietly closed the door behind him.

"Where shall I put the tray?" asked the waiter.

A few moments slipped away; no sound came out of the darkness. The waiter remained a few steps away from the door in an attitude of expectancy. Presently he cleared his throat, discreetly but pointedly, and at last the gentleman who lay motionless in bed, the bedclothes up to his chin, answered: "By the bed, please—here on the table, my friend. . . ."

His voice was soft, and he spoke German with a drawling, singing intonation. The waiter smiled. It amused him to wait on foreigners. The fact that they had to struggle with a language that came easily to him gave him a pleasant feeling of superiority.

"Here you are, sir," he said, and there was something fatherly in the tone of his voice. He took the few steps from the door to the bed and placed the tray on the little round table, which he pushed forward. "Shall I draw the curtains, sir?" he asked, pronouncing every word very clearly; after all, the person he addressed was only a foreigner, an elderly gentleman with a soft voice—best to treat him indulgently, but respectfully, and thus insure a good tip.

"Thanks," said the gentleman, who still remained motionless beneath the quilt. "Please be good enough to draw them halfway. I can't stand harsh light," he added somewhat plaintively, and at last moved his head in order to have a look at the waiter. The latter was tackling the heavy velvet curtains that covered the windows, making the gentle, careful movements proper to

[67]

a sick chamber. Light burst into the room and dazzled the man lying in bed. He blinked as his eyes took in the disorder of this foreign hotel room: a half-unpacked trunk, articles of clothing and books scattered chaotically on the plush-upholstered couch and on the mock-Renaissance chest of drawers. "I must have been in a fine state when I arrived yesterday evening," the gentleman thought. "Oh, yes, of course, that brandy I had on the journey. . . ." He closed his eyes in disgust.

"It's a fine day today," said the waiter at the window, at once briskly and respectfully. "An uncommonly fine winter's day," he added cheerfully, as the foreigner remained silent.

His silence was not withering or forbidding, such as the waiter was accustomed to endure from other guests; there was something sad and helpless, almost stupid, about it. For this reason the waiter decided to treat the man like a child. He began energetically to instruct him: "That is the morning paper next to the teapot," and after a short pause went on, not without a certain severity: "Will the gentleman settle his bill now?"

But the gentleman did not at once understand. Somewhat perplexed, he looked at the waiter, who stood there, tall and slim as a Prussian Guards officer, in his greasy tailcoat. A glance from the foreigner's deep-blue eyes induced the hearty young man to become gentler.

"I only asked whether the gentleman would like to pay at once?" he said, bowing slightly.

The foreigner half raised himself, hastily opened the drawer of the bedside table, in which silver coins and papers lay in confusion. "Oh, of course," he said, "of course—how much is it?"

The clumsy, hurried movements of the gray-bearded gentleman, as he groped for coins among envelopes, notebooks, sheets of music-manuscript paper, aroused a feeling almost of compassion in the waiter. But at the same time his quick mind realized that a man in his position could not afford to be compassionate, and certainly not towards a somewhat comical foreigner. "One breakfast—that comes to three marks," he said with precision, and with a bold look from his bright eyes: he had asked three times as much as he had the right to. If there was any unpleasantness afterwards one could always say that there had been a misunderstanding.

"Of course . . . please . . ." said the gentleman and went on rummaging eagerly in the drawer. And now the waiter looked at him with undisguised goodwill and with some pity. The scanty, feathery curly hair on the foreigner's head was nearly white; his short rounded beard was also grayish white, and beneath his drooping moustache full, soft, and very red lips were visible. When he readjusted himself after his search in the drawer, his face was dark red, and he gasped a little.

He handed the waiter two coins—a taler and a mark: this allowed a mark as tip, on top of the outrageous price which he had been charged. "It is rather expensive," he said, smiling somewhat wearily, but with an expression that revealed that he had not been taken in.

"Yes, it is, sir," said the waiter, and to his own amazement turned red. He stood there irresolutely, the money in his hand. He actually considered for a couple of seconds in sober earnest whether he would give the gentleman something back.

"Do you come from Berlin?" the gentleman asked. The waiter was once more aware of that sad, blue, penetrating glance.

"No, sir, I come from Hamburg," he answered, clicking his heels together respectfully.

"Oh, from Hamburg," said the gentleman. He lay quietly on his back, but turned his head so that he could look at the young man. "I have to go to Hamburg next," he added; "it is a fine town."

"What is the gentleman's nationality, if I may ask?" said the waiter, and was proud of the elegant manner in which he had expressed himself.

"I'm a Russian," replied the gentleman and turned his reclining head. Without looking at the waiter again, he indicated by a movement of the hand that he might now go. The waiter withdrew and quietly shut the door.

The man in bed remained motionless, his eyes closed. "Why on earth am I here?" he thought. "Why am I here, what is there here for me? Why am I not where I belong? O Thou Inscrutable God, why am I not at home? Here I know nobody and practically nobody knows me. People will try to get a laugh out of me. It is all a plot against me. The whole of this tour is madness." Then the thought assailed him with crippling vehemence: "I can no longer move my body," he decided. "Everything is so abominable and meaningless, and wrong, that I simply can't move any more."

Nevertheless, he moved. He sat up and poured himself out some tea. Before lifting the teacup to his mouth, however, he unfolded the morning paper—the *Vossische Zeitung*, dated December 29, 1887. He turned over the pages and came across this announcement:

> "Today, 29th December, the well-known Russian composer Tchaikovsky arrives in Berlin. Numerous friends and admirers intend paying their respects to him at a gathering in Lutter and Wegener's restaurant this morning at 10.30."

Peter Ilych screwed the newspaper into a ball and flung it to the floor. He sat upright in bed and groaned in anguish. His face became dark red; on his high domed forehead the veins swelled. He muttered such curses as are employed by cabmen and soldiers at home in Russia. He beat the bedclothes with his fist in order to dissipate some of his anger. At last a consecutive furious utterance extricated itself from the inarticulate curses. "That is monstrous," he shouted into the room. "That is quite unprecedented! A scoundrelly trick! They want to make a laughing-stock of me! They want to bring me into disrepute. That is what might have been expected. Oh, these hounds of agents! Oh, that Neugebauer! That damned Herr Siegfried Neugebauer!"

The name of the agent increased his anger to such an extent that he could no longer remain in bed. Sitting on the edge of the bed, he tried with his toes to fish out his slippers, which he imagined were under the bed; he failed to find them; for some seconds he was disgusted by the contact which his naked feet made with the dusty bedside mat—an imitation bearskin; then he forgot his disgust in his anger, and rushed about the room barefoot. His long silk nightshirt fluttered; gesticulating and complaining, he ran to and fro between window and door; his reckless gait was at once heavy and airy. Barefoot, bearded, in his billowy white garment, he gave the impression of a hermit possessed by holy wrath, pacing his cell as in a cage, denouncing the abominable wickedness of the world.

" 'Numerous friends and admirers indeed!' " cried the enraged man scornfully; and then stood still in the middle of the room, raising his arms and clenching his fists. " 'Numerous friends and admirers!' That is to pour scorn on me! They put that in their damned paper solely to ridicule me! Not a soul knows me here, not a single soul; I'm entirely unknown. I wonder how anybody got to know that I would be in Berlin today? I am only passing through; today was to have been a quiet day. I wanted to hide myself. That fellow Neugebauer must have his spies in Moscow and St. Petersburg. He discovered on what day I should arrive here. Oh, that fellow Neugebauer! Oh!" He broke out afresh. As he could not grapple with Neugebauer in person, he trampled all over the crumpled-up newspaper.

While thus engaged he caught sight of his own reflection in the mirror. He beheld the angry graybeard garbed in white— the enraged hermit with the flushed brow; he saw the prancing, stamping ridiculous old fellow—and was ashamed of himself. "I must calm myself," he murmured. "It does me no good, working myself up like this. I shall take a dose of valerian."

He sat down on the bed, leaned over the bedside table for

the medicine, and meantime found his slippers just under his feet. As he allowed the drops to fall into a little glass, he went on muttering in anger that gradually subsided. " 'Friends and admirers!' That is outrageous!"

As he swallowed the dose of medicine an artful and pleased grin spread over his face. "I'll play a joke on him," he thought, and this sudden idea worked wonders in improving his temper. "I'll play a joke on him, that fellow Neugebauer! I'll make him sit up. I shall simply not be available when he wants me. He can have this morning reception all by himself. *I* shall be elsewhere; I, unhappily for him, shall not be there. He doesn't happen to know which hotel I've come to—even he can't have spied out everything. Then early tomorrow morning I'll go to Leipzig, and I shall make myself known only to the gentlemen of the Berlin Philharmonic when I have to come back here for the concert. Today I shall make myself scarce; today I am nowhere to be found! I hope my fine friends and admirers will enjoy themselves at Lutter and Wegener's restaurant. I shall take my morning walk.

"Now I'll gradually get dressed," he decided, seeing that it was nearly ten o'clock. "When that festive gathering of people meets in Lutter and Wegener's restaurant I shall already be taking my morning walk."

He washed his face and the upper part of his body with cold water. While he was getting together the various garments which had been scattered about on tables and chairs, he hummed a short sweet tune. "Mozart . . ." he murmured, as he dived for his socks. "How charming that is! That does one good; it's just as if suddenly everything became easier, as if everything were magically and delightfully put in order. How grateful one ought to be that *that* exists. . . . Perhaps they are doing something of Mozart's at the Opera tonight. I should very much like to hear *Figaro;* but probably they're only doing *Lohengrin.*"

He now saw for himself that it was a fine winter's day. The

window was covered with pretty, fantastic frost-shapes, on which the sunlight played. "That looks charming," thought Peter Ilych. He lighted a cigarette: in his excitement he had forgotten to smoke. As a rule, his cigarettes were the first things for which he craved on waking.

The mirror, which had recently revealed him as a dancing hermit, now showed him as a reasonable, elegant gentleman, in a black coat beautified by silk braid. As he tied his cravat and went on humming a few more bars of the magical, comforting, delightful melody, there was a knock at the door. Peter Ilych thought: "That will be the waiter come to collect the breakfast things. Why, I haven't eaten a bit of anything—just because I was upset by that dreadful newspaper. What a fantastic price the young scamp rushed me for his tea! Apart from that, he's rather a nice fellow, really a very nice fellow. *Entrez!*" said Peter Ilych without turning from the glass.

The door opened. Peter Ilych, at the mirror, expected to hear the clatter of crockery and the sharp but respectful voice of the young waiter; yes, he must admit that he took pleasure in the sound of that voice: it was a *young* voice. And possibly for that reason he stood there without turning round, in order cunningly to prolong the slight pleasure of anticipation. But at last some-body, who had stood hesitatingly at the door, and whose nasal voice was by no means young, said in a tone that was both over-discreet and importunate:

"Mr. Tchaikovsky, if I'm not mistaken."

Peter Ilych turned round. First he went white with fear, and then red with wrath. "Whom have I the pleasure . . ." he be-gan threateningly, and once more the veins stood out on his forehead.

"I am Siegfried Neugebauer, your agent, Mr. Tchaikovsky," said the man at the door in a quiet voice, and smiled sweetly.

Peter Ilych stood speechless for a few moments, as if para-lyzed. At last he said softly: "That is going too far," and stared at Mr. Siegfried Neugebauer as if he were an evil apparition.

"I am very happy to make your acquaintance, Master," said the agent, and walked a few steps towards Tchaikovsky.

Siegfried Neugebauer was a remarkable sight. His reddish hair was sparse, and was spread over his somewhat long head in a few carefully barbered strands. Sparse, also, was his beard, and of a rather intenser red than the hair of his head; it hung like a thin transparent curtain from the edge of his chin, leaving his smooth pink face—a long-nosed, inquisitive but melancholy face with light lashless eyes—astonishingly naked. Even his upper lip was clean-shaven, which the fashion of the time did not exact, and in conjunction with the thin red fabric of his beard produced an astonishing effect. His mouth wore a sickly-sweet but at the same time permanently injured expression; ugly discolored fangs were visible beneath his upper lip; these, combined with his long, inquisitive, sniffing, rosy, proudly arched nose, gave his face a surprisingly animal-like appearance, reminding one both of a hare and of a goat.

"That is a devilish man," thought Peter Ilych, who looked at his guest with disgust but a keen interest. Siegfried Neugebauer met his glance with a mild smile—indeed he seemed, in an absent-minded, insensitive way, to be unaware of the other's scrutiny. A film spread over his bright, wide-open, lashless eyes, and it was this film that seemed to make the whole man unassailable. However much one shouted at him, he would only smile sweetly, almost as if he felt flattered, sniff curiously with his long nose; his veiled eyes would reveal no trace of astonishment, certainly none of indignation. Long before he had bellowed at the man Peter Ilych had decided: "It is no good. He could never understand me. He's the most worthless fellow I've ever come across. Nevertheless, there's a certain *grandezza* in his manner—and that is astonishing! It is not merely a matter of his stand-up collar and his long dark-brown checked frock-coat; it has something to do with his high, broad, and thickly padded shoulders and the surprisingly slim waist. Yes, this remarkable man, with the head of a snuffling dwarf king, really has a fine figure! There is something imposing too in that absent-minded expression of his veiled eyes—dreadful eyes! My agent has meek but at the same time cruel eyes!"

"How did you know in which hotel I was staying?" asked Tchaikovsky in a subdued and somewhat hoarse voice. He had made up his mind not to shout; he would not raise his voice at the man. "Indeed, how did you know I was here at all?"

"It was my business to know, so that I could accompany you, Master," answered the agent, and he smiled enigmatically.

"Accompany me—where?" Peter Ilych's face once more turned a disquieting red.

"To Lutter and Wegener's restaurant," said Siegfried Neuge-bauer gently; he showed his fangs and stared with his filmy eyes, screwed up his nose and sniffed happily; prepared for anything, he waited for what would happen next.

Peter Ilych clenched his fists, took two steps towards the agent. The desire to strike this man was strong within him, but he felt that Neugebauer would receive even a blow from his fist with the same sweet pouting smile under his screwed-up nose, so he restrained himself and only said, in a somewhat husky voice: "This is really monstrous; you actually dare to talk to me about that grotesque meeting at Lutter and Wege-ner's?"

"But, Master!" Neugebauer's oily voice became reproachful. "Did I not write to you weeks ago telling you that I would organize such a gathering?"

"And didn't I write back weeks ago and say that I wouldn't take part in any such gathering?" exclaimed Tchaikovsky. "I told you that I hated strangers; that I am nervous and shy of meeting people; I forbade you to organize receptions or any other nonsense in connection with me. Did I not specifically forbid you?" asked Peter Ilych threateningly.

And what did Siegfried do? Siegfried sniffed and smiled as

if flattered. "Oh, I didn't take that too seriously," he said with horrible coyness.

Peter Ilych realized that he must bring this interview to an end as quickly as possible. "I am not a match for this sort of encounter," he thought. "Oh, I ought never to go traveling. It is madness for me to travel, particularly alone. Such encounters are bound to occur; such contacts with this horrible world can't be avoided." "Whether you took it seriously or not, my good sir," he said, unnaturally calm, "I don't intend to come to your gathering."

Neugebauer stroked his scanty beard, which crackled as if charged with electricity. "It will soon be half-past ten," he said gently. "The gentlemen await us at Lutter and Wegener's." Whereupon Peter Ilych turned his back upon him. "You have more friends in our city than you imagine," Neugebauer continued, with forbearing persuasiveness.

"Friends and admirers!" hissed Tchaikovsky. "Friends and admirers—I know!"

"Undoubtedly," repeated Siegfried softly, and his tone was quite reasonable, even convincing. "And among your friends and admirers I number myself."

Peter Ilych turned to him. The agent stood there in a hypocritical attitude, his head on one side, his hands folded across his stomach. Meeting Peter Ilych's astonished, puzzled glance, he said with a certain solemnity in a voice that was especially nasal and long-drawn-out: "Indeed, Master, I love all your compositions."

To his own dismay Peter Ilych felt that he must believe him. Perhaps this persistent, sinister creature really did love all his works; perhaps he really did know them all, played them on the piano of an evening; and something stirred in his heart: what a touching, terrible thought that was! Tchaikovsky was filled with compassion for the man—yes, he felt a compassion which was almost as strong and violent as his anger and disgust had been; indeed, it sometimes seemed to him that in his soul compassion and anger quickly and surprisingly resolved into one another.

"Maybe *you* really do understand something about my music," he said hurriedly; "but you mustn't judge others by yourself. I am entirely unknown here."

"How dreadful of you!" said the distressed Neugebauer, his hands still folded across his stomach. "How very dreadful of you to talk like that! You *are* known. Kapellmeister Bilse has frequently included the popular Andánte from your quartet in his concert programs."

"The popular Andante—I know." Tchaikovsky's lip curled with disgust. "I shall probably cancel the whole tour," he declared suddenly. He felt greatly eased by the utterance of these words. "It was a mistake ever to have let myself in for such a thing. I'm not equal to such things. Moreover, I'm not a conductor." A lump had come into his throat. "I want to be alone and weep," he thought.

"You are nervous, Master," said Neugebauer reproachfully.

"I am *not* nervous!" exclaimed Peter Ilych. "I know exactly what I am talking about. I lack all the physical and moral requirements of a conductor. Whenever I stand before the public I am so ashamed that I want to sink into the ground. I can hardly raise my arms, and when I do manage to raise them I move them awkwardly and impotently. I spoil my own works when I conduct them. My idea is to do them some service—that's why I took on this martyrdom; but the contrary happens: it's been proved that I do them harm, that I completely ruin them, so miserably clumsy am I. Have you any idea by what an idiotic accident I came to be a conductor?"

Neugebauer was silent, but there was something about his silence, a suppressed curiosity, which seemed to stimulate Tchaikovsky to continue his story, or rather confession.

"It is the fault of my Moscow friends," continued Peter Ilych with bitter emphasis. "My Moscow friends talked me into it. It began by the conductor Altani getting ill during the rehearsals of my opera *The Woman's Shoe*. Do you know my opera, *The Woman's Shoe?*" asked Tchaikovsky and glanced grimly round; "a dreadful potboiler!"

Neugebauer caressed the crackling fabric of his red beard. "I have played through the pianoforte score," he declared with a dreamy look in his eyes. Tchaikovsky made an impatient gesture.

"They wanted to put a substitute in Altani's place," he exclaimed precipitately. It was as if he were trying to excuse himself—not so much to his agent as to himself—for the position in which he had found himself. "But the man they supplied was a mediocre conductor. Naturally I had to insist that my work should have a good performance—yes, even though it is a poor work, in fact especially for that reason. One is always running the risk of seriously damaging one's reputation. To cut a long story short: I turned him down. And then some of those in charge came to me with the ridiculous notion that I should conduct my own opera. Of course I said no. Nobody could be less intended than I to stand before the public. So the production was postponed. At the beginning of the next season my friend Altani was perfectly well again; there was absolutely nothing the matter with him. Now comes the delightful part of it: in the meantime the opera board had got it into their heads that I must conduct the performance. I don't know what they hoped to gain by it—perhaps some comical sensational success. They pressed me; they just wouldn't yield; Altani himself was the keenest of all in telling me what I ought to do. At last I gave way. I no longer know how the first night went off; no doubt the audience suppressed its laughter out of politeness. Yes, our public is better brought-up than they imagine in the West."

"How can you so disparage your own genius?" said Neugebauer distressfully. "That is really dreadful of you. Everybody knows what a brilliant conductor you have proved yourself to be —not only in the opera house, but in the concert hall. Your great

concert at the St. Petersburg Philharmonic Society on the fourth
of March this year was a triumph for you, Master."

"You actually keep the date in your head?" muttered Tchaikovsky, and he thought with pitying astonishment: "The fellow really is an admirer of mine!" "But it was in no way a
triumph," he said. "I have already told you: our public is well
brought-up. Perhaps when I stepped up onto the platform, in
all my awkwardness and misery, they wanted to show their appreciation of services I had previously rendered them—although
even those services were of questionable value. . . ."

"You are the greatest living composer," said Siegfried Neugebauer softly and looked at the Master out of his filmy eyes with
unashamed devotion. Tchaikovsky appeared not to hear him.

"Of course," he said thoughtfully, "when big offers came
from abroad I naturally felt flattered. My first thought was always, What do they want from me? What does the world
want from me? No doubt they want to make fun of me. But
my second thought was, Here is a chance to strengthen your
fame and at the same time the fame of your country. Yes,
Russia's fame is enhanced by everything I do for my own. Up
to now, so few Russian musicians have had an opportunity of
appearing before a foreign public. Only Glinka once gave a
concert in Paris, and Rubinstein, naturally Anton Rubinstein
. . ." "But why am I talking like this to this odious foreigner?"
he thought suddenly. "He makes me talkative. I am a garrulous
old fool."

He lapsed into silence and seated himself on the bed with his
head bent. Then he rose and strode about the room. "As for the
great Russian concert that I'm going to give in Paris at my own
risk, please understand, Mr. Neugebauer, that it is *that* which
matters to me. At that concert I shall conduct nothing of my
own, not the smallest trifle. I will give Europeans an opportunity of hearing our classics—the great Glinka and Dargomizhsky—they don't know about them; and I'll introduce them to a

few of our best living composers. It's true those gentry have done nothing to deserve it, but I shan't be doing it for their sake. Probably the Moscow and St. Petersburg papers will preserve a dead silence about this concert, for they're not eager to admit that anybody takes any notice of me abroad, and they wouldn't want to acknowledge that I can do anything for Russia. They call me a 'Westerner' and not a genuine representative of Russian art. But nevertheless, I will show the French what Russia can do in the way of music. It is *this* concert that is important to me. I will show people that I didn't make this journey out of vanity, just for the sake of making my own things better known."

"But," said the agent with a soft, distracted smile, "it's that very concert which will never be given."

Peter Ilych was completely taken aback. "How is that?" he asked, looking at Neugebauer with large astonished eyes.

The agent shrugged his padded shoulders skeptically.

"Because it will fall through," he said kindly. "The costs are far too high. You couldn't afford it. Apart from that, not a soul in Paris is interested in Dargomizhsky, whose name moreover nobody can pronounce." There was a note of intense pity in his voice.

"Shut up!" Peter Ilych commanded. "Thank God my Paris arrangements have nothing to do with you. It's bad enough that I should have entrusted you with such a large part of my tour—and *that* I shall take away. How should *you* know what I am capable of achieving in Paris? I have a great name there and powerful friends," he declared, flinging back his head. "How should *you* know what I can achieve in Paris? I shall most certainly give the great Russian concert."

"It will never be given," repeated the agent with a sort of detached obstinacy. "It is a simple question of money," he continued in the same ecstatic whispering tone as he had used when speaking of Tchaikovsky's works.

"Obviously the concert would never take place if it were entrusted to you," remarked Peter Ilych haughtily. "I should have been better advised to entrust nothing to you at all. You are a wretched agent. . . ."

Neugebauer smiled and screwed up his nose as if he enjoyed this attack. "That is, of course, extremely unjust," he said, drawling out each syllable in a nasal singing voice, as if deprecating an expression of exaggerated flattery.

"You've spoiled everything for me," asserted Peter Ilych. "You bring about nothing but intrigues and confusion. You've put me up for sale all over the place at the same time, like some cheap-jack. You've upset people and let them down. In your brilliant fashion, you fixed the same evening for the concert in Vienna as you'd fixed for Paris, so that I had to abandon Vienna —and it was the Viennese public that I particularly wanted to conquer. You made a mess of Dresden for me; you made a mess of Copenhagen—all because of your muddleheadedness and because you wanted to be overcunning. You spoil everything!" shouted Peter Ilych and paced about the room.

"Everybody is likely to make little mistakes sometimes," protested the agent with a kind of vague solemnity.

"Moreover," continued Peter Ilych angrily, "I will *not* give a performance of the *1812 Overture* here. I've written to you a dozen times telling you that I intend to do the *Francesca da Rimini*. The *1812* is a wretched work; I can't stand it. It was written to order, for a religious-patriotic occasion; it's absolutely worthless. Nothing would induce me to make my début in Berlin with it."

"But the public wants to hear it," threw out the distracted Neugebauer with a thoughtful shrug of the shoulders.

"I don't care a hang about the public!" cried Peter Ilych. "I don't intend to make my first appearance abroad with my most commonplace work. It made a certain impression when it was performed at the dedication ceremony at the Church of the Redeemer in Moscow—with the Russian anthem triumphing over the *Marseillaise,* and with the firing of cannon and pealing of bells. I suppose you think one could have cannon fired and bells rung in a concert-hall? A dozen times I wrote to you and told you I'd have nothing more to do with *1812*—and now I find it on the program!"

"Everybody was in favor of *1812*," remarked Neugebauer with a somewhat weary lack of interest, as if it were hardly worth while discussing the matter. "Herr Schneider, president of the Philharmonic Society, was in favor of *1812*, and even Herr von Bülow."

"I honor Hans von Bülow as a great musician and owe him a great deal of gratitude," Peter Ilych said hastily and with considerable emphasis, because he feared that the odious Neugebauer might make mischief between him and Bülow, "but I understand my own works better even than he does."

"Of course," agreed Siegfried, whose eyes seemed even more veiled than usual. "But you ought to take our patriotic feelings into consideration. *Naturally* we should be delighted to hear the *Marseillaise* triumphed over by *any* other national anthem, no matter which."

"I suppose you think I ought to have pitted the German anthem against the *Marseillaise!*" Peter Ilych was furious. "If I'd done that, I might have had the honor of meeting Prince Bismarck at my concert. I stick to *Francesca da Rimini.*"

"We here are all agreed, Master," said Neugebauer, his nose tightly screwed up, and with sudden unblushing familiarity, "that *Francesca da Rimini* is somewhat boring."

Tchaikovsky's face turned red. "I've had enough of this," he said quietly and sourly.

"Quite right. We have no more time for talking." Neugebauer became bright and enterprising. "It's high time we went to Lutter and Wegener's."

This piece of audacity struck Peter Ilych as so incredible that, instead of answering, he simply stared at the agent.

"I have sent out invitations for a reception to meet the Master this morning," added Neugebauer casually, sniffing. "And apart

from that, there are many things still to be arranged for today,"
he went on confidingly. "I've made several appointments for
you—with the members of the Philharmonic Society, with a few
journalists . . ."

"You are going to get me mixed up with all these people, are
you, and have arranged interviews with them against my will!"
Tchaikovsky spoke without looking at the agent. "I will visit
nobody and receive nobody. I'm exhausted by the journey. This
is my day for resting. I don't want people."

"Have you no desire at all to come with me now to Lutter and
Wegener's?" asked Neugebauer, as if he were making an entirely new proposal. His sleepy, long-nosed, pink face remained
immobile.

"Oh, let's go, then," said Tchaikovsky harshly.

He allowed Neugebauer to help him on with his fur coat.
The agent handed him his large round cap. Thus muffled up,
Tchaikovsky suddenly looked like a cross between a Russian
prince and a Russian peasant.

Neugebauer politely allowed him to go first. They went
silently along the carpeted corridor, their footsteps making no
sound; they went noiselessly and quickly, Siegfried Neugebauer
half a yard behind Peter Ilych. The wide staircase was also
covered with a thick red carpet. On every landing stood a dusty
palm in a gaudy enamel pot. The hall was also adorned with
many palms, and on mock-Renaissance sofas sat gentlemen with
large moustaches and stand-up collars, studying the newspapers.
The porter, who had the largest moustache of all, stood stal-
wartly erect, as if on guard, in his box under the picture of the
old Kaiser. The porter had the face of an angry tomcat. He
greeted the composer and his agent with a brusque military
nod.

At a pianoforte, which was decorated with many little twisted
columns, sat a black-maned young man wearing a strip of loosely
knotted black silk as a tie. He struck the keys of the pianoforte;
it was out of tune. "Wagner—of course," thought Peter Ilych,

disgusted. "The *Pilgrims' Chorus*—and he is playing it like a military march. Oh, these Germans!"

He passed by the military porter and stepped into the open air. Neugebauer followed him.

Outside it was sunny but cold. Peter Ilych breathed in deep drafts of fresh air. A cab came by; he beckoned to the driver and the cab pulled up. The cabman, who had a friendly gray beard, looked very much like the cabmen at home.

Siegfried Neugebauer made as if to get into the cab with him, but Peter Ilych shut the door in his face. From inside he opened the window. "Enjoy yourself at Lutter and Wegener's!" he cried and broke into a laugh; it was the happy laugh of a naughty boy and made him look younger. "I'm going for a drive!"

Neugebauer ran a few paces after the cab: Peter Ilych made a sign to the cabman to drive faster. The desperate agent gesticulated wildly in grief and disappointment, flapping his long arms like wings as if in protest to Heaven. Then he remained standing there. Tchaikovsky was still able to see how Neugebauer's face slowly took on its sweet sickly smile and how he, unaccountable fellow that he was, seemed to enjoy this fresh injury.

"Drive through the Tiergarten!" Peter Ilych called out to the cabman. As usual, when speaking to humble people, his voice had a soft pleading tone.

Every time Peter Ilych came to Berlin his first excursion was to the Tiergarten. It was the part of the capital that he liked most, or hated least. It was the only spot in this mighty city where he felt a little at home; the rest of Berlin remained foreign to him, although he had been there many times.

The cab turned out of Friedrichstrasse into the broad and showy avenue Unter den Linden. Under the feet of pedestrians and the coachwheels a light fall of frozen snow crackled pleasantly. The sun shone on the snow; it was a lovely day. The wide street displayed its beauty triumphantly. One beheld the Brandenburger Tor, which formed an impressive termination to a fine perspective: it was built solely that conquering troops might pass under its arch, to the sound of trumpets and the roll of drums. What a show street it was indeed! It was quite clear that the street and all who walked in it—not only the well-dressed, energetic-looking ladies and gentlemen, but also the poor and feeble (but these were fewer)—enjoyed its splendor, which was enhanced by the sunshine and the sparkling snow. What a city! The right capital for this triumphant country—the most feared country in the world, a country which nobody quite trusted, which nobody quite liked, but which everybody had to reckon with.

The foreign gentleman in the cab—Peter Ilych Tchaikovsky from Moscow—was rendered uneasy by this hard, aggressive beauty; it had something threatening about it, he thought. He looked through the cab window, and his glance was melancholy and somewhat scared. "Every one of you is a little Bismarck," thought Peter Ilych from Moscow. Overawed rather than scornful, he scrutinized the martial appearance of the men: the bristly moustaches, the bushy eyebrows, and the menacing determination of their expressions certainly inspired not a little alarm. A considerable number of them wore uniforms; one felt they might at any moment draw their swords. They cast enterprising and impudent glances at the ladies, who for their part walked with heads erect, every one of them a Germania, fully aware of her inviolable worth, carrying her large fur muff before her like a trophy. Successful commercial magnates, wearing dazzling rings on their fat fingers, drove by in elegant carriages drawn by vigorous horses which looked well-nourished and were smartly caparisoned. The commercial magnates and the officers seemed to own this gala thoroughfare; now and then a professor in a soft hat, with a shaggy beard and wearing a coarse but esthetic waterproof cape, might be seen hurrying, distracted, and not without a certain suspicious self-consciousness, and in his obstinately bent head appear to be hatching some evil plot.

The foreign gentleman in the cab saw all these things over-distinctly, simplified, like ghostly figures out of a comic paper. He was ashamed of his malicious scrutiny. But he could not help thinking: "Oh, these Germans! Wasn't there almost a war this very year between them and France? It's true I don't understand much about such things, but nevertheless I feel how unsettled everything is. Haven't they been increasing their army again? Some new army bill or other has just gone through."

The cab drove across the gleaming expanse of the Pariser Platz. The triumphant Brandenburger Tor received it, and then it continued steadily on, over the crisp snow. And now the Tiergarten . . . !

"It was in this city that dear Kotek had his worst time," thought Peter Ilych, and suddenly felt a lump in his throat. Why did he wait so long before he went to Davos? Why did he have to die? He was young; he was charming and talented. I was fond of him; for a long time he meant a great deal to me, and he might have meant a great deal more to me if he had wanted to and there had been more time. Why couldn't I have died and he gone on living? Then I shouldn't be sitting here in this damned cab; while he would be in some room or other, his thoughtful young head on one side, playing the fiddle marvelously. Yes, he was an excellent violinist; that's why I dedicated that valse-scherzo to him, quite a nice piece, for violin and piano. How I enjoyed listening to his playing when I went to see him at Davos for the last time! I stayed a whole week, we had such a lot to talk about. He was delightful, Kotek, although he was so ill. My dear Kotek, I wonder where you are hiding yourself now? My dear, are you allowed to make music where you are now? My dear . . ."

Peter Ilych was torn out of his tender-sorrowful musings by a noise that seemed to him terrifying; but it was only a large dog barking at the cab. Even this barking had a threatening tone. Threatening also was the look which a policeman with bushy eyebrows threw at the cab, at the cabman, and at the foreigner sitting inside. The stern keeper of order looked as if he had decided, on some pretext or other, to arrest this melancholy-looking foreigner on the spot. A horde of children went by in military formation, and what they sang was all about German honor and how France would soon be beaten again. A well-equipped gentleman with a conquering gesture stretched out a long sword over barking dog, singing children, and suspicious policeman. The gentleman was made of white stone—a statue in a challenging attitude adorning a frozen fountain. All these things Peter Ilych saw, and he was scared. He had a sense of fear and hate surrounding him. Everything seemed unfriendly. He felt isolated, delivered up, attacked from all sides. Even the dazzling sky seemed to threaten him.

He hated the stone statue, he hated the street, the snow-covered Tiergarten, the whole pompous and imperial city. With overwhelming intensity he wished he were anywhere else—"anywhere but here, anywhere but here . . ."

He was used to attacks like this—a suffocating, unspeakably urgent desire for an immediate radical change in his surroundings. This paralyzing, lacerating torment, more powerful than a physical pain, was apt to seize hold of him anywhere, even at home—if he could think of any place as "home." But more and more did Peter Ilych fasten his hate and disgust with great earnestness on the place where he happened to be. "I *won't* drive here," he thought angrily. "I refuse to drive about in this strange and abominable city, in which my friend Kotek suffered. If only I were not here! The sparkle of the sun on the snow infuriates me and makes me ill. If only I were somewhere else! Best of all, nowhere at all; but at least not here!

"If only it were autumn and I were sitting somewhere in Maidanovo, my dear, tranquil Maidanovo! But no! I should not be sitting at all; I should be walking across the open field flying a kite—it's lovely to fly kites. Or I should be walking through the wood looking for mushrooms—it is so peaceful bending down after mushrooms. I know all of them. The wood at Maidanovo is beautiful; true it has been mercilessly thinned out, but it is still splendid. Perhaps my dear brother Modest would be with me, or my sister Sasha's young son, or that lazy old chap, La-roche. I must have somebody with me who is good and whom I have known for a long time, with whom I share common memories, and whom I love. It is not good for me to be alone. In any case, I'm not going to go on driving here."

"Turn round!" he cried to the cabman. "Drive me back to the hotel!" The cabman turned his bearded old face with fatherly astonishment towards his passenger. The gentleman who had previously spoken with such a gentle voice was now showing that he could speak harshly.

*   *   *

Peter Ilych stamped through the hotel hall with angry strides. To the ladies and gentlemen sitting on the mock-Renaissance sofas, he must have looked somewhat terrifying, in his long fur coat, with his round astrakhan cap surmounting the unusually dark red face.

As he hurried down the corridor he was annoyed by the noise-lessness of his own footsteps; he would have liked them to make a menacing noise. With a hand that trembled slightly, he went to unlock the door of his room. Before entering, he cast a look about him; he had the impression of a veiled but importunate glance behind him. From round the corner formed by this part of the corridor there protruded something long, rosy, and in-quisitively sniffing. It was the nose of Siegfried Neugebauer; and there stood the man himself, the padded shoulders raised, the immovable smile on his lips disclosing his fangs. He had been lying in ambush. His reddish forehead was quite trans-figured by the joy which this disgraceful situation gave him. "So you left me in the lurch," he said, sniffing for pleasure, and drew a couple of steps nearer.

"*Fichez-moi la paix!*" shouted Peter Ilych, and went on speak-ing in French, either in order to upset Neugebauer or perhaps because in his excitement he lapsed into the language that came easier to him. "I'll have nothing more to do with you. I cancel our agreement. You will hear further from me."

"How terribly unjust!" cried the agent plaintively, nevertheless enjoying the situation.

Peter Ilych banged the door behind him and locked it from within. He heard Neugebauer fumble for a time with the doorknob, turning it and pushing it; he heard his soft, complaining, whispering voice outside, like that of an importunate but not dangerous animal who had been shut out.

Tchaikovsky had remained standing in the middle of the room. For a few moments he stood there motionless, with eyes closed. "I will darken the room," he thought. "Yes, I will draw the curtains too. I will sit down in this armchair and hold myself quite still. I close my eyes. I am thinking of the few people who are still left to me. This day must pass by. Tomorrow I go to Leipzig; that is at any rate another place. No doubt they're decoying me there to make fun of me—but it can't be worse there than it is here. O God! How terrible! How terrible! O Thou great, powerful, remote God, in Whom I believe, how terrible hast Thou made everything! Why must I put up with all this? Simply in order to transform it all into melody? And perhaps not even good melody. . . . I will hold myself quite still. It will pass. . . ."

*   *   *

◈◈◈◈◈◈◈◈◈◈◈◈

He doesn't seem to have come," said one of the gentlemen who were waiting on the platform. The last passengers alighted from the Berlin express. Tchaikovsky, whom they had come to meet, did not appear to be among them.

"But that is impossible," said the youngest of the men, whose name was Alexander Siloti. While the other three appeared large and shapeless in their fur coats, he, in a dark tight-fitting overcoat, looked youthfully slim. In a voice that had a bold, attractive, and curiously resonant ring, suddenly he called out, holding his head back and making a horn of his two hands: "Peter Ilych, Peter Ilych, where are you?"

It was as if Peter Ilych had only been waiting for this call. A moment later his tall, broad, somewhat bent figure appeared at the door of a first-class carriage.

"Peter Ilych! Why don't you get out?" called young Siloti in his beautiful resonant voice.

At last he was seen by Tchaikovsky, who stood there completely bewildered, as if blind, staring about him. "Oh, it's you, Siloti," he said, and a slow smile spread over his features. "Yes; the fact is something seems to be wrong with my luggage. I have a great many bags."

Siloti ran up to him; his gait was charged with the same vibrating energy as his voice. "My dear Siloti," Tchaikovsky greeted him, feeling a lump come into his throat. "How nice of you to come!" They shook hands. "I seem to be so frightfully incapable." Peter Ilych laughed apologetically. "You see, I'm not in the habit of traveling without somebody to help me. I've always had my good Alexey with me." He took Siloti's arm. In the meantime, one of the other men had called a porter.

A great welcoming took place. Peter Ilych embraced his old friend Brodsky, the violinist, and shook both hands of the pianist Arthur Friedheim. The fourth, an agile little man with a black goatee and pince-nez which were constantly shifting towards the blunt tip of his nose, introduced himself.

"My name is Krause," he said eagerly. "Martin Krause, music critic of the *Leipziger Tageblatt,* an admirer of your music. Welcome to Leipzig!" he cried with sudden solemnity, striking an attitude, as if he were the leader of an official deputation, with flags and a brass band. With a slight, triumphant bow, of the kind made by a conjurer when to everybody's astonishment he produces a dove or a bottle of red wine out of his ear, he presented Tchaikovsky with a great bunch of roses which till that moment he had concealed with careful cunning behind his back.

"Roses! How beautiful!" said Tchaikovsky, much moved. "And in the middle of winter too!" He wanted to take the flowers, but as he had no hand free he had to put down one of his handbags; this interfered with his cigarette, which he just allowed to drop from his lips, leaving Siloti dutifully to put it out.

"Welcome to Leipzig!" said Brodsky also, somewhat belatedly, in his deep booming voice. Arthur Friedheim gave utterance to a hearty laugh.

"How nice it is of you all to come!" Tchaikovsky linked one of his arms in Siloti's and placed the other over Brodsky's shoulder. "You know, I simply didn't dare to get out of the train. I had already quite made up my mind to travel on—and then to send a telegram from some little foreign town or other saying I'd been prevented from coming to Leipzig."

Brodsky laughed, and the noise of it echoed through the station hall. "What notions you get!" He could hardly breathe for laughing. "You are the same crazy old fellow as ever!" They all laughed; but on Siloti's handsome young face there was a serious, radiant smile. "I'm very glad I called out to you," he said

quietly, while Brodsky wiped away the moisture which laughing
had brought to his eyes.

"It was an absolute hallucination," explained Tchaikovsky,
looking at Siloti. "I thought to myself: You simply *can't* get out.
Either nobody will be waiting for you at the station, which
would be dreadful, and you will discover that everything has
gone wrong; or there will be many strange people there—and
that would have been even more unbearable. But now I'm
saved."

He laid his arms still more firmly on the shoulders of his two
friends. People looked at the three of them as they walked
through the station hall towards the exit. Friedheim, the music
critic Krause, and the porters followed on behind. Tchaikovsky
leaned so heavily on Brodsky and Siloti that it looked as if they
were supporting him. As he walked between them, in the midst
of his admirers, whose attentions seemed to exhaust him, he
swayed slightly and looked like an old man.

"I can't stand these railway journeys any more," he said.
"They make me ill. They upset me; and in order to cope with
them in some way or other, I generally take a full bottle of
brandy with me; and by the end of the journey, lo! it is suddenly empty . . . and yet from Berlin to Leipzig isn't really
a very long stretch, is it? But I simply can't endure these journeys any longer; I've done with them! I'm a wreck, as you see.
And I can't even compose any more."

"Ha, ha, ha!" laughed Brodsky; but Siloti shook his head
gravely and smiled reproachfully.

"What am I doing?" asked Tchaikovsky. "Here I go on
chattering and chattering and don't let any of you get in a word.
Well, how are you all? I know already that old Brodsky is a
firmly established professor at the Leipzig Conservatory."

"A well-established violin professor," explained his friend
Brodsky, booming cheerfully.

"And my little Siloti?" Tchaikovsky turned round and looked

him full in the face. "My little Siloti goes from triumph to triumph. The whole world is talking about him. That's marvelous! Good heavens!" cried Peter Ilych and stood still in the middle of the station hall, "how well I remember giving you the composition course at the Moscow Conservatory! Some years ago, that was. Afterward came the period of the great schools for you—Rubinstein, Liszt! But at that time in Moscow you were quite a youngster. You were a wonderful youngster. And have remained so," added Peter Ilych.

A fleeting blush passed over the ivory-colored face of young Siloti, leaving a few hectic patches on the cheekbones.

"How quickly you have become famous!" said Peter Ilych, still looking at him.

"Have you seen Anton Rubinstein lately?" asked Siloti.

"I meet him seldom." Peter Ilych at last turned his glance away from Siloti and continued: "He has always been very severe and reserved with me."

Brodsky laughed, but young Siloti remained serious.

"Nothing can compensate me for the loss of his brother," said Tchaikovsky, staring in front of him with an absent-minded expression. "I miss good Nikolay terribly. Yes, Brodsky," he went on, turning suddenly towards his old friend, "so many have gone!" Brodsky nodded with a somewhat embarrassed solemnity. They were standing in the square in front of the station.

In the wan light of the late afternoon, the snow had a slate-colored sheen. It was rather cold. Over the snow-covered houses the sky hung in glassy purity.

The critic Krause, who had overtaken the three Russians, said with a gesture that took in the buildings, cabs, sleighs, and the whole square: "Allow me to introduce you to our Leipzig, Master—the musical center of the German Empire!" Like a good Saxon, he pronounced the "p" in Leipzig very softly and drawled the name of his native town in an inimitably broad and genial fashion. Everybody laughed. "The musical capital of

the kingdom ever since Mendelssohn-Bartholdy worked here,"
added the little man solemnly as his pince-nez slipped down his
blunt-tipped nose.

They hailed a sleigh. "What a queer shape it has," said Peter
Ilych as he got in.

"It hasn't a queer shape," explained Brodsky; "it only has a
different shape from ours at home."

The vehicle was open; they wrapped themselves up in the
rugs. Peter Ilych sat at the back with Brodsky and Siloti; Friedheim and Krause took the seats opposite. The critic proposed:
"It would be best if we were to give the luggage to the hotel
manager to deal with and then go on at once to friend Brodsky's,
so that we should all get something warm in our insides."

Peter Ilych observed him, amused and appreciative. "What
organizers these Germans are!" he declared. " 'Something warm
in our insides'—that's a brilliant idea."

The keen wind gave them all red cheeks and noses; only
Siloti's face remained ivory-pale: in the dim light of the dying
afternoon it seemed to shine as if it were made of some other
material than flesh and blood. Peter Ilych was very excited
and talked a great deal. "You don't know how lucky you are
that I was alone when I stepped out of the train," he chattered,
laughing. "My friend Siegfried Neugebauer fully intended to
accompany me to Leipzig; my most cunning tricks I had to employ to prevent it."

The name of Siegfried Neugebauer had a very animating effect on the company. They all knew him. They laughed at him
and abused him among themselves. "Oh, that fellow Neugebauer!" they cried. "That monster! That jackanapes!" Peter Ilych
was amused and laughed louder than any of them. "That's
right; he is a monster." He repeated with joy every separate insult that was directed against Siegfried. "But I assure you, the
fellow has a sort of demoniacal strength. You simply can't get at
him; he is as tenacious as life itself. Do you imagine I could
get rid of him? Not a bit of it! In the morning I turned him out

neck and crop. In the evening Herr Neugebauer accompanied me to the concert, although I hadn't the slightest wish to go out at all, and certainly not with him. I was obliged to hear the *Requiem* of Berlioz under the direction of Mr. Scharwenka. *Entre nous,* if Neugebauer hadn't been with me it might have been very painful. Scharwenka behaved in a somewhat aggrieved fashion towards me, because Neugebauer had made appointments with him on my behalf both for the morning and for the afternoon, although he knew I wouldn't keep them. So I was not only bored, but was badly treated too. Oh, that fellow Siegfried! He is just as I have imagined Richard Wagner's wood boy to be! I didn't dare to ask the hotel porter if there were any mail for me, knowing full well that there would be at least two telegrams from him—and what telegrams!"

Throughout the whole sleigh-ride they talked about the agent Neugebauer. Each had had some dreadful experience with him, each of them had some grotesque anecdote about him to relate. Arthur Friedheim declared that he had once boxed his ears on the platform in the presence of the whole audience, because at the end of the concert Neugebauer had wanted to kiss and embrace him.

Professor Brodsky lived on the outskirts of the town in a quiet, well-kept suburban street. The houses here had the appearance of comfortable little knights' castles, adorned with many projections, pinnacles, little towers, balconies, and round bottle-glass windows. "Like the scenery for the *Meistersinger* at a provincial theater," laughed Peter Ilych. "Nevertheless, it is no doubt very pleasant to live here. It looks bourgeois and comfortable."

Brodsky's flat was on the second floor of a homely little Saxon knight's castle. While the gentlemen were mounting the stairs, two ladies appeared up above; they nodded and called out. They were Brodsky's wife and sister-in-law—both of them had full figures and they resembled each other. Their broad faces looked very friendly under their high headdress; both had long cigarettes between their soft lips. Madame Brodsky wore a Japanese kimono of black silk embroidered with great yellow flowers; the sister-in-law wore a white linen Russian blouse fastened all the way up, with a red embroidered collar as stiff as the collar of a uniform. Brodsky embraced his wife, who at once reproached him for driving in an open sledge and for looking frozen.

"But ladies," cried Peter Ilych, "it's such a lovely evening!" He had known Madame Brodsky in Moscow and waited for her to introduce him to the sister-in-law. With quaintly old-fashioned and exaggerated gallantry, he bowed very low to the two ladies. To Madame Brodsky he handed the red roses with which Herr Krause had presented him.

In the sitting-room there was a smell of pine trees, honey-cakes, and the samovar. On the round table in the middle stood the Christmas tree, a fine, well-loaded, sturdy, well-proportioned example, lavishly decked with colored balls, fruits, silvered pine cones, all sorts of twisted cakes, wax angels, and allegorical figures. The candles burned, sending their fragrance and mild fitful light into the room.

"Yes, Peter Ilych," declared Madame Brodsky, "we have decorated the tree with new candles in your honor."

Peter Ilych showed his pleasure. "Oh, a Christmas tree!" he cried again and again. "That's splendid. Now at last I see I am really in Germany. Yes, Brodsky, my dear old Brodsky, you have become a real German professor and family man! But no, you have also remained a good Russian. For I see you've actually got a samovar, and the tea glasses, and preserved cherries, and cigarettes with long mouthpieces, and bottles of vodka, and the nice sweets!" He took one of the soft brownish fondants. Beside himself with pleasure, he pranced about the room. "Ah, and what sort of things have you got in the bookcase, I wonder? Pushkin and Gogol and *War and Peace*. How glad I am to be here! It's like being back in Russia. That is good. That is good," he repeated softly, and a lump came into his throat. "And at the same time I am in the middle of Germany," he added, "and have the Christmas tree and the mask of Beethoven. You really have the best of both countries."

"But you must take some tea, Peter Ilych," cried Madame Brodsky. "You mustn't spend all your time talking; first of all you must have some tea, and I've baked some genuine *piroggen* for you."

"Isn't it beautiful here?" said Peter Ilych to Siloti, who had remained standing by the Christmas tree. Siloti's flawless face was turned towards the candlelight.

"Marvelous!" he said gravely.

"No, no, I'm not in the 'enemy's camp,' not 'caught in a trap,'" cried Tchaikovsky and turned away from young Siloti and towards the others. "That was all my imagination. I was terribly alarmed. But now I am happy."

"You must have some tea!" repeated Madame Brodsky with cheerful obstinacy, and the sister-in-law in the Russian blouse added like a merry echo: "Now you really must have some tea, Peter Ilych."

Peter Ilych had his tea. While thus partaking of the good things of Moscow and Leipzig, he said to Brodsky: "You are treating me like a prince! It is splendid of you. If it hadn't been for your hospitality, I should certainly not have survived this evening. You have already saved my violin concerto, and now you save my life. I don't know which action was the more worth while," he added. "I am eternally grateful to our old friend Brodsky," he went on, turning to the critic Krause, who listened eagerly as he plucked at his beard. "Our wonderful old friend Brodsky took on my violin concerto at a time when not a soul would have anything to do with it. I had dedicated it to my friend Auer, and my friend Auer professed himself to be enormously flattered and charmed. His great joy in the dedication showed itself in his never wanting to play the thing; it was unplayable, declared friend Auer—it was in fact too difficult. You can well believe that this authoritative judgment on my poor concerto was not particularly useful. It lay idle; nobody dared to attempt it—until Brodsky came along, and he played my poor old concerto in Vienna. And what did he get for his pains? The most influential critic on the Danube, Herr Hanslick it was, wrote . . ."

Peter Ilych leaned back in his chair with satisfaction, in order to quote Herr Hanslick's review exactly, stressing each word with enjoyment: " 'We know that in contemporary literature there appear more and more works in which the authors love to produce the most offensive physiological phenomena, including even obscene smells.' " Peter Ilych spoke very gravely, with raised index finger. " 'Such literature can be described as stinking. Mr. Tchaikovsky's concerto has shown us that there is also such a thing as stinking music.' "

"Disgraceful, disgraceful!" cried Mr. Krause, and in his indignation his pince-nez, which were fastened to a black ribbon, fell from his nose. Arthur Friedheim was also enraged. "By such criticism as that, Herr Hanslick ought to have condemned himself!" he said with severity and with an angry jerk of his shoulders. But Brodsky growled reproachfully: "You've actually learned the stuff by heart! Did it really upset you?"

"It upset me terribly, old fellow." There was an almost tender softness in Peter Ilych's voice. "For my part, I've got accustomed to that sort of thing. I've had to read a great many similar things about myself in Russia. But you had given yourself so much trouble. . . ."

"Well," said Brodsky, "in the meantime your concerto has been played all over Europe; I wasn't left to be the only one to play it."

"But you were the first." Tchaikovsky gave him a friendly smile.

"It is a lovely concerto," said Siloti breaking a short silence. Tchaikovsky looked at him for a moment, and then turned his glance away from him and said laughingly to the critic Krause: "I'm now curious to see whether the critical gentry of Leipzig will characterize my orchestral Suite as 'stinking.' "

At this, Martin Krause suddenly became highly agitated. "But, Master!" he cried indignantly. "That's almost an insult. You may take it for granted that you'll find here a greater understanding of art than in Vienna. And as you are being sponsored by the Gewandhaus," he added eagerly, "you can rest assured that you will be treated with the utmost respect."

"I know it is a great honor," said Peter Ilych hastily, with a politeness which was neither assumed nor ironical. "I shall prove myself quite unworthy of it; I shall fail completely. . . ."

"Whether it is a great honor or not is neither here nor there." In Mr. Krause's tone there was a shade of severity. "At any rate, the occasion has the value of great unusualness. Generally speaking, they are very conservative at the Gewandhaus. They favor classical programs: Haydn, Mozart, Beethoven, Schumann, Mendelssohn. Only rarely do they venture on Wagner, Berlioz, or Liszt—and then it is a timid concession to the moderns. Otherwise, such things are left entirely to the Liszt-Verein, from whom, in my own opinion, you can always count on getting an interesting program. And now they are going to do *you* in the Gewandhaus! It is a sensation! Here you are regarded as a representative of the ultramodern movement."

"Yes, Peter," declared Brodsky, "here you are looked upon as one of the wildest ones!"

On hearing this Tchaikovsky could not help laughing heartily.

"Certain people in St. Petersburg ought to know that!" He chuckled and rubbed his hands: "Certain people who look upon me as belonging to a played-out generation, and make out that I am an arch-conservative bore!"

"One contention is, of course, just as false as the other," remarked Friedheim. "The truth is, your place is midway between the two extremes, Peter Ilych."

Tchaikovsky stood up. "What does this mean?" he exclaimed walking about the room. "We talk the whole time about me and my petty doings; and that disturbs me, not only for the sake of

those here in the flesh, but also on account of those over there—
the Masters." He had remained standing by the mantelpiece,
which was adorned with pictures of the great musicians. They
stood in a row: Glinka and Wagner, Schumann and Berlioz,
Liszt and Brahms. "What a fine head Liszt had!" said Peter Ilych
reverently. "The eagle in the cassock! . . ."

Suddenly they all began to talk about Liszt. Both Friedheim
and Siloti had been pupils of his. "Nobody ever had a finer
mastery of the instrument than he," declared Friedheim, tap-
ping the black shining surface of the closed grand piano with
his thin, trained fingers. "Not even Rubinstein," he added contentiously.

"No, not even Anton Rubinstein," confirmed the resonant
voice of young Siloti.

"And yet the piano to him, and perhaps the whole of music,
was only a means of seduction," said Friedheim thoughtfully.

"Liszt, or the School of Velocity—after Woman!" added
Martin Krause with a titter. "That is how a German poet-philoso-
pher branded him."

"It's remarkable," said Tchaikovsky; "it's hardly more than a
year since he died, and already he is a legend. In his own lifetime he made legends out of himself. The great seducer in the
garments of an abbé, the unconquerable virtuoso of the pianoforte, and of love . . . I never went to visit him," he added
slowly. "He was so sought after, and only wanted to have his
admirers around him. He could not make much of my work,
so I've been told."

They went on talking about Liszt, and of his famous love
affairs, his travels, the varied and princely life he spent between
Rome, Paris, Weimar, and Budapest; and of the extraordinary
combination of worldliness and piety which characterized him;
of his stimulating pedagogic activities, his tirelessness in helping,
discovering, and promoting. "Yes, he was a great *arrangeur*,"
said Peter Ilych, summing up, "and a great wizard. He was cast
in the same mold as Paganini. I wonder if anyone now living has

inherited his secrets? And this, this is Brahms," he added, bending down over another portrait.

"Yes, that is Johannes Brahms," repeated Brodsky solemnly.

There followed a short silence. Tchaikovsky, his back to the rest of the company, had remained standing in front of the fireplace. "You are one of his admirers also?" he said at last, turning round to Brodsky.

"We all admire him," answered Brodsky, his voice still solemn.

Peter Ilych bit his lips. "I know, I know," he said. "They have worked up a kind of religious cult for him here. It is rather disconcerting to find oneself in the midst of a cult in which one can take no part."

"What have you against Brahms, Master?" Martin Krause drew nearer rather officiously, with the air of one who meant to whip out a notebook and take down the actual words of the Russian visitor.

"What have I against him?" asked Peter Ilych, putting one foot on the other nervously. "Well, I find him completely incomprehensible—I must admit it. Of course I recognize and appreciate his qualities: he is serious, and deep, and even noble. He is solid and distinguished; he will never make use of crude, superficial effects, as some of our contemporaries do—as, maybe, I do at times. But I simply can't bring myself to love him; I simply cannot *love* him, try as I may. It upsets me to have to speak like this about your country's celebrated Master," he added with a slight bow in the direction of the critic Krause.

"Oh, not at all; please go on," pleaded the contributor to the *Leipziger Tageblatt* animatedly. "What you say is extremely interesting."

"Very well, then, if you really want to hear what I think," said Tchaikovsky, "I find in Brahms's music something dry, cold, nebulous, repellent. In everything he does there is a tendency towards the excessive, the *bottomless*, which repels me. You will forgive this crude word. When I hear this music no warmth comes into my heart; on the contrary, I feel as if I had been attacked by an icy wind. It freezes me—do you understand that? I feel that there is something lacking. There is a lack of beauty, melody. In his work a musical thought is never quite allowed full expression. No sooner is a musical theme hinted at than harmonic modulations, luscious and mysterious, grow rankly all over it. It is as if the composer had set himself the task of being incomprehensible and profound—profound at any cost, even at the cost of boredom. I've often asked myself: Is this German master really so deep—deep all the time and in every phrase? Or is he only flirting with profundity in order to cover up the appalling poverty and dryness of his imagination? That, of course, is a question which cannot be decided. But this profundity and this sublimity, whether genuine or faked, don't move me—no, they don't move me at all, they have no power whatever to stir anything in my heart."

"You will think differently when you have steeped yourself with greater devotion in his music—music which is so rich in marvels," said Brodsky, gently rebuking. "You will certainly come to recognize its greatness."

"Well—perhaps . . ." said Tchaikovsky and turned again towards the tea table. "Musical Germany is divided into two great camps—on the one side Wagner, on the other Brahms. Now, if I have to choose between those two, I plump for . . . Mozart!"

They laughed. The tension that had held the little company during the last few minutes was released.

"In spite of everything," said Brodsky, "I want you to know Brahms personally. Perhaps the effect of a personal contact with him will be to change your opinion of his work. Tomorrow evening he'll be coming here to make music. Will you give us the pleasure of your company too?"

"I shall regard it as a great honor to make the acquaintance of a man who is so famous and so much discussed," Tchaikovsky hastened to assure him. "Many thanks. Of course I shall be pleased to come."

He allowed Madame Brodsky to pour him out a second glass of vodka. Arthur Friedheim inquired about various acquaintances in Russia. Anecdotes were related about Rimsky-Korsakov and César Cui, and about various virtuosos, music critics, and singers. Peter Ilych laughed a great deal and allowed them to fill up his glass repeatedly.

The four Russians hardly noticed that for some considerable time the conversation had been carried on in their own language. The music critic Krause felt out in the cold and at first made a somewhat sour grimace, but presently he engaged the two ladies in conversation about the state of the Leipzig Opera House. Both from the German-speaking and the Russian-speaking groups came loud outbursts of laughter.

When somebody called attention to the fact that it was nearly midnight, they were all astonished. While they were helping one another into their fur coats in the little cloakroom, Peter Ilych invited young Siloti to come and have lunch with him next day. He kissed his friend Brodsky good-bye on both cheeks, and paid exaggerated compliments to the ladies, whose faces were flushed with alcohol and pleasure.

*   *   *

"Please don't go away yet," Peter Ilych begged of young Siloti, who was taking his leave of him an hour after lunch. "Stay just a little longer. I have such a horror nowadays of being alone. . . ."

They sat drinking coffee in the hall of the hotel, which was resplendent with imitation marble, gilded stucco, and all sorts of exuberant commonplace ornaments. Behind the little table at which they were sitting an enormous white plaster angel grew out of a massive column of imitation yellow and black marble. Beneath a mass of curly hair the angel had a low forehead and puffed-out spherical cheeks; in his two coarse hands he held a mighty wind instrument to his mouth, a cross between an overgrown flute and a warlike trumpet. Like a dangerous weapon, it towered over the heads of the two musicians.

"Isn't it dreadful here?" said Tchaikovsky, and threw a startled glance at the threatening cherub. "Perhaps you will be good enough to keep me company for a while in my room. . . ."

Young Siloti bowed gravely, and a courteous smile spread over his marble face. Peter Ilych's cheeks were red from the food and drink provided by the interminable hotel repast; Siloti's face and forehead had remained the color of ivory, and his long black eyebrows looked as if they had been drawn with Indian ink.

"You must forgive me, my boy, for keeping you so long." Peter Ilych spoke somewhat hurriedly. "But I am in such a nervous state that it is painful to me to be alone. I have taken on far too much. I am terrified at the thought of the concert in the Gewandhaus. It is the first time that I have undertaken to conduct abroad. I shall misfire, I feel quite sure. . . ."

"I am very happy to be allowed to be with you," said young Siloti, in his very clear, vibrant, but somewhat soulless voice.

"How distant he is from me!" thought Peter Ilych. And the dismay with which he made this discovery was so intense that for some moments he could not move. "He is incalculably far removed from me. I wonder what he is thinking about? Only about himself and his early fame? How uncanny it is that one can never really grasp what another is thinking and feeling. And this strange smiling young man, with his strange way of speaking, I have known for years; he has been a pupil of mine; I can still see his attentive childish face as he sat next to me at the piano. . . ."

"Is it really so wonderful to be famous?" asked Tchaikovsky, who was suddenly thinking of Kotek—poor little Kotek who had been so avid of fame!

"You certainly ought to know what it is like to be famous," said young Siloti, and as he met the sad, thoughtful look of his former teacher, no expression disturbed the flawless perfection of his face. "You must know more about it than I do, Peter Ilych. I am only just beginning. And of what importance is a little pianist? He is merely an interpreter. . . . It is you who must tell me what fame means, *real* fame."

Peter Ilych made a tired gesture. "Oh, I . . ." he began slowly, his head drooping. "I don't know much about it. More than anything else I find it fatiguing, this so-called fame. Moreover, in my case it has come too late. I'm finished, I'm played out; I've nothing more to say: Since the violin concerto I haven't written anything that really matters. . . . But you are young, you are ambitious; how enviable that is! I doubt if there is as much fame in the world as you demand and expect."

"Naturally I am ambitious," said young Siloti, sitting very upright. "But you're not being sincere," he went on, smiling as he inclined his head slightly towards the Master. "You don't believe you're played out—why, you are just forty-eight! Nor have you ever been indifferent to fame. We all need it." Suddenly Siloti had spoken very loudly, almost triumphantly, as if addressing the chubby-faced music-making angel above him.

Peter Ilych sat with bent head between these two young musical divinities—the one imperfect and commonplace and made of plaster; the other perfectly and nobly formed of flesh and blood—and said without lifting his glance from the ground: "We all need it—perhaps! Yes, no doubt I wasn't being sincere. We do all need it—but for what? As a substitute for what? As a substitute for what, I ask you, Siloti?"

"As a substitute for that, and only that, which we are willing to sacrifice for it," said the pupil, his young face frozen in an icy, radiant smile.

Up in his room, Peter Ilych asked for permission to lie down. "I feel terribly done-up," he said complainingly. "Last night I didn't sleep at all." He took both bicarbonate of soda and valerian drops. For Siloti he pulled up the armchair next to the chaise longue on which he stretched himself.

The young pianist remained with Tchaikovsky the whole afternoon. There were many long pauses in their conversation; once, indeed, Peter Ilych remained a whole quarter of an hour with his eyes closed. It was impossible to tell whether he was asleep or not. Siloti kept quite still. Then they began to talk again, and their conversation remained on the same quiet friendly plane, whether they related some gossip of the musical world, or some moving reminiscence of Nikolay Rubinstein or of somebody else whom they both knew. Every now and again Peter Ilych asked young Alexander Siloti about his plans: he loved listening to the controlled voice, which nevertheless trembled from secret ambition as he spoke of the tours and concerts which were destined to enhance his reputation.

The room had become quite dark—they had forgotten to light the lamps—when Siloti declared he must leave, in order to change for the soiree at Brodsky's.

"Come and call for me in an hour's time," Tchaikovsky begged. "We will go together to Brodsky's. It is painful for me to appear alone in company—and particularly this evening. I am in mortal terror of making the acquaintance of the Master, Brahms. I've no doubt it has come to his ears that I don't speak of him with becoming respect."

An hour later they were walking side by side through the snow-covered streets. It was even colder than it had been the previous evening. In spite of that, Tchaikovsky was bent on going the whole way on foot. "One must be careful to see that one gets enough exercise," he cried; "otherwise one becomes stiff. I'm already old and infirm enough!"

As they approached Brodsky's flat he said: "Although I'm so full of anxiety about this evening—you mark my words, it's going to be a distressing affair!—I am very happy when I think of Brodsky's home. It's so nice and warm there. Perhaps they will even have some punch," he added excitedly, and with his soft, sensuous mouth he seemed to enjoy the hot spicy liquid in anticipation.

"There is bound to be punch," Siloti promised him, kicking vigorously at the freshly fallen snow with his right foot. "Why, it's New Year's Eve!"

Peter Ilych stood still in the middle of the snow-covered street. "Well, well, so it's New Year's Eve, is it?" he said. "I never remember that you have a different calendar here. . . . Yes, of course, you are quite right: it is New Year's Eve. A new year! How dreadful, Alexander! A new year!"

He stared, with a disconsolate expression, into the star-filled night sky. His horror-stricken glance, released from the glittering frosty wastes of the winter sky, fell on his companion. "A new year . . ." murmured Tchaikovsky once more, and slowly stretched out his arm towards Siloti as if he must have his support. He let his arm fall as slowly as he had raised it, without having touched the shoulders of the young man at his side.

"A new year," said Siloti in a friendly, calming voice; "what is there so frightful about that? It only means: a new chance to achieve something else."

"Yes, yes." But Peter Ilych shook his head, and standing there, somewhat bent, he suddenly looked like a quite old man. "It terrifies me every time," he said. "I don't know why. . . . Every time it terrifies me. . . ."

When they arrived at Brodsky's flat they were greeted by both ladies, the wife and the sister-in-law. "A hearty welcome to you!" cried the opulent Madame Brodsky, who was fantastically decked out in an extremely low-necked evening dress of purplish red velvet, while the sister-in-law shone in a similarly cut gown of green taffeta. "A hearty welcome, dear Peter Ilych, and a happy new year to you!" They shook hands, the two ladies retaining the long cigarettes between their lips. Of course Peter Ilych had to embrace Madame Brodsky. Her bosom heaved and she exhaled a strong odor of some sweet oriental musk perfume.

Professor Brodsky had joined them. He wore a solemn evening suit; his face was hot and flushed and he appeared to be somewhat excited. "The Master, Brahms, will be here soon," he said, as if reassuringly. "Come inside, old fellows. Other friends are expecting you."

There was a buzz of voices in the sitting-room. In the soft flickering candlelight which came from the Christmas tree, Tchaikovsky could scarcely distinguish one face from another. He shook many hands. The old gentleman who greeted him with particular warmth was Carl Reinecke, the honored conductor of the Gewandhaus orchestra. "We are all so glad to have you here," said Reinecke. Peter Ilych bowed gratefully. Another gentleman came in, and he also had shrewd, good-natured eyes: this was Joachim, the great violinist, Kotek's former teacher and an old friend of the Master for whom everybody was waiting.

Peter Ilych would have been pleased to talk with the two worthy and experienced musicians, but it was not possible to escape from the tall lean woman who was approaching him. Her gray sports costume—a sort of eccentric hunting outfit—did not fit into the picture of the serious middle-class, dressed-up company. On a short leather lead she had following her a narrow-backed, evil-looking greyhound. "You are Mr. Tchaikovsky?" she asked, attacking him at once. From her first German word it became clear that she was an Englishwoman. "*Very interesting!* I don't happen to know your compositions, but I have been told about you. I am Miss Brown, a colleague of yours. Yes, I also write music."

"Delighted . . ." murmured Peter Ilych.

"So you have also come to make the acquaintance of the Master, Brahms?" asked Miss Brown. "Are you seeing him for the first time? I envy you! Between ourselves, he is divine!" She cupped her hand round her loquacious mouth as if she were betraying a secret. Peter Ilych wanted to turn his back on her, but forced himself out of politeness to listen to her further chatter. "We must all be proud that we are contemporaries of his." He heard her tinny voice as through a fog. He gazed angrily beyond her longish, yellow, old-maidish face, which looked like creased and crumpled parchment. He noticed that Brodsky was coming towards him; at Brodsky's side was a somewhat slender and gentle-looking young man, walking with tripping steps.

The young man remained standing in front of Tchaikovsky; his blond hair was wavy and at the same time rather sparse. When close to him, one could perceive that his bright, strikingly pure, and innocent-looking eyes were surrounded by a whole colony of tiny wrinkles. Brodsky laid his hand on Peter Ilych's shoulder. "Edvard Grieg is anxious to make your acquaintance," he said.

"Edvard Grieg!" exclaimed Peter Ilych. "But my dear Brodsky, why didn't you tell me that Edvard Grieg would be coming? If you had told me, all day long I should have had something pleasant to look forward to."

They shook hands. Grieg stood there in a timid attitude, one shoulder raised in a nervous manner. "It is very nice to make your acquaintance," he said in a high-pitched, clear voice. He spoke German with a very attractive, slightly singsong Norwegian accent.

"And I have wanted to make your acquaintance for such a long time," said Peter Ilych, with great cordiality, speaking much louder than usual. He was unusually moved and charmed by the sight of this shy and still youthful-looking man, whose famous melodies—a whole treasure-house of unpretentious charm and freshness—he knew and loved. "And how young you look!" he exclaimed. "You must forgive me for coming out with that at once; but I don't suppose I'm so very much older than you. I had been thinking to myself: 'Grieg is an old colleague'—and now I find a youth!"

"But you also look quite young, dear Tchaikovsky," declared Grieg, with quaint courtesy.

"Ah, my friend, don't make fun of an old man!" Peter Ilych playfully covered his worn features with both his hands.

"Nina!" called Edvard Grieg eagerly. "Nina, come along and be introduced to Tchaikovsky."

From a corner of the room there came an answer in a pure high voice which was rather like his own. "Yes, Edvard, yes!" And Nina Grieg approached them; her step was rather tripping like her husband's; she was small like her husband, and she had a face which curiously resembled his; but she was already somewhat gray.

"This is Nina Hagerup-Grieg," said her husband, "my wife and cousin." They stood in front of Tchaikovsky hand in hand like two good children.

"It's marvelous to find you both here," said Peter Ilych, kissing Mrs. Grieg's hand. He had completely forgotten that anybody else was there. The presence of the rest of the company entered his consciousness only when their chatter and laughter ceased. All of a sudden a reverential hush descended upon the room. Johannes Brahms had entered.

Peter Ilych had already observed his solid and portly form at the door, but behaved as if he had not done so. Breaking into the silence, he turned to Mrs. Nina Hagerup-Grieg and said in a quite loud voice: "You can't imagine how much I love those melodies of your husband, dear lady."

Professor Brodsky prodded him from behind. "Peter Ilych, Brahms is here!" he whispered to him.

"Oh, has Herr Brahms arrived?" Peter Ilych took on the attitude of an indifferent man of the world. Brahms had already come up to him.

"So this is our Russian guest," said the German Master, and holding his head back he observed Peter Ilych out of his somewhat screwed-up gray eyes.

"A happy new year to you, Herr Brahms!" said Peter Ilych; and to his great annoyance he felt himself turn red as he spoke.

"But the old year isn't over yet." Brahms broke into a short harsh laugh which ceased as abruptly as it had broken out. This amusing observation of the Master provoked reverential laughter from the circle which had formed itself round the two composers, Peter Ilych Tchaikovsky and Johannes Brahms. Loudest of all was the laughter of the music critic Krause, whom Peter Ilych now saw for the first time among the guests.

Brahms stood there with legs astraddle. He held his arms slightly separated from his thickset body, and this gave a heavy clumsiness to his appearance.

"He looks as if he suffered from shortness of breath," thought Tchaikovsky, "and yet his breath comes quietly and steadily."

"How do you like Leipzig?" asked Brahms, and slowly raised his right hand in order to put a large black cigar—which looked terribly heavy and awkward—into his mouth.

"It is very kind of you to inquire," answered Peter Ilych, lighting a new cigarette from one which he had just smoked to its end. "My friends here have welcomed me so charmingly I already feel almost at home."

"I'm glad to hear that," said Brahms, leaning his head backwards, his mouth slightly open, holding at arm's length the heavy cigar and allowing the smoke to rise. "Yes, it is always nice and comfortable at the Brodskys'," he added with a slight smile in the direction where Brodsky was standing. "And you get the best coffee in Leipzig here." Whereupon a short and silvery ripple of laughter was heard to come from Madame Brodsky.

Brahms spoke with a strong North German accent, somewhat jerkily, strongly emphasizing the first syllable of each word. "Vienna hasn't affected him at all," thought Peter Ilych; "neither him nor his music. And the rounded soft lines of his face don't go with his sharp way of speaking. His face rather reminds me of a Russian priest, with its luxuriant grayish beard and the fine long gray hair—nice hair . . . but it is already quite thin. His long dark coat has also something priestly about it. I must have known a priest at some time or other whom he resembles. But I wonder why he wears such short trousers? They look awkward, and so does the long coat; and he's got dreadfully clumsy boots on. . . ."

"We'll have a little music later on," said the German Master, to whom somebody was handing a cup of coffee. Peter Ilych suddenly remembered having heard that Brahms drank strong coffee half the day: he must have an extraordinarily strong heart! "I hope you won't be bored, Herr Tchaikovsky."

"I should be very proud if I might be allowed to hear your new trio." Peter Ilych bowed slightly.

"Well, perhaps it won't be altogether to your taste." Brahms continued to stand with his legs astraddle in front of this foreigner who he knew did not appreciate his work, in one hand the coffee cup, in the other, the cigar. "It is not highly seasoned; there is nothing brilliant about it." He looked at Peter Ilych in a friendly fashion, but not without a tinge of mockery.

"I am convinced that it is beautiful," said Tchaikovsky, and was annoyed with himself for having answered so ineptly. Everybody in the room had been waiting with strained attention to see how he would react to the great man's somewhat direct and undistinguished attack, and now they must all be disappointed.

"It is generally known," began Brahms with a look that was friendly but keenly scrutinizing, "that after the music of your own country, you prefer the contemporary French composers: Gounod, Massenet, Saint-Saëns." He pronounced the French names rather laboriously and with false emphases, perhaps out of animosity.

"The composers you mention are certainly estimable," said Tchaikovsky, his high forehead flushing. "But, as a matter of fact, in Paris they contend that I am all too strongly under the German influence."

"In Paris," declared the composer of the *German Requiem*, again laughing harshly, "in Paris they suspect a German influ-

ence everywhere. But I understand your mother was French?"
he asked suddenly, and screwed up his eyes a little.

"My mother came from a French family." Peter Ilych found
this conversation unbearable; if it lasted many more minutes it
might provoke him to a distressing outburst which he would
never be able to live down. Brahms must have felt similarly, for
he brought the conversation to an end, as a royal personage
might terminate an audience.

"In any case, I wish you a pleasant stay in our country," he
said and turned away.

The gaunt Englishwoman with the greyhound leaped towards Brahms like an Amazon against the foe. "When does the
concert start?" she inquired eagerly. "We are all *so very happy* to
hear your latest creation!"

Peter Ilych sought out Grieg, who with his Nina had retired
into a corner. Breathing a deep sigh of relief, he sat down between the lovable little couple on the sofa. "We will listen all
together to the trio," he said.

*   *   *

Peter Ilych passed such a bad night that he felt a wreck the
whole of the next day; he ached in every limb. He canceled
all his engagements and remained in bed. Full of anxiety, he
was afraid that every ill came from heart trouble. He had un-
defined but terrifying notions of some serious heart disease with
which he believed himself to be afflicted—something which the
doctors—those crafty fools—were too ignorant to discover, but
which he nevertheless, in fact therefore, was the more painfully
convinced would some day be the death of him. "My heart is
completely ruined. It has practically ceased to function," he was
in the habit of declaring gloomily. Nevertheless, he smoked
cigarettes the whole day long, even today, when he was lying in
bed trying to get well. The pasteboard mouthpieces piled themselves up beside him in the ashtray. Peter Ilych lay on his back.

He endeavored to remember the dreams which had been tormenting him during the whole of this past dreadful night. But his dreams eluded him. His mother had appeared in them in some way or other; so much he still remembered. She had been unfriendly towards him—how was it that one could dream such hateful things? Yes, he was standing on a table, or it may have been on a chest, and his mother had wanted to hurl him into the abyss. She was amused because he was so alarmed. How came one to dream such things?

He did not eat a mouthful of the lunch which the waiter brought to his room. At about four o'clock he ordered for himself a bottle of cognac. He drank and smoked. Time went by. Peter Ilych realized with anxiety that it would grow dark. "At seven o'clock," he said to himself, "I must get up and dress myself. I must go to the Brahms concert at the Gewandhaus without fail. It is the great New Year's Festival; the whole of musical Leipzig will be there. If I failed to turn up, it would be regarded as a demonstration."

In the evening Brodsky and Siloti called for him. They took a cab to the Gewandhaus. Practically all those who had been present the previous evening at the Brodskys' musical soiree were gathered in a group in the foyer of the concert hall. Peter Ilych heard Miss Brown declaring: "I tell you, my friends, he is the Real Thing, the Fulfilment. I feel that he is the Real Thing. I believe in the three great B's: Bach, Beethoven, Brahms. But the first two were only a preparation for the third and greatest. No, not even Beethoven was the final Fulfilment. And certainly not Wagner; *his* appalling bluff is not a preparation, but a noisy aberration. So it is agreed, then, that the real Fulfilment is Brahms."

Nobody laughed at her. She was regarded as amusing but not ludicrous. As the Master tolerated, with friendly patience, her unbounded admiration, she was counted among the chosen circle of his intimates. She was to be seen at all concerts and at all musical festivals.

"Now you will make the acquaintance of our new Gewand-haus," said the critic Krause animatedly to Peter Ilych, "your new sphere of activity! You will open your eyes, honored sir!"

Peter Ilych admired the hall and assured everybody who wished to hear that it was the handsomest concert hall that he had ever seen. Before coming to the "Fulfilment"—the new Brahms Double Concerto for violin and 'cello—the Thomas-kirche Boys' Choir sang a motet by Bach. Peter Ilych was moved by the rather shrill, white, and angelically pure tone of the children's voices and by the straining, enraptured, and fervent expressions on the childish faces, with their somewhat frowning foreheads and wide-opened mouths; the transfigured boys held the music away from them as if they were all a little farsighted. They were like a group of slender singing angels, raising their voices in harmony to the Almighty.

"They sing even better than *our* church choirs," whispered Peter Ilych to Siloti. "Heavens, how beautifully they sing!"

When Brahms mounted to the conductor's desk, he was greeted with applause that was more respectful than enthusias-tic. But from the moment that he gave the signal to begin and stood there, plump and solid, the baton in his upraised hand, complete silence reigned in the hall, as if some sacrament were about to be celebrated. The violin part was played by the master Joachim; the 'cellist was Hausmann, who had come from Berlin. Peter Ilych listened with reverence to the strong, pure attack of the strings. "It is the best orchestra I have ever heard," he thought, impressed. "In Russia we have nothing to compare with it." With close and completely objective attention he ob-served the movements of the conductor-composer—movements which were heavy, almost awkward, but strong and full of feel-ing; the almost angry jerk of the head and stiffly raised arm in the *forte* passages; and immediately afterwards, the sudden softening of the attitude, the tender curving of the pleading, entreating arms, which vibrated like the strings of an instrument; the appearance of inward emotion on the backward-leaning, inspired face.

Peter Ilych found it difficult to concentrate on the music. He was very nervous. He was thinking of the orchestral rehearsal which he had to take in this very hall next day.

*   *   *

The Russian composer, who was about to be introduced to the Gewandhaus orchestra by the conductor Reinecke, had a white and agitated face which at times flushed a dark red on the slightest provocation; his too-soft mouth, under the drooping gray-white moustache, trembled.

"You all know the great composer Tchaikovsky," said good-natured old Reinecke. "Gentlemen, allow me to introduce you to both the conductor and the man, Tchaikovsky."

The great composer, conductor, and man, Tchaikovsky, stepped onto the rostrum, bowed down with anxiety and nervousness. The violinists, viola players, and 'cellists tapped on their instruments with their bows as a sign of their approval, but simultaneously grimaced peevishly: they were not very keen on collaborating with foreign composers who were known to be eccentric. With a timid glance Peter Ilych looked at these cool, noncommittal faces. "Now I've got to make my speech," he thought as the dark red hue spread over his countenance. "They will jeer at me; they will make a laughing-stock of me." He began in a husky voice: "Gentlemen, I cannot speak German, but I am proud to be in such a . . . such a . . . how shall I express it? I am proud . . . I cannot . . ." The leader of the orchestra, who sat next to Peter Ilych, suppressed a laugh. Tchaikovsky, suddenly holding himself erect, tapped on the desk with his baton. "Let us begin, gentlemen!" he cried in a voice which had suddenly become loud, easy, and well under control. They rehearsed the First Orchestral Suite.

Peter Ilych worked with passion. He frequently interrupted the playing and asked for repetitions, but he was never impatient or irritable; on the contrary, he treated the members of the orchestra with the most careful and kindly consideration; indeed, he almost coquetted with them in order to gain their good will. "Gentlemen, my dear sirs!" he cried in his soft, singing German, and raised his arms in a comically pleading gesture. "I implore you: once more—and with more tenderness—a more floating quality, lighter, quite, quite light!"

The first movement, Introduzione e Fuga, gave the winds a lot of trouble. Just at the beginning the two bassoons had to play the theme in unison; they could not keep the high-pitched notes clean, and Peter Ilych insisted on having them repeated. During the second movement, the Divertimento, a stocky figure appeared at the back of the half-dark hall. It was Brahms. He carefully took a seat in the back row of the stalls. Peter Ilych had noticed him as soon as he entered. "What a good thing it is we are doing the Divertimento," thought Tchaikovsky. "It is a successful piece; it must impress him as something novel. Yes, the way I have combined our folk-tunes—our tragic, beloved tunes—with German waltz-rhythms is certainly new. The result is something more than a mere Valse Triste: it is a Tragic Waltz. It is a mixture of grace and sorrow—a graceful lament. Do you understand what is meant by that, Herr Brahms? To lament gracefully . . . ? I put in the Divertimento as an afterthought. . . . I am glad I fitted it in. . . ."

The musicians were now in an excellent mood. The great and genuine zeal of this foreign composer had stimulated their ambition, and his flattering and ingratiating amiability had put them in a good humor. After the Divertimento they rehearsed the Intermezzo, and they put a good face on it when they were constantly interrupted. When they came to the third movement, the Marche Miniature, Peter Ilych became a little uneasy. He knew that Brahms, in the gloom at the back of the hall, would assume an expression of contempt. "I ought to have cut out the Marche Miniature," he thought, as he begged of the orchestra to play with the greatest possible lightness. "This little piece must sound as if it were being played on a music box," he explained to the musicians. "I am well aware that this little joke of mine is somewhat trivial; that's why I have marked it *ad libitum*. But no conductor will ever hear of leaving it out; the public likes such jokes. Why should I abandon something that is invariably effective?"

"Moreover, it sounds very pretty," he thought, with a feeling of defiance that was directed at the man in the semi-darkness. Only a small section of the orchestra was employed: two flutes and a piccolo, two clarinets, two oboes, four divided violins, a triangle, and the glockenspiel. "It really sounds very nice," thought Peter Ilych, and as his movements became more and more dancelike and unrestrained, he called out: "Lightly, my friends! Very, very lightly! A music box, my friends!" At this very moment he heard Brahms clear his throat disapprovingly.

After the rehearsal, Peter Ilych expressed a few words of warm thanks to the orchestra. "It will be all right," he declared exhaustedly, wiping the perspiration from his brow. "But the Marche Miniature must be even lighter, please. It ought to have no weight at all!"

Old Reinecke shook him by the hand, paid him compliments, and made one or two criticisms. Brahms's stocky silhouette emerged from the dark background. He came up to them and greeted Tchaikovsky with formal friendliness. He said not a word about the Orchestral Suite. He behaved as if he simply had not heard it. The greetings over, he began to discuss with Reinecke a concert that would be given at the Gewandhaus after the Tchaikovsky evening.

Peter Ilych was in a position to feel after the rehearsal that he no longer had any excuse for crippling, agonizing anxiety. A good friendly relationship had been established between him and the orchestra; they had made themselves thoroughly acquainted with one another; a complete fiasco would now appear to be out of the question. Nevertheless when he went next morning to the general rehearsal, which was open to the public, he was again agitated and apprehensive. All night long he had been imagining that Brahms or one of his admirers might stage an attack on him in Leipzig; that they might even go so far as to engage rowdies with whistles and stink bombs.

However, the morning arrangements were carried out in an entirely friendly manner. The large concert hall was well filled; probably free tickets had been distributed; Peter Ilych noticed a large group of Russian students. It was they whom he had to thank for the hearty applause; after the Marche Miniature, which never failed of its effect on the public, the applause expanded into an ovation; it dropped again after the fourth movement, the Scherzo, and rose to enthusiasm after the Finale, a gavotte. The young Russians shouted and showed their approval of their compatriot. He bowed his thanks to them, and as he did so he was aware once again of tears—tears of emotion, of pride, of homesickness, and of fatigue. He was glad when at last he found himself alone in the cab which took him back to the hotel.

The porter handed him a note which had just been delivered. Peter Ilych read: "It was splendid! Many thanks. Your friend and admirer, Edvard Grieg." He smiled and was fearful lest the moustached hotel employee should observe the great tears which ran down his cheeks.

He put the note carefully in his breast-pocket, and carried it with him as a talisman when he drove to the concert next evening.

He had been warned beforehand that the very serious German audiences were not given to rash and exaggerated manifestations. In spite of this, he was somewhat disconcerted when not a hand stirred as he stepped onto the rostrum. There was complete silence. This evening there were no Russian students in the hall. Peter Ilych bowed awkwardly. The undemonstrative public allowed itself to be won over; the applause grew with every movement. At the end it was very hearty. Peter Ilych had to take two calls, and he was assured that this was something out of the ordinary for Leipzig.

"And now may I go home?" thought Peter Ilych. "Now may I go to my room in the hotel, fall down on the bed, and close my eyes? What shall I think of then? Let us hope that my thoughts will soon calm themselves down and torment me no longer. . . .

"I wonder why Siloti is not here? I haven't seen Siloti the whole evening. Where can he be? Wasn't he at the concert? Remarkable! He who of all people should have been there, failed! There is always a certain person one wants to come, and he nearly always fails. . . ."

Next morning Peter Ilych was awakened early. It was not yet seven o'clock when somebody knocked loudly on his door. The reception manager of the hotel stepped in and called out breathlessly: "You must get up at once, Herr Tchaikovsky! The military band has come to serenade you!"

"Where?" asked the bewildered Peter Ilych. "Here in my room?"

"Of course not!" replied the excited manager. "In the courtyard of the hotel. It is a great honor. You must look out of the window and listen. It is a great honor, Herr Tchaikovsky! Here is the program."

With a bow he handed him the program: it was painted with broad brush-strokes on a piece of stiff cardboard and looked rather like an elegant bill-of-fare. At the top was inscribed: "Morning Concert in honor of the Russian Composer, Peter Tchaikovsky." Then followed, in a beautiful and carefully arranged group, framed by a garland of roses, the titles of eight pieces of music. Before Peter Ilych could decipher them, a brass band down below played the Russian national anthem. The hotel reception manager handed Peter Ilych his long flannel dressing-gown; Peter Ilych put it on and went to the window.

"Must I open the window?" he asked.

"Of course," said the manager excitedly.

"But I shall catch cold," grumbled Peter Ilych.

He opened the window. The fresh morning air entered the room. Down below, in the snow-covered courtyard, the military band was playing with all its might. The bandmaster saluted Peter Ilych, who returned the greeting politely. He thought it was frightfully cold; his breath floated upward like a little cloud into the clear and frosty air; he held the brown dressing-gown close to his chest. As the Russian anthem boomed and crashed to its end, the guests who had been aroused appeared at all the windows of the hotel, which was built in a square round the courtyard. They had thrown furs or woolen shawls over their sleeping garments. They did not quite understand what was happening down below, but they were happy because the morning was fresh and bright, and because there was military music to be heard. A stout lady, with her hair in curl-papers, leaned well out of the window in a way that gave cause for anxiety—she was fat and awkward and might fall out—in order to applaud the band. Waiters, scullery-maids, kitchen-boys, and cooks in their white caps had emerged from their basement into the courtyard, that they might be as near as possible to what was going on. After the Russian anthem, the uniformed brass band played an aria from *Aida*; after that followed a Viennese waltz and a short and very varied Wagner potpourri; after several other highly effective pieces, played with praiseworthy accuracy, the program closed with the *Marche Solennelle* in D major by Tchaikovsky. The principal theme bore a certain resemblance to the *Wacht am Rhein*. The hotel guests and staff, under the impression that one of their national songs was being played, with slight changes, clapped delightedly. Some of the waiters sang the patriotic refrain with wide-open mouths, standing at attention, with their hands pressed to their sides: "Dear Fatherland, may Thou be peaceful!" It did not quite fit the music, but that troubled nobody. Peter Ilych, acknowledging the applause and bowing his thanks, not recognized either by the people in the courtyard or by those at the windows, drew back into his room.

Two minutes later, the bandmaster, who had conducted the band like a solemn marionette, entered the room. His rather grumpy yet good-natured face and heavy beard made him look like an old dog. His uniform, with its elegant epaulettes, was as smart as a general's, and on his chest gleamed many medals.

"Allow me to introduce myself," boomed the old musician and soldier; "my name is Saro." He clicked his heels.

"I thank you, dear Herr Saro, for the wonderful morning concert. I am really touched." Peter Ilych extended his hand.

"It was a great pleasure to me . . . a little attention for our famous guest. . . ." Military-bandmaster Saro stammered and turned red. "I am a great admirer . . . your works, Herr Tchaikovsky . . . many masterpieces among them. One is not a philistine." The good fellow perspired in his embarrassment. "No sort of prejudice . . . against Russian music. . . ." He cleared his throat and became more and more embarrassed. "On the contrary—great reverence. . . . Music and politics have nothing to do with one another," he finished up suddenly, and looked at Peter Ilych with dull, honest eyes.

"I thank you with all my heart," said Tchaikovsky once again.

"It has been a great pleasure to me," said Saro and stood at attention once more. "To my regret—duty calls me!" With a sudden movement he turned round, and in a moment had left the room.

The reception manager followed him. Before closing the door behind him, he bowed to Peter Ilych. "That is fame, Herr Tchaikovsky," he said softly. His tallowy, overtired face was very serious.

Peter Ilych stood alone in the middle of the room. Suddenly he began to laugh: loud, piercing laughter shook his whole body. "Ha, ha, ha!" he laughed, and sank into the armchair, swaying backwards and forwards with laughter, and striking his knees with the flat of his hands. "That is fame . . . ha, ha, ha!"

His head was drooping, his mouth was wide open, as if in lamentation. . . .

◈◈◈◈◈◈◈◈◈◈◈◈◈

PETER ILYCH REMAINED some days longer in Leipzig. When he awoke of a morning in his room at the hotel and
beheld all the trinkets on the whatnot—among them was a
Trumpeter of Säckingen complete with a saucy feather in his
hat, which he particularly hated—then the old, old sensation,
always more and more overwhelming, always more and more
paralyzing, assailed him: "Why am I here? How ridiculous,
how pointless, how horrible it is that I should be here!" But
then he saw from his little notebook that the day was full up
with appointments; he must get up lest he should miss the first
of them. It would be a noisy, strenuous day. As a rule the day
began with a telegram, handed to him by a waiter on a silver
tray—a bewildering, fussy, quarrelsome, humble telegram from
Siegfried Neugebauer; and it ended with music.

His first visitor this morning was Brodsky, who appeared with
a bundle of newspapers under his arm. "I congratulate you, my
dear Peter Ilych," he cried. His face was flushed by the fresh
air, some of which he seemed to have brought with him. "You
have a good press."

"Is there no Hanslick among them?"

They laughed. "No, they have treated you with great respect."

Brodsky spread out the papers on the breakfast table. "This is
the most important," he declared and handed Peter Ilych one
of the pages. "That is Bernsdorf, in the *Signale für die Musi-
kalische Welt*."

"So he is the most important?" asked Peter Ilych. He read:

"Until now only some two or three works by Peter Tchaikovsky, who belongs to the neo- or young-Russian *Sturm und
Drang* school, have become known to us, and these, to be can-

did, have inspired but little sympathy, not because we failed to
recognize the gifts and ability of the composer, but because
the manner in which he applied his talents was repellent to us.
With like frankness we confess that it was not without some
aversion that we sought to become acquainted with the Suite
included in the above-mentioned program, because we feared
that once more a hotchpotch of monstrosities, distortions, and
perversities would be placed before us. It has turned out otherwise. In the work mentioned, Tchaikovsky appears to us to
have become more moderate and clearer; his method is no
longer conspicuously marked by overdecoration or extrava-
gances, no longer seeks salvation in baroque effects. We say
'no longer conspicuously marked by' for details still intrude
which belong to the earlier manner and smack strongly of mere
caprice or even leg-pulling."

Peter Ilych laughed. " 'Seeks salvation in baroque effects.'
That, of course, one should on no account do," he said. "From
now on, I'll try to avoid it."
The review in the *Signalen* closed:

"He will certainly therefore take away with him the conviction that in musical Leipzig there can be no possible question of Russophobia."

"That is what Bandmaster Saro with the big epaulettes has
already assured me," said Peter Ilych with satisfaction. "The
people are awfully proud because they don't allow their musical
taste to be dictated by Bismarck."
At midday there was a little party at Reinecke's. Peter Ilych
sat next to the young composer, Ferruccio Busoni. He was
drawn but at the same time overawed and disconcerted by his
neighbor's seraphically pure, ascetic face; it was a tormented
face and yet wore an ecstatic expression born of intellectual
earnestness. A superficial, conventional conversation between
these two men was not possible; as the place and the occasion

forbade anything very profound or serious, however, their intercourse was restricted, but not without a certain warmth.

In the evening they had a box at the opera. *Die Meistersinger*
was being performed. After the overture Peter Ilych said to
Reinecke: "Your young conductor is wonderful; I am delighted
with him. He seems to have a magical power over the orchestra.
And yet by Heaven, he *does* practically nothing. An old be-
ginner like me toils and writhes and jumps and dances, whereas
that fellow dispenses with every superfluous gesture. He keeps
quite calm, excitingly calm—and in that way seems to compel
the orchestra to thunder like a thousand Jericho trumpets and
then to coo as softly as—as what? Why, as softly as a little dove,
and to fade away with such sweetness . . . well, it takes your
breath away. Do you realize what you've got there in that man?"

"Do we know what we've got in Artur Nikisch?" All the gentlemen who had taken their places in the management's box
broke out excitedly. "Nikisch is our pride and our hope," explained honest old Reinecke. And Martin Krause declared:
"There are no interpreters of the later Wagner who can be
compared with this young master—no, not even Bülow!" he
cried with a challenging expression.

In the interval Peter Ilych allowed himself to be taken round
to meet the conductor. Nikisch was only a little over thirty years
of age; he was slim and gentle; his eyes shone from a pale face.

"I am ashamed," said Peter Ilych to the young conductor. "I
am ashamed, my friend. How could anybody like myself dare
to go before the public as if he were a conductor? You are *really*
one!"

The young conductor Artur Nikisch, whose pale face was
delicately framed by his dark hair and beard, bowed low before
Peter Ilych Tchaikovsky. As he slowly drew himself up, he said:
"I am proud to meet the composer of *Eugen Onegin* and the
Fourth Symphony face to face."

Peter Ilych flushed. "You know my works," he began hurriedly. "I am very pleased that you should have chosen to men-

tion the Fourth Symphony. I don't think it altogether failed—no, not altogether. . . ." Then he added softly, almost secretively, as if it was something which the young conductor might hear but nobody else: "But it's not my last word, in any sense. It will not be my last word."

Peter Ilych had the impression, as he took his leave of Nikisch, that it was a friend whose hand he was shaking; not one of those friends whom one gains and loses in a fleeting exchange of sympathy, the sort of attachment which comes unexpectedly and may just as unexpectedly depart; but a real friend—a friend of his work, and therefore a definitely constructive part of his essential being, which no accident could affect.

*   *   *

Next evening the Liszt Society gave a Tchaikovsky concert in the hall of the old Gewandhaus. The room thus devoted to the cultivation of modernism in Leipzig—for the pursuit of the audacious, the new, and the not-yet-classical was the particular aim and achievement of the Liszt Society—was not outwardly suitable. The hall of the old Gewandhaus was small, uncomfortable, and almost grubby. Nevertheless it was with pardonable pride that the critic Krause remarked to Peter Ilych, as the latter took off his fur coat in the artists' room: "In this room Mendelssohn and Schumann were at home. You know, Master," he added, tugging complacently at his little beard, "our Liszt Society has been in existence for only three years and yet it already has its own steady and faithful public. The hall is quite full." Krause, like Artur Nikisch and Alexander Siloti, was among the special patrons of the Society.

The violinist Halir from Weimar had been engaged for the Tchaikovsky evening. He had made a specialty of that concerto in D major which Auer had turned down and which Brodsky had taken over. The audience at the old Gewandhaus—an audience consisting for the most part of young people—was very enthusiastic about the work that Hanslick had dubbed "stinking"; Peter Ilych, who sat on the platform on one side of the orchestra, whispered the words of the well-known and odious criticism in his neighbor's ear as the applause burst out; his neighbor was Grieg.

The triumph of the violinist Halir was made quite clear after the great and dazzling cadenza which came as a climax in the middle of the first movement and established the brilliant victory of the audacious, isolated solo instrument in its passionate battle against the combined forces of the orchestra. The triumph of the concerto itself was made clear after the delirious success of the first movement. The audience rose to its feet and applauded with admiringly raised hands. The hall attendant came up to Tchaikovsky trailing a great wreath. Peter Ilych did not know exactly what to do with it. "To the Russian Master" was inscribed in gold letters on a gigantic red silk ribbon. No, this young and exacting German public did not regard the playful lightness of the allegro theme and the melancholy lyricism of the slow movement as trivial and lacking in seriousness; they had not been scandalized by the birdlike chatter of the flute and clarinet in the second movement, nor by the wild dancing extravagance of the Finale. In this town, where the cult of music was taken with solemn seriousness, the public was open-minded and receptive to this kind of music-making—the half-melancholy but newly inspired music of a convalescent.

For Tchaikovsky had been a convalescent when he wrote the violin concerto. Ah, how besieged by recollections was his memory-laden heart now, as he made his embarrassed bow in response to the acclamation of these enthusiastic young foreigners! What a lot had taken place before he had been able to start to work on this violin concerto! . . . It didn't bear thinking of.

The concert continued. They played the Pianoforte Trio in A minor, the dedication of which was "à la mémoire d'un grand artiste." And while the 'cellist played that mournful melody of the elegy, Peter Ilych once more had time and occasion to look inside himself where memories dwelt. For the *"grand artiste"* was his friend Nikolay Rubinstein, the irreplaceable; yes, he was quite irreplaceable, for all his disturbing and irritating qualities, his rudeness, his blustering temperament, his everlasting pedantic sense of superiority. But one owed him so much gratitude that one had to forgive him everything; and now, as the mournful theme of the first movement sang out, it was like a lament wrung from his very heart. Peter Ilych listened and did not move; he sat on the platform between Nina and Edvard, stared at by an indiscreet and curious public which was still in the grip of emotion—an elderly man, older than his years, he sat there, his head bent as if under a burden, for there had been much bitterness in his life which ought to have been transmuted into musical sounds, and such transmutations as had been made had perhaps not always altogether succeeded; something impure had inserted itself in the course of the difficult, sacred process; he had sometimes made concessions, had sought to create effects, and, as a punishment, a residue of bitterness had remained, a residue of unredeemed, untransmuted life—and it tasted bitter on the tongue, like a bitter herb.

Pictures and faces, which he had believed to be sunk in oblivion, rose up during the second movement, with its ingenious variations. Into what an abundance of skilfully wrought beauty had the memories which had tasted so bitter been transformed! The listener on the platform had the right to feel proud, and indeed his heart was full of melancholy elation. "Good Nikolay may feel satisfied with his memorial," thought the listener. "I wonder if he would have indulged in his usual abuse and faultfinding and even declined the dedication, as he did in the case of the pianoforte concerto, when he made me so annoyed with him? No, no! This time he would have been pleasant, and perhaps somewhere or other he is listening now and looking pleased, for he is a connoisseur. How beautifully they play, *à la mémoire d'un grand artiste!* It is really no longer chamber music; it is a symphony for three instruments. It has great style. This time you ought not to grumble, old Nikolay! You really must admit that it is not an unworthy memorial!"

Their ensemble was indeed splendid: young Siloti at the piano, Halir, and the 'cellist Schröder, whom Peter Ilych had known in Moscow. Siloti's flawless face glowed with earnestness and an austere and reverential concentration. "There he sits and transmutes my memories into sounds," thought Peter Ilych emotionally. "Surely he must be near to me at this moment? But as soon as the performance is over, he will retire once again into his beautiful aloofness. It is not my memories that move him, but the form in which I have expressed them; merely the formula that I have used!"

Peter Ilych had invited Edvard and Nina Grieg to lunch with him in his hotel next day.

"Here you are, my children!" he cried to the friendly couple when he met them in the hall before lunch.

"Why your children, Papa Tchaikovsky?" demanded Grieg, about whose bright eyes the good-humored little wrinkles played.

"Oh, don't you know?" Peter Ilych laughed. "Brodsky explained it to me yesterday at the concert, during the interval. You and I displayed ourselves to the public on the platform side by side, in such wonderful harmony, that Brodsky heard a Leipzig lady inform her daughter: 'Look, Luise, there sits Tchaikovsky with his two children.' And the children were—you!" They all laughed. "But as a matter of fact it is really sad," said Peter Ilych as he offered Nina his arm. "I am only a couple of years older than Edvard—I'm not yet fifty—and I am taken for his father. Sometimes I startle even myself when I look in the mirror. It is uncanny and dreadful, how quickly one changes, day by day, without noticing it. Only a few years ago I looked quite different. When I see a picture of myself belonging to that period, I say: that is a strange young man. Yes," he went on, as the reception manager conducted them to a table in the corner of the dining-room, "if I had had a wife like you all my life, dear Madame Nina, things would be quite different with me today; I should be better preserved."

Peter Ilych loved the dancing, singing cadence of Grieg's voice as he rejoined: "A better wife could not be found! Without her I should have made nothing of my life; it would have been a short, empty life."

Nina turned very red. "What are you talking about, Edvard!" she cried and shook her head disapprovingly. "You were already on the heights when you married me. You were already a great man, and I was your little country cousin, who was able to sing your songs a little."

The tone of her voice, her way of speaking, was very much like his. "How alike they are!" thought Peter Ilych.

"Nina Hagerup was never merely my little cousin," said Grieg, reproaching her tenderly. "You were already a great artist, my child, when you sang to me for the first time. But I was ill and depressed. If it hadn't been for you at that time I should have come to an end."

"Oh, Edvard, Edvard!" The little woman shook her head; the childlike face under the grayish hair turned red. To Peter Ilych their gentle conflict sounded like the twittering that might pass between two birds in their nests or from tree to tree.

The menu was selected with great care. Peter Ilych loved to play the host: he spent time and trouble over the choice of wine and dishes.

"You are spoiling us," said Nina, and Edvard supported her in almost the same voice and with exactly the same cadence.

"You like being in Leipzig?" asked Tchaikovsky.

Grieg explained: "I feel practically at home here. You see I lived here for a long time when I was young."

"Of course you did," said Peter Ilych, recollecting. "You studied here."

"But now I don't want to stay much longer away from the

north." Grieg's clear eyes looked past Tchaikovsky at the wall, as if he expected to find something there—a beloved picture that might suddenly become visible behind the plaster ornaments. "You must come up there to see us without fail, dear Tchaikovsky," he said.

"Yes, you certainly must come sometime, without fail," repeated Nina in a chirruping echo.

Peter Ilych asked: "Is your home up in the north, in the neighborhood of Bergen?"

"It is called Troldhaugen," said Grieg. "Troll Hill—of course you know what a troll is? It is a very simple house. But how beautiful it is there!"

"Yes, how lovely it is there!" came the twittering echo.

"I have many good memories of Leipzig." Grieg's eyes, pensive in the midst of many merry wrinkles, stared in front of him. "I was so young, and so inexperienced, when I came here. Great impressions were made on me! I had very few connections. Yes, the northern towns are delightful; but for young people who want to make a start, a real start—do you know what I mean?—for such a one the circumstances of a little northern town soon become oppressive. There are nothing but cliques in our delightful towns, and everybody knows everything about everybody; and there are intrigues, and hate, and envy, and an appalling egoism. No, no! A young man who really wants to get on is bound to be demoralized."

Nina, who listened eagerly to her husband and cousin as if she were hearing all this for the first time—sometimes silently mouthing the words he uttered—nodded in confirmation.

"But our national music," went on Edvard, "nobody can take that away from us; and no intrigues can stifle its melody. When we were still quite young we discovered it, this northern melody!" He turned his face towards Peter Ilych: it was bright red with enthusiasm. "You understand that perfectly, my dear Tchaikovsky!" he cried; "that is something that you must understand through and through. For you have done for your Russia what a few of us have been able to do for our Norway, and what Smetana and Dvořák do for the Czechs. You have given Russia a national music."

Peter Ilych bowed his head as if for shame. "Leave me out of it!" he said, and he pondered—his head bent like that of one who has received honors that are not his due—on all the reproaches and insults he had to hear and read in Moscow and St. Petersburg: that his music was not genuine, not authentic, not Russian, that it was impersonal, conventional, westernized, unhealthily influenced by the international Jew, Anton Rubinstein, that it was in no sense Russian music; that the genuine, The Real Thing, came only from the Five Innovators, who derived from folk music and had learned nothing, and of these, the most genuine of all was Mussorgsky, who came from and belonged to the people, that inarticulate genius whom Peter Ilych himself had called a "noisy dilettante."

"Leave me out of it!" Tchaikovsky begged. But already Edvard was back with his Norwegians. "We may not be a *grande nation*," he said, "but we have great national figures. So much at least we can say!"

They spoke of famous Norwegians—Ole Bull, the great violinist and adventurer; Henrik Ibsen, "the most uncanny creature I've ever met," as Edvard confessed in a shy whisper; Björnstjerne Björnson, their beloved poet, "the uncrowned king of the North."

"But we are talking only about *our* country," Grieg finally interrupted himself. "And we are so eager to hear something from you about Russia, that great Russia which is so rich in mysteries and treasures!"

Peter Ilych had to tell the Griegs all about his meeting with Leo Tolstoy in Moscow, more than ten years ago. "Nikolay Rubinstein and I had arranged a musical evening for him at the Conservatory," he said. "Heavens, how excited I was to meet the great man! And how frightened! He was something like a demigod to me, you know—and still is, at that."

"How was he?" the Griegs asked eagerly. "How did he act? Was he friendly? Did he enjoy the concert?"

"Yes, he seemed to enjoy himself. He is exceedingly fond of music. They played the Andante from my first Quartet. Tolstoy cried—I was sitting next to him, so I could see that he was actually shedding tears over my composition. I don't believe I'll ever be so flattered and touched again."

"And then? Did you make friends with him? Did you see him again?"

"He returned to Yasnaya Polyana a few days after the concert," Peter Ilych replied. "He wrote me from there and sent me some of his poems I wanted to set to music. His letters were delightful. 'For God's sake,' he wrote to me, 'arrange my poems after the Mozart-Haydn style, not the artificial Beethoven-Berlioz style that tries only for effect.' Isn't that a charming way of putting it?"

"Charming," the Griegs agreed. "But didn't you see him again?"

"No, I didn't." Peter Ilych looked strangely pensive and absent-minded.

"And why not?" the Griegs went on asking with naïve persistence. "Why didn't you cultivate so valuable a contact?"

He shrugged his shoulders. "I suppose I am rather shy," he said, without looking at Edvard and Nina. "And he is such a great man, such a genius."

How could he explain to this curiously innocent, childlike couple what it actually was that had prevented him from calling on Tolstoy again? The plain truth was that he had been afraid—mortally afraid of the great writer's psychological intuition, his penetrating eye. The man who had created the stupendous sagas of *War and Peace* and *Anna Karenina* might have enough divinatory power to see through his, Peter Ilych's, problematical character, to identify his disgrace, his incurable disease—"THIS."

They began to speak about other Russian authors—Pushkin,

Gogol, Dostoevsky, whose works were known and admired by
the Norwegian composer and his keen, open-minded little wife.
When they reached the subject of Turgeniev their voices took
on a quality of warmth and tenderness. They vied with one
another in the warmth of their praise of his humanity and personality and of the perfection of his works. They related inci-
dents and intimate details about his life.

"Do you know that he also is reproached with not being Russian enough, 'westernized'?" asked Peter Ilych, as Brodsky
came towards the table.

Grieg, turning somewhat red—and Nina also smiled in a
rather shamefaced manner as if a fine but somewhat indelicate
scheme were in the wind—said: "I asked our friend Brodsky to
come; I wanted to play to you, with his help, a new work of
mine, if it won't bore you, dear Tchaikovsky. It is a violin
sonata: I have only recently finished it. Yes, and I have dedicated it to the German painter Franz von Lenbach." He spoke
hurriedly and confusedly, as if he ought to apologize for wanting to play his new sonata.

"But that's splendid!" exclaimed Peter Ilych.

They played in Tchaikovsky's little sitting-room, which led
out of his bedroom. "The Bechstein piano is quite respectable,"
declared Peter Ilych. "I haven't made any attack on it myself
yet, but that is entirely my own fault." He sat down with Nina
on the sofa, under the lamp, the long silk fringe of which gave
the room an intimate character.

When Grieg sought out the first chord on the pianoforte, his
shy, boyishly soft face took on an earnest, very concentrated, almost threatening expression. With triumphant impetuosity, the
song of the violin broke out. Tchaikovsky, leaning his head
against the gilded back of the sofa, listened with his legs crossed
and his mouth slightly open. In this position he remained during
the whole performance.

The first movement had been as startling and wild as a sudden scream. "Where does this pale and slender fellow get his

strength from? Where does it come from?" thought Tchaikovsky, his soft, brooding eyes dwelling on Grieg. After the scream
came the more peaceful elegy. But what angry, protesting defiance there was in the hammering, tramping theme of the
third movement! And the little man at the piano seemed to
grow with the theme. He sat there rigidly, and over his countenance came such lines of determination as one would in the
ordinary way never suspect to exist. Boldness had conquered.
The heroic determination to sublimate suffering through art had
succeeded. "What a victory for the slender, youthful-looking
man at the piano!" thought Peter Ilych with emotion; his head,
which had been leaning against the hard ornamented back of
the sofa, was hurting him, but he scarcely perceived it. "What a
victory for slight but unyielding strength! You are ill; you are
not sufficiently well equipped to offer resistance; people are convinced that you will soon go to the wall. . . . But against all
this threatening onslaught you oppose a short tramping melody
and demonstrate that it is the stronger. How beautifully you
have played, my slender friend at the piano! It was inspiring,
and it was instructive! What a happy accident it was that you
should have played this particular thing, at this particular time,
giving me encouragement to hold up my head again and grow
strong." Thus his thoughts ran.

"Thank you," cried Peter Ilych, springing to his feet. "I thank
you. It was splendid. That is the most beautiful thing you have
done. And it is the finest music that has come out of your country."

Already Grieg's face had again become childlike, soft, and
anxious. "Dear Tchaikovsky, dear Tchaikovsky," he said. "How
happy you make me!" And tears of emotion ran down the cheeks
of his Nina.

Brodsky loudly and eagerly kept on praising details of the
composition. "It's a masterpiece," he repeated in his booming
voice. "Our Grieg has created a masterpiece."

"Nobody can *sing* more beautifully than you," said Tchaikovsky going close to Grieg.

"But it is for one's pleasing little pieces that one becomes famous," declared Grieg, on whose lips there suddenly appeared a thin, peevish smile, the smile of one who had been much slighted in his native land, the smile of one who had experienced pain and anger, the fruits of narrow-mindedness in a provincial town. "One becomes famous for drawing-room pieces that are nice and easy to play."

"And now I have the impression that even I am not altogether played out," said Tchaikovsky, who, having suddenly become concentrated on himself, his hopes and fears, appeared not to have heard Grieg's last remark. "You wait, Grieg; something new will come from me, something or other will come. . . ."

He had laid both hands on Grieg's shoulders, and as his glance seemed to go through and beyond his new-found friend, he shook the little man's hand slowly, in a definite rhythm, backwards and forwards. "Just you wait, just you wait!" he said in a deep, singing, remarkably resonant voice, right into Grieg's astonished face. "We are not yet done for—we are in no way done for. We must not give in before our time. . . ."

*   *   *

Places and faces changed. They appeared and disappeared. Peter Ilych gazed on them and gazed after them, with his soft, brooding glance. He made many acquaintances; he shook many hands. A somewhat timid "man of the world"—kindly but easily perturbed—he moved in all sorts of society and took part in all sorts of conversations. Many a time he was alarmed by all these strange faces, by all this laughter, these unfamiliar eyes and the meaningless movements of unfamiliar lips.

Once more he stayed a day in Berlin. Discussions about his concert there were held. He found himself frequently with a very influential gentleman named Hugo Bock. Kommerzienrat

Bock insisted that Peter Ilych should perform the *1812 Overture* at the Philharmonic. "Our public likes it," he contended. Siegfried Neugebauer never failed to be present at such conferences. Joyously sniffing with his screwed-up nose, he reveled in the insults which Peter Ilych hurled at him, even in the presence of a third party. Siegfried Neugebauer meddled in everything, created confusions; he made the most ridiculous suggestions in a genteel nasal voice, the tone of which implied that he was giving utterance to the most illuminating statements; when he was spoken to sharply, he looked from his filmy eyes and smiled sweetly; he was cunning, mercilessly importunate, and disarmingly devoted; he said: "You are utterly unjust, Master, but I remain at your service," and an hour after he had been ejected by the porter, he would thrust his rosy, troubled countenance back into the room. For Peter Ilych he embodied all the most unpleasant things in life. Finally he paid the unhappy creature a considerable sum of money in order to free himself from a painful contract. He swore to himself that he would never receive the man again, never open another telegram or letter from him.

From Berlin Peter Ilych went on to Hamburg. There he saw Hans von Bülow again, finding that the conductor had aged considerably. The furrows on the high brow, the lines that began above the wings of the nose and ended in the bushy moustache, had grown painfully deeper, like great clefts. The narrow, nervous, highly intelligent face, with the pointed goatee jutting out from the short chin, had changed in a remarkable fashion. It seemed less vivacious, less sensitive than formerly; a bitter peacefulness had spread itself over features which had once been tense and restless. Bülow—famous for his wild caprices and for his mordant wit—spoke cautiously and quietly. Sometimes, indeed, the malicious but bewitching spark flashed from his eyes, and then, in the rapid French that he employed when speaking to Tchaikovsky, he who had been the tragic victim of so much discreditable gossip that clung to him like an unpleasant aura, gave utterance to one of those sardonic phrases which went the round of the musical circles of two continents.

On the other hand, sometimes his glance seemed to become remote, his voice took on a faraway, mysterious tone, and he spoke inconsequently of irrelevant things, smiling obliquely in a gloomy fashion. "He has not got over that deplorable private affair of his which aroused so much discussion everywhere," thought Peter Ilych in dismay. "How cruelly life seizes hold of us! It won't suffer us to hold our heads erect; it exposes us to ridicule and humiliates us whenever it can; it has a particular kind of pain and humiliation ready for everybody. This man, for instance, it has made the most notorious cuckold of his time. He has become the victim of Richard Wagner with his merciless lust for conquest, a sacrifice on the altar of the unscrupulous Frau Cosima."

The conversation between Hans von Bülow and Tchaikovsky was animated and intimate, but Peter Ilych felt that it no longer had the friendly flavor that had characterized their talk last time, in Russia. "The reason may be that I am not here for the Society which he directs," he thought uneasily, "but for the rival company; for it is obvious that there are two competing enterprises. It would distress me very much if he felt like that; I owe this remarkable man so much. But after all, it was the rival concern that approached me first, and apart from that, it has a far better reputation."

However, within a very few minutes Bülow had disposed of any misgivings which Peter Ilych may have had. On his own account he complained of the orchestra he had to work with, which was at the same time the orchestra of the Hamburg Opera House. "For this reason," he said bitterly, "the players come to me half dead from the rehearsals, in a state of exhaustion." He spoke scornfully of Pollini, the all-powerful director of the Hamburg theater, who had obstinately brought this new symphonic undertaking into existence. "There is something of the circus manager about our great boss," he declared, "with his

shiny matted black moustache and his merciless activity. I can
see him before me, cracking his whip in the menagerie. . . ."
Continuing to talk of the theater-impresario Pollini, he gradually worked himself into a nervous anger; he made ugly faces,
and suddenly he contended that Pollini had designs on his life.
When bidding Peter Ilych good-bye, he gave him some remarkable souvenirs: for example, a series of pictures of the Social
Democratic members of the German Parliament and a large
mother-of-pearl button. "In order to give you pleasure, my
friend," he said hurriedly.

Later, Peter Ilych was told that Bülow had developed this
curiously distrait manner and at times uncannily violent tone
against his old friends. Many ventured to intimate that they
feared for his reason. Moreover, Peter Ilych discovered that Bülow, after the devastating Wagner disillusionment and the ab-
surdly exaggerated deification of Brahms, was on the point of
launching a new genius, a young composer about whom the people at the Hamburg Conservatory spoke with a certain timid, still
half-skeptical curiosity (was this, perhaps, another whim of the
overexcitable Bülow, who was always after a new sensation?):
his name was Richard Strauss. Peter Ilych knew a symphonic
work of his. He considered it detestable; pretentiously extravagant, dissonant, and almost devoid of talent.

"That is why I am no longer on Bülow's agenda," remarked
Tchaikovsky, and he recalled the sympathetic enthusiasm which
the great conductor had demonstrated formerly in St. Petersburg
—it was scarcely three years ago—when he contributed to the
triumph of the Third Suite and created an international sensation with its first performance . . . that very Third Suite
which Peter Ilych himself was now going to conduct in a quarter that was antagonistic to Bülow. After the brilliant performance under Bülow he had regarded it as his best work; but in
the meantime he had become uncertain about it; and it was not
without some doubt and pondering that he now turned over the
pages of the score.

Many hands had to be shaken and many strange faces had to be seen. In the evening he had a concert to attend: Bülow was conducting the *Eroica*. Peter Ilych made up his mind that next morning he would flee to some little strange town; for there were still some days to pass before the rehearsals for his Hamburg concert would begin.

The little strange town—it was Lübeck—was gray and full of nooks and crannies. Peter Ilych walked along the narrow courts lined with houses with pointed gables; he contemplated an old town hall and an old church. The hotel appeared to be fairly comfortable; he engaged a bedroom with a small sitting-room adjoining, and found that it was not at all cheap.

Peter Ilych was suddenly seized by the fear that his money would not hold out, that he would have to remain somewhere or other, his hotel bill unpaid; his fur coat and even his beautiful watch would have to be pawned. The fear of sudden, catastrophic proverty sometimes attacked him in much the same way as he was attacked by the unwarranted but no less violent fear of a malignant heart disease—although he had a very handsome revenue, and over and above this he could always count on the help of his mysterious friend and benefactress, Madame von Meck, from whom he now drew an income of no less than six thousand rubles. "Once again I have to pay out too much," he thought with anxiety; and with a cigarette in his mouth he paced backwards and forwards between the sitting-room and the bedroom. "Everything has been disproportionately expensive, and the income has been very small. How dear it was at that restaurant yesterday after the concert! Unfortunately I had invited a gentleman from the Philharmonic; moreover Pollini joined us. Things can't go on like this! If no reply comes from St. Petersburg today about my respectful petition to the Emperor for a civil pension, then I shall have to telegraph to publisher Jürgenson, and in addition to that I shall be obliged to ask my good Nadezhda for an extra allowance. I should find that most distressing because I have already cost her a great deal of money;

but it will have to be; obviously I can't pawn my warm fur coat and my beautiful watch."

The answer came from Petersburg two days later and was magnificent. His Imperial Majesty, the Tsar, had been graciously pleased to grant a yearly pension of three thousand rubles to the composer Peter Ilych Tchaikovsky. It was the Director of the Imperial Theater, a friend and patron of the composer, who had recommended and agitated for this grant, and who now transmitted the news with his congratulations. All this was uncommonly pleasant; now one could once more burn the candle at both ends—for the idea of giving up part of the allowance made by Madame von Meck, in view of this new source of revenue, never entered Peter Ilych's head.

Unfortunately, in the meantime other distressing things had happened. The quiet days had been good; he had been able to write letters—to his brother Modest, to the benefactress; he had been able to sit down with a book, and to go for walks in the crooked streets, and of an evening sit drinking schnapps at an inn. The solitude tasted good, like fresh air when one has been sitting too long in a smoky tavern. But alas, the hotel proprietor's son was interested in music. He discovered the name of the Russian composer in the visitors' book; and together with his father he called upon their famous client. The scene was extremely painful; father and son stammered; the faces of both of them turned red; Peter Ilych's face also turned red, and he devoutly wished himself anywhere else. "M'yes," said the Lübeck hotel proprietor, "my dear departed wife sang very nicely, but the jollier sort of things. . . ." Peter Ilych became desperate.

He had his evening meal in his own room. After eating, he drove to the State theater, where the famous Barnay was appearing as a guest actor in the role of Othello. Peter Ilych—who was rather dejected and distrait—remained throughout the performance in the background of his box, which was musty with the smell of dusty plush. In the interval he promenaded in the foyer among the prominent citizens of Lübeck; he marveled at the

costumes of the ladies and at the forbidding, almost aggressive
expressions on their faces. Nevertheless, it was pleasing to know
that of all these people certainly not one had ever heard the
name of Tchaikovsky. But as luck would have it, the hotel proprietor's son—a thin, earnest young man wearing large spectacles
on his pimply face—chose to be at the theater. Peter Ilych
stepped a pace backwards when he noticed him but could not
get to his box in time; the culture-hungry young man sprang
forward and blocked his way. Abruptly he declared that he
worshiped Shakespeare, that he couldn't possibly live without
music and Shakespeare; he inquired—and his hands perspired
with the effort—if Shakespeare was also understood in Russia,
and if he might be allowed to bring along some acquaintances of
his father. Peter Ilych nodded, horrified. As if they had been
waiting in ambush round the corner, several gentlemen stepped
up, most of them corpulent and red of visage; one, in a frock
coat, tall and bald—he obviously felt himself superior to the rest
of them and suffered deeply on account of his superiority, as
was betrayed by the bitter lines around his mouth. He drew
Peter Ilych aside and asked him in a whisper if he did not consider the town of Lübeck appallingly provincial; he for his part
was Doctor Plöschke, a private tutor, and moreover an atheist,
and was only interested in the most advanced ideas. Peter
Ilych replied that he liked Lübeck enormously. He had a ghastly
suspicion that the hotel proprietor's son had plotted all this, prepared and organized it. The man at the box office had perhaps
divulged the fact that a box had been ordered by the Russian
gentleman, whereupon the ambitious young man had told all
his family's acquaintances to come to the theater. "This is unspeakable!" thought Peter Ilych, as he suffered one of the
corpulent gentlemen, whose breath smelled of alcohol, to puff in
his face. The collection of gentlemen showed a certain disposition
to laugh often and for no reason; they said "Famous!" "Splendid!" and "Magnificent!" without Peter Ilych's understanding
exactly what they were referring to; and they asked him if he

were not immensely proud to be allowed to give concerts in Germany; if the work of composition was very exacting; if there were any fine Russian military marches; what he thought of Richard Wagner; whether he knew the Tsar, and whether it was also cold in the summer in Moscow. Peter Ilych decided that very night that he would go back to Hamburg next morning at the latest.

In Hamburg he lived in the room adjoining that occupied by the young pianist Sapelnikov, who was going to play the B-flat minor Pianoforte Concerto at the Philharmonic. He began to practise of a morning at nine o'clock; Peter Ilych was awakened out of sleep by his own melodies. Sapelnikov repeated the same phrase endlessly, ten times, fifteen times, thirty times. Finally, he came dashing into Peter Ilych's bedroom.

"I can't do it, Master, I simply can't!" cried Sapelnikov, drops of sweat standing out on his forehead. "Oh, I want to bite my hands!" And he really did bite the knuckles of his despairingly raised fist.

"It will soon come!" said Peter Ilych softly from the bed.

"Oh, these hands, these stupid, obstinate, crippled hands!" moaned Sapelnikov, and he drummed with his fingers—long, hard-working, lean but powerful fingers, with closely cut nails which looked as if they had been gnawed. "And this concert is so terribly important to me!" he groaned, falling into an armchair and stretching out his long legs in front of him. In his big-boned, thin face the dark, deep-set eyes looked hungry, hungry for that fame which Siloti's more beautiful and calmer expression seemed to take for granted as something bound to come to him, claimed by him, and expected as a necessity of life, but which Sapelnikov, with a desperate effort, wished to force towards him, at any cost.

"I had a telegram from London yesterday from Sophie Menter," he reported. "She is of the opinion that I should put all I know into this concert, which may be a determining point in my career." Once again he stretched and bent his long muscular fingers.

Peter Ilych knew Madame Sophie Menter, Sapelnikov's famous teacher; he had met her in St. Petersburg and Moscow. He valued her; she was a very distinguished pianist, a very charming but scatterbrained person. She had often invited him to her country house in the Tyrol, and he had always wanted to go there some time, but the plan had never materialized.

"Give Madame Sophie my greetings!" said Peter Ilych.

"I *must* have a success!" shouted Sapelnikov, and bounded from the chair as if it were inconceivable that one should pronounce the word "success" and remain seated.

"You will have a success, my friend." Peter Ilych spoke to him as one would speak to an invalid. "It will be splendid." And as he looked with a weary and somewhat pitying smile at the excited Sapelnikov, who was pacing up and down the room, he thought to himself: "I must help him; this feverish desire must be calmed down. I shall arrange a concert for him in Berlin; I'll speak about him in all interviews in order to make him better known. The boy will go off his head if he doesn't soon get that fame he wants—his miserable fame!"

"You are so good to me, Master!" said Sapelnikov, with tears in his burning eyes. He gripped Peter Ilych's hand firmly and then went back to his own room to continue practising. He practised ten hours every day.

Sapelnikov had a great success with the B-flat minor Piano Concerto, a much greater success than Tchaikovsky had. For Peter Ilych saw clearly that the composition had not pleased. It was Sapelnikov who was recalled again and again.

"They don't appear to be exactly enthusiastic about my dear Opus 23," thought Tchaikovsky, sitting in the artists' room, while Sapelnikov, burning with excitement and happiness, was outside, bowing. "They don't seem to respond to whatever charm it may have. . . ."

He embraced Sapelnikov, who emerged breathing heavily

from his triumph. "I congratulate you, I congratulate you," said Peter Ilych time after time, and he thumped the thin back of the young man, whose whole body was trembling. "You played splendidly!" Sapelnikov gulped and then beamed. "Did I? Really?" he asked, eager for words of praise. "At the beginning I was terribly excited; in fact, I struck a wrong note in the first phrase. . . . But that is all on account of the weather," he chattered on. "I'm always nervous when the clouds hang down like that—Sophie Menter often warned me about it." This reference to the weather was entirely meaningless; it had been a cloudless winter day. "It was magnificent, my boy!" said Peter Ilych, and gave him another thump on the back.

And now for the first time it occurred to Sapelnikov that Tchaikovsky had not been recalled and that this unfair distribution of the applause might upset him. "Why didn't you show yourself again, Master?" he asked.

"Because they didn't call for me," said Peter Ilych. "They didn't care for the concerto; it was only your playing that they liked."

"Hans von Bülow is in the hall," said Sapelnikov, his breath still fluttering. He seemed quite incapable of calming down after the excitement and triumph of the evening. "If only I knew whether he was pleased with my performance!"

"It was charming of him to come," said Tchaikovsky. "I was afraid he might be offended because I did not work with his orchestra. Of course, the Serenade will not have made any special impression on him," he added mournfully. "It hasn't very much to it. I like doing it at the beginning of a program because it is so unexacting to conduct. It conducts itself. That helps me to conquer my dreadful nervousness."

The Third Suite also met with a cool reception. During the first movement there was a lot of coughing. The variations of the last movement failed of their proper effect on account of the festive noisiness of the turbulent Finale, the "Polacca," that very Finale which had aroused so much enthusiasm when it was performed under Bülow in St. Petersburg. Here it seemed to repel and alienate the audience. Trombones, cymbals, big drums, and the whole body of the strings worked up to a brilliant, noisy, and irresistible climax; but the audience sat cold and aloof. Such riotous outpourings did not please them. They preferred work that was restrained and serious. Here the Brahms cult had its own center. Here the Master was honored even more unreservedly than in Leipzig. This inflexible public had been brought up on Brahms and the classics, and conservative cautiousness had kept it anti-Wagnerian. The newspapers declared daily that they were utterly opposed to the "brilliant and the piquant."

As Peter Ilych was aware with every nerve in his body that the festive noise which he had to conduct would find no sympathetic echo here, he hated it—yes, he was really disgusted by the triumphant, clangorous, booming uproar. His arm, when it should have been particularly dominating, was tired; he had a bad taste in his mouth, and he found it unspeakably distressing that he should be compelled to stand there and conduct this endlessly repeating orchestral intoxication, which went from climax to climax and finally overreached itself. "Oh, why do I always let myself go so abominably in the finales?" he asked himself miserably. "I don't know when to stop; I work myself into a state of joyful intoxication, which I'm not in the mood for. How commonplace and false and tricked-out it all sounds! I feel so wretched, I'd like to sink into the earth!"

After the sparse applause had petered out and Tchaikovsky, trembling with shame, had left the platform, Hans von Bülow came to the artists' room and shook him by the hand. Peter Ilych turned to him in a state of exhaustion. "During the Finale," he said, "I had the greatest desire to fling down the baton. When you conducted it in St. Petersburg it was much finer. . . ."

Bülow paid a few shrewd compliments to Sapelnikov, whose thin face was hectically flushed. Once more it struck Peter Ilych how old and weary Bülow looked. Yes, he was played out.

("Does one know oneself when one is played out? Yes, one still goes about, but a shadow on one's face betrays the secret to others: you are done for!") Bülow went on speaking: "Today I've once more savored the real beauty of the music with which I formerly had so much to do. Our friend Tchaikovsky is a great man." Leaving the hungrily attentive Sapelnikov, he turned his face—lined and wrinkled by the many bitter experiences through which he had passed, and now showing signs of real emotion—towards Peter Ilych.

Peter Ilych had to go to the great reception which the Philharmonic had arranged in his honor. Hundreds of people had been invited. They all sat at little tables. Tchaikovsky had the place of honor next to a distinguished graybeard, Herr Avé-Lallemant, the president of the Society. He liked the gentle old man immensely. He had a very small, alabaster-hued face, lined with innumerable wrinkles, very carefully trimmed side-whiskers, and expressive dark eyes surmounting an old-fashioned stand-up collar.

"You will permit me to be quite frank with you, my dear Tchaikovsky," said this ancient gentleman, peeling an orange with his fragile but supple little hands. "I am eighty years of age, so may perhaps allow myself that privilege." He had a very high-pitched, rather querulous voice.

"I shall be grateful for your frankness," asserted Peter Ilych, speaking rather more loudly than usual, on the assumption that his companion might be a little hard of hearing.

"You are very talented," said Herr Avé-Lallemant, still busy with his orange, "enormously talented!" He jerked the white joint of his index finger warningly. "But you are on the wrong track." He shook his gentle old head rebukingly: "There is something wild, Asiatic—yes, forgive the harsh word, something barbaric in your music, and it offends my ears." With a sensitive gesture he laid his two small hands, which were like pointed forks, over his ears, as if Tchaikovsky's noisy music still hurt them. "You misuse the percussion," he said plaintively. "Really, now! What a noise! The Finale of your Third Suite—why, it is an explosion of dynamite! It was quite ear-splitting! Oh, dear! Such a noise is *nihilistic*—do you understand what I mean? It expresses nothing; it is fundamentally empty."

Peter Ilych listened attentively, his head bent close to the old man's, although the latter spoke by no means indistinctly.

"You could become a really great man—yes, a really great man," contended the old man in his high, querulous voice, "if you would only give up some of your unmannerliness. You must learn to do better! Improve yourself! Take another course! You are still young!" Peter Ilych recoiled before this last remark; it staggered but enchanted him. He listened again to the venerable gentleman who regarded him as young.

"Profit by our great Masters," he continued, "by their noble moderation and their perfection! Come to Germany! Stay with us. Our country is the only one that possesses a real and serious musical culture."

You could become a great man—yes, a really great man, rang in Peter Ilych's ears, and *You are still young!* Suddenly he felt so tired that he could hardly keep his eyes open. The shrewd, fragile countenance of the old man became blurred, and Tchaikovsky saw the whole eating, drinking, chattering, breathing, smelling company of strangers as if it were enveloped in a vaporous haze.

"I will fly away to some unknown place," he thought, "before going again among people in Berlin. I have heard that Magdeburg is a very small and quaint town."

*　　*　　*

Places and faces changed. They appeared and disappeared. Peter Ilych gazed on them and gazed after them with his soft brooding glance.

From Magdeburg he went back again to Leipzig, and from Leipzig he went on to Berlin. There it was more strenuous than it had been in the other towns. Before the concert, he had to cope with receptions and dinners. Peter Ilych arranged with the big concert agent Wolff that Sapelnikov should play to a group of influential people—critics, musicians, and patrons of music. "So that something after all may come out of the whole business!" said Peter Ilych, who found a certain melancholy satisfaction in being useful to young people, all of whom were anxious to get on at any cost. Their ambition had the power to move him. "They wouldn't speak to me," he thought, "not a single word—if I weren't able to be of use to them. So I *must* be of use to them—because they're young." He felt that his great fame had served some purpose if he could use it on behalf of the young.

Sapelnikov played before the influential and was a success. At another reception—this was in the pompous home of Herr Kommerzienrat Bock—Peter Ilych saw again a face which long ago had had the power to move and charm him. Now it had changed; it had developed soft layers of fat!

The face of the singer Désirée Artôt was broad and very lavishly powdered. The too carefully tended skin of her cheeks and double chin was somewhat downy. On her upper lip there was a trace of dark hair, like a faint shadow, but the shape of this upper lip was still beautiful. Perhaps it was principally the charming line of her lip that had made Madame Artôt so seductive twenty years ago; and when she smiled, she revealed beautiful teeth. And then there were also her dark, experienced eyes beneath lids which she raised with an accomplished technique in order to reveal the bold vivacious glance that Peter Ilych at one time liked to think he loved better than anything in the world. True, these eyes could also look very tired and apathetic when Madame Désirée sat still and believed herself to be unobserved.

For the first few moments they did not recognize each other. Peter Ilych had noticed among the other guests only something very pompous and very *projecting*—in a very décolleté evening dress of raspberry-hued satin, with dazzling jewelry on a gleaming white bosom whose opulence was rather alarming: the back, however, was beautiful. Peter, cool and detached, like one looking at an object in an exhibition, marveled at the blinding whiteness of this back before he recognized the face of his old friend.

Madame Artôt knew that Tchaikovsky was expected; nevertheless she looked past the gray-bearded gentleman who, rather tightly confined in his evening clothes, stood close to her chair. This strained face, with the high brow, the somewhat too heavy eyelids over the pensive preoccupied glance, the too-soft mouth, appeared strange to her. But when she observed his smile, she suddenly knew who he was, and she stretched forth her white, voluptuous arms, so that her jewelry jingled. "Pierre!" called Madame Artôt, and suddenly tears filled the lovely eyes, perhaps simply on account of the shock of meeting, but perhaps also in dismay at seeing her friend so aged and so greatly altered. *"Pierre! Ce n'est pas vrai!"*

Peter Ilych said quite softly: "Désirée!" The gray-bearded old man and the overfat woman stood facing each other for a long moment motionless and without speaking. Peter Ilych trembled as he bent down over her hand. This hand, at least, had remained slim. It had always pleased him that she, for all her love of jewels, wore no rings.

"How long is it since we last saw each other?" It was Peter Ilych who first gave expression to the question that was in the minds of both.

"Oh, never mind about that, never mind about that, naughty Pierre!" Madame Désirée shook her raspberry-colored handkerchief at him chidingly. Peter Ilych appeared not to hear.

"It is exactly twenty years," he said cruelly with a preoccupied punctiliousness.

At this, she allowed the silk handkerchief to sink. "Oh, is it really twenty years ago, dear Pierre?" she said complainingly in a soft fine voice. "Her '*piano*' must still be wonderful," thought Peter Ilych. "I have been told that in the upper register her voice has become shrill, like a knife, and that altogether she hasn't much to recommend her now. But I'm quite sure that her soft voice is still magical. As a matter of fact her voice was not altogether up to its best form when I last heard her—at the Moscow Opera House; that was a year after our affair. She had already got married to that chap, the Spanish baritone; now what was his name? Even at that time the press thought she was past her prime. However, she had a great success; her talent triumphed. What a brilliant showman she was!" He said aloud:

"I had the chance of seeing you once again later—true, it was only on the stage—when you had certainly forgotten all about me. That was a year after—your sudden departure. I sat hidden in a box and admired you. I remember still—you had twenty curtain calls after the *Huguenots*."

"Twenty curtain calls!" The Artôt was touched. "How sweet of you to count, Pierre—and to remember how many!" She gave him a moist, tenderly melancholy glance.

"I shall never forget that performance of the *Huguenots*," said Tchaikovsky, and this was no exaggeration. Every detail of that evening was indeed unforgettable, for once more he had seen Désirée Artôt, now Madame Padilla (yes, Padilla was the name of her Spanish husband), on the stage of the Moscow Opera House. During the whole of the performance he had not moved the opera glasses from his eyes; he still recalled that his arm hurt him because he held the glasses in one position for so long—not, however, in order to see more clearly (it was of no consequence to him what he saw, and moreover he was sitting quite close to the stage), but so that the friends who were with him in the box should not perceive that he was weeping. When the audience greeted the beloved Artôt with their applause, he could not help crying, and his tears continued to flow during the twenty curtain calls at the close of the opera. What did Peter Ilych weep about? Not, surely, because he had lost her? Would he have had to lose her if he had really wanted to keep her? Could he then lose what he had never possessed? Could he possess what he had not passionately wished to possess? Were

his tears really those of a betrayed lover seeing his faithless beloved again? If they were tears of grief, for what was he griev-
ing? Certainly not because he had loved in vain. (Ah, with
what great tenderness had Désirée, the not-enough-desired,
come to him!) The fact that he had *not loved enough*—that was
something he might well grieve over; that was something over
which he might well shed tears. But perhaps they were not tears
of grief at all, but tears of shame. . . .

"You must tell me all that has been happening in your life,"
said Madame Artôt. "You have become world-famous; the little
Pierre of long ago is today a great man. You must come and see
me soon. Bring Madame Tchaikovsky with you! Of course you
are married, dear Pierre?" She asked this with soft, almost tender malice.

"I never got married," said Tchaikovsky.

"Oh," said Madame Artôt astonished. "But somebody once
told me—"

"It's not worth talking about," interrupted Peter Ilych in
a rough voice. "And you, Désirée?" he asked her. "One hears a
great deal about you. It appears that you are just as much a
favorite here in Berlin as you used to be in Warsaw, Moscow,
and St. Petersburg."

"People are very kind to me here." The large, flat face of the
singer suddenly looked wretched; double chin and down-cov-
ered, powdered cheeks sagged disconsolately. "But I am no
longer young," she declared, and slightly lowered her bejeweled
head.

"You must be a welcome guest at Court," said Peter Ilych.
"No doubt you regale their Germanic Majesties with your incomparable trills and runs. I envy the German Emperor. Oh,
Désirée, you are indestructible! I can picture you making your
curtsey at Court: you must do it with delicious *grandezza!*"

They both laughed. A booming voice called out: "You appear
to be amusing yourself marvelously, my sweet!" And behind
Désirée appeared a giant in evening dress; a greasy black mane

framed a bloated but good-natured face, with moist lips and small fiery, very black eyes, which gleamed between layers of fat: it was Mariano Padilla y Ramos, the Artôt's husband.

She turned smilingly to him. *"Chéri,"* she said, "I want to introduce you to my old friend, Pierre Tchaikovsky."

Whereupon Señor Padilla shouted "Ho, ho!" and thumped Peter Ilych on the shoulder so heavily that it resounded and hurt. "Ho, ho! But this is an immense pleasure!"

"The pleasure is on my side, Monsieur Padilla," said Peter Ilych, shattered by the mighty voice and physical force of the giant.

"So at last I can see what my wife's former fiancé looks like!" Padilla laughed immoderately over the tactlessness to which he had given utterance in such a stentorian voice.

"Padilla, what are you talking about?" cried Madame Désirée, and struck at him with her little handkerchief.

But Peter Ilych was thinking: "Fiancé? Was I ever her fiancé? True, all Moscow talked about it, and my old father sent a letter of blessing. 'If you love each other, my children . . .' Was I really your fiancé, Désirée?"

"You must soon come and dine with us, dear Tchaikovsky," said Padilla, "without fail." The Artôt added archly: "I have already asked him to do so, my dear!"

* * *

Nina and Edvard Grieg traveled all the way from Leipzig especially to be present at Tchaikovsky's concert. The intimate dinner party at the Padillas' had been fixed for the evening before the concert, "as a preliminary celebration of the great success that you are bound to have, dear Pierre," said Désirée. Peter Ilych had then asked her if she would also invite the Griegs. The company, therefore, consisted of five persons: Padilla and his wife, the two Griegs, and Tchaikovsky.

Peter Ilych discovered that Padilla was really a good sort, once one had got used to his boisterous manner and his naïve tactlessness. Other things had to be overcome, such as the sounding thump on the shoulder with which he greeted one, the sudden outbursts of laughter, and the misplaced jokes. But on the whole one felt happy in his company; he was a warm-hearted fellow.

"How cosy it is here, Désirée," said Peter Ilych. "You have made a real home."

She leaned coquettishly towards her powerful husband, who at that moment had for some reason burst out laughing. "Yes, we are very happy," she said and smiled at Peter Ilych. "It is too bad that I can't introduce you to our daughter. She is charming, much more charming, I fancy, than I was that time in Moscow. And she is gifted. She will have a great career."

Today Madame Artôt was looking more matronly, less gaudy, than she had looked in the grand gown she had worn at the soiree. The splendor of her bosom was veiled in black silk.

Everybody was already feeling in the best of humor when dinner was announced. The conversation was conducted in French, although neither of the Griegs spoke that language with ease. Their hurried chirruping, singsong way of speaking, at times comically hesitant, contrasted pleasantly with the drawling, very fluent, soft, singing French of Tchaikovsky, with Padilla's rough jargon with its hard consonants and rolling r's, and with the perfect Parisian of the Artôt.

"Here we are, all sitting in a Berlin dining-room," said Grieg, his wife Nina forming every word with her lips after him—"a Frenchwoman, a Russian, a Spaniard, and two Norwegians. We musicians are a model for the international society of the future."

"Good health!" cried Padilla somewhat pointlessly, raising his glass of port; they were still at the soup stage. "We must drink to the fact that you didn't get each other!" and he turned with a particularly boisterous laugh towards his wife and Peter Ilych.

Edvard and Nina looked disconcerted, while Peter Ilych, flushing, bent his head. "He is scoffing at me," he thought unhappily. "Perhaps he intends it to be harmless and amusing, but it sounds like the most appalling mockery." The Artôt dabbed with her silk handkerchief at her impossible husband; today she wore, with her dark gown, a cream-colored handkerchief with a black-pointed border. "But, Padilla," she complained, "you are horrid!"

"Why?" asked the baritone, breathless with laughter. "Why? We are bearing up splendidly, your old flame and I." He raised his glass to Peter Ilych.

Madame Désirée, somewhat abruptly, inquired after her old teacher, Pauline Viardot; Tchaikovsky had run across her during his last stay in Paris. "The old lady was good enough to invite me to lunch," he said, his eyes still fastened on his soup plate. "It is astonishing how fresh and vivacious she still is."

"Yes, a wonderful person," said the Artôt, somewhat distrait.

Between the courses, Grieg asked Peter Ilych how the Hamburg concert had succeeded. Peter Ilych spoke about Sapelnikov and Hans von Bülow. "It was very curious seeing Bülow again," he said. "I found him greatly altered. Something in him seems to have collapsed."

The Artôt, following with her eyes the movements of the servant who was handing round the hors d'œuvres, said: "He has certainly never really got over the Cosima tragedy."

"People ask too much of us," said Peter Ilych somewhat irrelevantly. But Nina exclaimed, and seemed terrified by the independence of her utterance: "I shall never understand how a woman can behave like that . . . I mean in such shocking circumstances. It was really dreadful. Bülow worked for Richard Wagner in Munich; he devoted all his strength to the work of his great friend; and all the time she was carrying on behind his back with the same great friend!"

Edvard stroked her hand pacifyingly. "Certain people seem to be linked to one another by destiny—certain people of heroic mold; do you understand, my child? And we little outsiders have no right to judge them," he said at once instructively and confidingly.

Padilla began to tell them an anecdote about adultery in the Paris Grand Opera circle; but the Artôt returned to the Wagner-Cosima-Bülow theme.

"Yes," she said, "Grieg is right. We are dealing here with people built on a grand scale; we ought not to measure them by the standards of humdrum philistines. I once had an opportunity of seeing Cosima. What a woman! The true daughter of the great Liszt and the Comtesse d'Agoult! Of course she could not abide by normal rules. Who says that free love is immoral in a case like hers?" she asked provocatively. Nina turned somewhat red; Padilla snickered inappropriately, and Peter Ilych thought: "Good Heavens, she has been reading Ibsen. Of course, she must make herself seem interesting—to whom, I wonder? To me? In reality she is not in the least in favor of free love; she always did have quite middle-class opinions; we often squabbled over such things."

"What is your attitude in the matter, Pierre?" asked the Artôt, turning her large face towards him; the still beautiful mouth smiled as if to reward him in anticipation for an answer which would support her audacious opinions.

Peter Ilych looked at her thoughtfully. "I am thinking of what the poor, betrayed Bülow said about Wagner to a relation of Cosima's. The Master, he said, was *aussi sublime dans ses œuvres qu'incomparablement abject dans ses actions.* So far as the second part of the formula is concerned," added Peter Ilych smiling, "that I agree with. At the same time, it is very entertaining to try to picture the whole of that famous constellation of legendary figures; the figure of the incomparable, handsome, and crazy young king of Bavaria puts the finishing touch to the dramatic array. One ought to have been present at that performance of the *Meistersinger* in Munich—but only if one could have been well behind the scenes and worn a cap of invisibility. Throned above everything, the melancholy young King and Maecenas—and at all the festivities, this deadly tension between Wagner and Bülow, who afterwards would never meet again. Liszt, the father of the fateful Cosima, was far away. It pleases me to think of him in Rome, following, diabolically and piously, the development of the whole situation, not giving his approval and not intervening. I have been told that on the day of the great première of the *Meistersinger* the crafty old abbé heard Mass in the Sistine Chapel, played to the Holy Father, Pius IX, on a Bechstein grand piano, after which the Holy Father handed him a box of cigars by way of recompense. All that is extremely amusing!"

"It seems to me that we take on too much when we try to explain the private life of Richard Wagner," remarked Grieg. "It is quite difficult enough, and more important, to cope with him as an artistic phenomenon; for we all know that he is the most amazing figure in the art of his time; without him none of us would have been conceivable. But which of us loves him?"

"Oh, he wrote some splendid baritone roles," said Padilla, who had not stopped eating.

And the Artôt—her voluptuous white arms resting on the table so that the black silk slipped and revealed their ripe beauty—declared excitedly: "I admire everything great!"

"She is not very clever," thought Peter Ilych, observing her with cool but intense curiosity. "Astonishing! At one time I considered her remarkably intelligent." And he said aggressively: "There are also great phenomena which we ought to hate. Perhaps Wagner belongs to that class."

With provocative zeal he kept the conversation throughout the whole of dinner-time to the great theme of Wagner, Bayreuth, and their significance for music—a subject which stimulated him to take up a more and more passionate and polemical attitude. It may be, however, that he clung to the subject so obstinately on this occasion in order that Padilla might be provided with no further opportunities of making coarse allusions to long-past and melancholy events, bringing blushes to the cheeks of all present.

So he entertained the company with outbursts of wrath and merriment on the subject of Bayreuth. Mingled with his violent and unjust assertions were ejaculations of admiration, such as "Naturally I am impressed by Wagner's enormous talent!" and so forth, admissions apparently designed to make his attacks more potent. "What a Don Quixote this Wagner was!" he said vehemently. "He paralyzed his own genius by his absurd theories. *Lohengrin, Tannhäuser,* the *Dutchman*—they are all bearable, they are at least *operas;* but the later period, the so-called music drama, which was designed to combine all the arts in a single work of art—what a mass of lies! How terribly remote from all artistic truth, simplicity, and beauty—how lacking in all humanity! Over-life-size figures, which have no relation to us, strut about on stilts; and the music which swamps their pompous gestures is both brutal and arid. Why is the later Wagner so unbearable?" asked Peter Ilych, throwing a challenging glance at the others. "Because he lost all sense of proportion!" he said triumphantly, answering himself. "Because his talent was completely ruined and swallowed up by his diabolical pride, by his dreadful imperialism, and by his devotion to a mongrel and typically German art-form. Absolutely swallowed up!" he repeated angrily, and gave himself some brandy. "A few years ago I heard *Tristan* for the first time, here in Berlin. What an appalling bore! Such things ought not to be allowed. The whole evening I was thinking: Here we have an artist who has taken the wrong turning! Was one obliged to remain and witness this highly distressing fiasco, this extravagant outpouring of a megalomaniac? On only one other occasion have I been similarly bored—at a performance of the *Götterdämmerung.*"

Peter Ilych—who seemed unwilling to drop the subject of Wagner for a single moment—told them about his stay in Bayreuth: that was in the summer of 1876, at the opening of the Festival Theater. At that time he was still writing Music Letters for the *Moscow News.* "It was like a gigantic fair!" he said. "The little German town was filled with international celebrities. In the highways and byways one saw all sorts of famous folk, although not many of the very first rank were to be seen. Verdi, Gounod, Brahms, Thomas, Bülow were conspicuous by their absence. I had come from Lyon, where I had been visiting my brother Modest. My good friend Nikolay Rubinstein met me at the Bayreuth station. I recall now that he said: 'You'd better be prepared for a shock!' My God, what I suffered in that Festival Theater! That 'Ring' which showed absolutely no sign of ever coming to an end; and when the last act of the *Götterdämmerung* was finally disposed of, I took a deep breath like one released from prison. I had only one feeling: 'Uff!'— Yes, I know quite well," he went on with a nod to Grieg, who was about to contradict him, "that there are beautiful things in it, magnificent things indeed. But the thing as a whole—well, it is simply devastating. Having gone through it, one needs a period of convalescence. Do you know what I most longed for after the completion of the 'Ring'? That bewitching ballet of Delibes, *Sylvia.* But that, of course, wasn't to be had in Bayreuth!"

Everybody laughed. The Artôt said: "Yes, *Sylvia* is charming; Paris is the place where one should see it. But I should not dare even to think of it in Bayreuth: I should feel quite wicked!"

While the maid was serving dessert, Tchaikovsky told them how difficult it had been to get anything to eat in Bayreuth at that time. "All that sort of thing was very badly organized," he said. "As for hot dishes, they weren't to be had for love or money, and in that consecrated Festival town one heard a good deal more about sausage and potato salad than about leitmotiv and heroic figures. How they besieged the beer-tents during the intervals of *Walküre* and *Siegfried!* I saw millionaires and world-famous personages fighting like wild animals for a sandwich. I hope the crowned heads, at any rate, had enough to eat."

He described very dramatically the arrival of the handsome

and gloomy young King of Bavaria at the little station of Bayreuth; how Richard Wagner shook hands with this royal Parsifal, the noblest of all his patrons and disciples. "I looked on from the platform," said Peter Ilych. "What a pinched and malicious mouth Wagner had! The poor young king looked beautiful and pale, like a statue, and he stared fixedly right past his master, right past his ungrateful friend and master. One felt that already an invisible wall had sprung up between them; they no longer understood each other, they were already widely estranged. And how terrified of people this much-loved king was! One could see the anxiety on his brow as he drove through the streets in his closed carriage to the cheers of the crowd; he only nodded, sitting there behind the carriage window, with a staring, white, disconsolate expression. After he had listened to the 'Ring' he went away at once, back to one of his legendary castles, which were reputed to be not only magnificent but enchanted. I am sure he had all sorts of special reasons for wanting to hurry away: in the first place, because he was disillusioned about Wagner, and above all because in the meantime the old Emperor Wilhelm had turned up in Bayreuth; and the romantic king of Bavaria was far too proud to greet the Prussian as his emperor."

Grieg broke a short silence to say: "But now they are both dead, the young king and his ambitious master."

They spoke of Richard Wagner's solemn death in Venice. "In her great grief, Frau Cosima let them cut off all her hair," said the Artôt emotionally; they spoke of the triumphal procession of his coffin through northern Italy and through southern Germany. "In Munich the populace paid homage to this dead man as they would have paid it to a prince," said Grieg; "and in Bayreuth they buried him like an emperor. Never before has a musician been accorded so much honor."

"His King Parsifal survived him only three years," said Peter Ilych. And they talked about the tragedy of the ill-fated king at the Starnberger See. "A doctor wanted to intervene," said Peter

Ilych, and suddenly an expression of bitterness, almost of disgust, came over his face. "What did a doctor expect to discover? Perhaps that young king was not so mad after all. He only wanted to be free. If a man wants to be free, others call him mad."

It was Padilla, whom the conversation had made uncomfortable, who first rose from the table. "What a solemn atmosphere we've created!" he cried. "We'd better have a glass of brandy at once, or better still, several glasses!"

When they reached the drawing-room, the baritone engaged Grieg in conversation first on the subject of Scandinavian schnapps, and then on the subject of liqueurs in general, while Désirée discovered her Pierre half-hidden behind a plush curtain in the window-bay.

"You have been speaking of thousands of things, my dear," she said, laying her beautiful hand gently on his shoulder. "And you only do that in order to avoid speaking about yourself. And yet I should so much like to know something about your life. How do you live, Pierre?"

"There is nothing much to tell you about my life," he said. "I work."

"And what else?" she asked—getting too close to him, he thought. "Are you alone?"

"I'm not asking questions of *you*," he said roughly, and, in contrast with his usual manner, almost rudely.

She retaliated softly: "Dear Pierre, the reason why you don't ask me questions is that you have never in your life—never in all your life, do you hear—been seriously interested in anybody."

"Do you really believe that, Désirée?" he asked hotly.

Désirée, whom people had spoken of as his fiancée, the lost Désirée, the completely estranged, elderly, fat, and affected Désirée, nodded her head earnestly. He was minded to flare out, perhaps in order to justify himself in his own eyes, perhaps the more bitterly to indict himself; but he broke off before he had begun. "Let's drop the subject," he said and turned away. "It would be nicer to have some music."

"It would be nicer to have some music!" repeated the elderly singer. Peter Ilych had already joined the others. They all gathered round the piano. It was decided that Nina should sing some of Grieg's songs and that Peter Ilych should accompany her; while the Artôt wished to sing a couple of Tchaikovsky's songs, with Grieg at the piano.

"That is a neat and just division!" declared Padilla contentedly. "You can't imagine how much my wife admires your music, Master Tchaikovsky. She makes a downright cult of your works."

"Really, Padilla! Do leave off!" Désirée shook her silk handkerchief at him, and it was touching to see how she blushed beneath her powder.

"Why, what's the matter?" boomed her husband. "Why shouldn't I be allowed to say that? Now, let's begin!" he commanded. Nina had already taken up her position at the piano, in that artificially negligent attitude adopted by singers at the opening of a great concert. "People like ourselves couldn't be engaged in anything better than music-making. Other things only lead to foolish thoughts. . . ."

Peter Ilych said: "You are right," and smiled at Señor Padilla. He went slowly to the piano with his heavy tread. He sat down on the revolving stool and lifted the lid of the piano. For a moment or two he closed his eyes and laid both of his heavy white hands on the keyboard of the instrument in front of him.

*　　*　　*

Peter Ilych parted from the Griegs outside the house where Désirée lived with Padilla and with her pretty daughter.

"I should not have seen you again, *ô toi que j'eusse aimée*," he was thinking as he walked alone through the strange streets of the German capital. "I am disappointed, and so are you, *ma pauvre petite Désirée.* Yes, I am sure you had imagined that our reunion would be something quite different—more dramatic, more sentimental. No doubt you feel that I was nothing like sufficiently shattered. As a matter of fact, I did experience something shattering, but it was only at the first moment, at the Kommerzienrat's party, when I saw how old you had grown: it made me reflect on all the time that has gone by in your life and in mine. After that everything became banal, and the fact that it was also tragic did not make it more exciting. A finale is always flat—a fussy and pompous flourish, hollow and conventional, without any relevance to the preceding drama.

"Nothing lasts, *ma pauvre*—not even real love; let alone the vague, equivocal feeling I once had for you, *ô toi que j'eusse aimée.* As no emotional tie can ever be permanent, it is only natural—isn't it?—that our meeting should have been anti-climactic, indeed, a little embarrassing.

"What do you say? . . . *Perhaps, dear Pierre, the reason is that you have never in your life—never in all your life, do you hear—been seriously interested in anybody.*

"Is that so? Are you so sure of that, *ma chérie?*——

"And what about Nadezhda?" he asked aloud, speaking to himself in Russian, much to the surprise of the passers-by.

He did not like to admit, even to himself, that this "ideal," "platonic" friendship, his spiritual romance with Madame von Meck, was beginning to wear out, to lose its initial freshness. Of course, the generous widow continued to send her always highly welcome checks ("*that* at least is something I can depend upon until the end of my life!" Peter Ilych was wont to think, not without a certain secret anxiety); but their correspondence was no longer what it used to be, eight or ten years before. If formerly they had exchanged tender and elaborate messages several times a week, now there were months without any communication.

Was it Tchaikovsky's fault? Naturally, he was busier now, more famous and consequently more harassed, than he had

been in the days of *Onegin* and the Violin Concerto. But it was
not he alone who neglected the correspondence: Nadezhda, too,
had lost her old diligence. Had it to do with her failing health?
Peter Ilych knew that the "beloved friend" was suffering from
tuberculosis—the ailment that had destroyed so many of those
close to him. Or was she simply losing interest in her idol and
protégé?

Peter Ilych, walking along the dark, quiet avenue Unter
den Linden, rejected this unpleasant notion. "She will never
lose interest in me—never!" he decided. "My guardian angel
is faithful. It's just that letter-writing now entails more of
an effort for her than it used to. After all, we are not getting
younger."

He recalled, not without sympathy, what Modest had written
him some time ago, having seen Nadezhda Filaretovna in
Rome: "How old she has become! And how queerly she
dresses!"

Yes, she had been dressed in rather a quaint, old-fashioned
style, even at the time Peter Ilych caught a first glimpse of her,
nine years ago in Florence. Both Madame von Meck and her
beloved composer were then spending several weeks in the
beautiful town on the Arno—without ever talking to each other,
naturally. But once in a while, by chance, Peter Ilych would
see his capricious friend passing by in an open carriage—an
unknown woman, a lady of distinction, even though queerly
dressed.

Maybe that Florentine period had marked the climax of
their peculiar relationship. Peter Ilych was then working on
his First Suite (dedicated to Madame von Meck) and began
outlining *The Maid of Orleans*—the long-planned opera based
on Schiller's drama. It had turned out a complete failure—a
grandiloquent, noisy affair strongly influenced by the terrible
Meyerbeer; but while working on it, the composer was full of
enthusiasm and confidence. Nadezhda, residing in grand style
at the Villa Oppenheim, would receive daily billets from the

Villa Bonciani where Tchaikovsky had his quarters, describing in the most buoyant terms every phase of his work in progress. The good fairy, in turn, had her man Ivan carry little gifts to her beloved friend's abode—for instance, three different brands of the most exquisite Turkish tobacco which, she said, would have an at once soothing and stimulating effect on his nerves. The letters accompanying such attentions ended with affectionate phrases like "Loving you with all my soul," or *"Au revoir, my dear friend beyond compare!"*

Was all this over and gone? The lonely wanderer stamping through the deserted streets of the Imperial city refused to believe it. Clearly, poor, frustrated Désirée was altogether mistaken! "My friendship with Nadezhda has lasted and will last," Peter Ilych thought with a sort of defiant triumph, "which proves that I have been, and still am, able to take a serious interest in another person."

He had reached his hotel. "What's my schedule for tomorrow?" he wondered while crossing the lobby. "Oh yes, I'd almost forgotten—I have to make the morning train to Prague!"

P ETER I LYCH ' S STAY in Prague, following on his engagement in Berlin, was a public festival with a definitely political significance. The lonely Tchaikovsky took pleasure in the ovations with which he was received, but he did not fail to observe that they were not solely inspired by him, but also by "Little Mother Russia." He was inexpressibly moved, almost to tears, by the cries of acclamation with which the Czech students greeted him and by the storm of applause raised by the Czech audience at the opera. He enjoyed these ten glittering days of triumph in Prague, the more because he spent them in the company of his handsome and aloof friend, Alexander Siloti. He was ravished by the beauty of the "Golden City," its bridges, squares, and mysterious alleys; he rejoiced in it as "the town which was the first to recognize Mozart." And what else did he know about it? He was happy about a connection he made with the most recent genius of the Czech people—Dvořák; and he felt a thrill of joy in his heart when he was assured that never before had a foreign artist been received with such an ovation as had been accorded him. Was he aware of the reason why the vanguard of the Czechs, their press and their high officials, stressed and overstressed these ovations with such remarkable enthusiasm?

Was he not aware, was he unable to grasp the fact that a battle was in progress and that he, the musician who had come to them with all his fame and his personality, had been drawn into this battle and was being made use of? Did he not suspect that this great struggle was taking place between two races, between two ages? That here was a young and robust people that wished to break free from fetters which had been laid upon it by the effete and tired and always cruel Austrian monarchy? That here was a spirited, ambitious nation resolved to stamp its own

[167]

culture, and its own political mode of life, on history? These people were intoxicated by the Slav flavor of Peter Ilych's music. This flavor symbolized not only a sweet and much-loved homeland, but also *power*: for it signified Russia against the Hapsburg and Hohenzollern monarchies. The homage paid to the unpolitical composer Tchaikovsky was a political demonstration.

*   *   *

After Prague, the next place of call on this tour was Paris. In Germany, a respectable musical élite had accepted the composer with a certain tempered understanding; in Prague, a Slav people, oppressed by a foreign power, had given him an extravagantly demonstrative triumph. But in Paris it was Society which pursued him. The musical world here was closely linked with the world of fashion; the foreigner who wished to make good in the one could not afford to neglect the other—a fact which his Russian friends were not slow to make known to their compatriot. He believed it, and accepted the musical-fashionable round as a duty imposed upon him by the necessities of his calling. A shy man, easily disconcerted by people, wearing a somewhat tight dress suit, his forehead rather flushed—he played his part in the receptions given in his honor at the most exalted houses. One had to suffer not only in order to create music, but also by having to mix with people in order to become famous! "Did I not once say to my ambitious young friend Siloti—or was it Kotek to whom I made the remark?— 'I am not interested in fame,'" ruminated Peter Ilych. "But he answered: 'We all need it—we all need it.' So in honor I must accept these invitations, even though I perspire with embarrassment and boredom, for perspire I certainly shall. Every contact with this importunate and unreliable world is so painful, so embarrassing, and so fatiguing—like a meeting with the agent Siegfried Neugebauer, who most uncannily and comically unites in himself all their bad qualities!"

Peter Ilych went on trying to persuade himself that all these social unpleasantnesses had to be endured for the sake of the great Russian concert: it was still his ambition to introduce the music of his native land to this most blasé public in the world. "For nobody here knows anything about us," he thought several times during the day, when people spoke to him about Russian affairs. Here in Paris there was a Russian cult, which, however, possessed very little knowledge of Russian achievements or Russian life. Here the cult had a political emphasis, like the genuine outpouring of sympathy in Prague: its darts were directed against a dangerous Germany. People were enthusiastic about Franco-Russian fraternity and wore "Franco-Russe" ties. In the salons and in the newspapers the novels of Tolstoy and Dostoevsky received a great deal of attention, while at the circus the Russian clown Durov had a triumph. Nevertheless, for serious Russian music the interest was so slight that Peter Ilych would have had to be a rich man to take on the risk of the concert himself. Without being guilty of any great extravagance, he had had to spend a considerable amount of money on this tour, which had cost much more than it had brought in. Already he knew that there was nothing for it but to give up the idea of a great Russian concert. Siegfried Neugebauer had been justified in his offensive skepticism, and it was just this that Peter Ilych did not wish to admit. So he took delight in talking about his beautiful concert, trying to get influential persons and fashionable social sets to be interested in it. Everywhere a polite curiosity was aroused, but it remained lukewarm, and nothing of a really helpful nature came of it.

In the meantime he put out feelers. It would advance his fame, and one needs fame, even though fame be a hallmark of the pariah and a miserable substitute. The round of solemn festivities began with a full-dress gala reception in the palace of M. Bernardacky, a rich Maecenas who kept open house in Paris. More than three hundred persons foregathered: Peter Ilych was informed that this was *"tout Paris."* The great conductor Colonne had been taking his orchestra through Tchaikovsky's String Serenade, and on the gala evening the composer himself conducted it. After Peter Ilych—who also played the pianoforte part in the Andante Cantabile of his first String Quartet—some of the most famous virtuosos followed, notably: the pianist Diémer and the brothers de Reszke, two singers whose voices were here held to be the most beautiful it was possible to conceive. In addition, the soprano Madame Bernardacky, *née* Liebrock, took part in the concert, together with her sister who was an opera singer. It was a brilliant evening: the publisher Maquart, who had arranged it, might well be contented. After the concert various world-famous notabilities congratulated the Russian visitor, who, gracious and timid in his somewhat too tight-fitting suit, and with his forehead flushed, bowed low to everybody who approached him. Among the congratulators were the great rivals Colonne and Lamoureux; Gounod, Massenet, and Saint-Saëns; old Pauline Viardot and Paderewski. The Russian guest listened politely to everybody who came to him, however gushing or garrulous. An old lady, who carried a fortune in jewelry on her neck, bosom, arms and fingers, asked him if he were aware how famous he was in France: his song *Nur wer die Sehnsucht kennt* played a quite important role in the novel *Le Froc* by one Emile Goudau. So great was his fame! When one's work figures in a French novel, then one really belongs to *"tout Paris."*

The round of solemn festivities showed no sign of coming to an end. M. Colonne gave a great soiree; an even more important party was given by the Baroness Tresdern, a patroness of music, who had once been able to arrange a private performance of Wagner's "Ring" in her drawing-room in the Place Vendôme. Now she was graciously pleased to give a reception in honor of the Russian visitor. Others were given by the Russian Embassy, Madame Pauline Viardot, and also, and in great style, by the management of *Figaro*. At this last-named, a performance of the third act of *The Powers of Darkness* was given in one of the flower-decorated halls of the distinguished newspaper; and all to honor the Russian guest. The pianist Diémer arranged a gala evening at which his students played only compositions by Tchaikovsky; that was a very good advertisement, not only for the virtuoso-pedagogue, but also for the composer, and—perhaps —for the young students. The boulevard press, large and small, took a lively part in all these events. True, people were less interested in Tchaikovsky's music than in *"la délicieuse toilette en satin et tulle blanc,"* worn by a Polignac or a Noailles; the *"grace de grande dame"* of Madame Bernardacky was lauded, as well as the floral decorations in the great *Figaro* hall: the name of the florist who had supplied the latter was not over-looked, for why should not he, too, participate in the general orgy of publicity?

When at last the two great public Tchaikovsky concerts came to be given at the Châtelet, the Russian visitor was already well known by the most important duchesses and in the re-ception rooms of the most important newspapers. He had paid visits everywhere, a timid man of the world, piloted and intro-duced by his zealous publisher, M. Maquart. And now, to wind up, the great French public would be given a chance to know him and the serious musical journals would be able to take an interest in him.

He was received by the audience at the Châtelet with great applause, which no doubt—so his sensitive apprehension readily informed him—was again directed more to "Little Mother Rus-sia" and to Franco-Russe fraternization than to the composer himself, of whom this public knew but little. However, after every separate piece, and at the end of the concert, there were great ovations.

The journals were restrained. Clearly, they had read César Cui's *La musique en Russie,* and from this they were able to extract their wisdom. The Paris press declared with severity: *"M. Tchaikovsky n'est pas un compositeur aussi russe qu'on voudrait le croire";* he possessed, so it was firmly stated, neither the audacity nor the strong originality that were the chief charm of the great Slavs—Borodin, Cui, Rimsky-Korsakov, Liadov. M. Tchaikovsky was unfortunately quite European. *"L'allemand dans son œuvre domine le slave, et l'absorbe."*

"Obviously at the Châtelet they had expected to hear *des impressions exotiques,"* thought Peter Ilych bitterly. "In Leipzig they reproached me with being French; in Hamburg, with being Asiatic; in Paris, with being German; in Russia, they consider me a hotchpotch of everything, and in any case quite unoriginal.

"Oh, these proud and brutal members of the neo-Russian school, these five gifted Innovators, who stick together as thick as thieves; this solemnly pledged brotherhood of musical nationalists: what harm you have all done to me! It is you and only you I have to thank for the cry that I am 'flat,' without strength, and 'western.' The students in Prague, who hailed me as the legitimate message-bringer and singer of the great Russia, did not think that; nor did that clever old Avé-Lallemant think it when he said that I was too Asiatic and should learn of the German masters. But César Cui thinks it. Rimsky-Korsakov is another matter. He is the only one of the group who understands something about his craft; his *Spanish Capriccio* is very interestingly orchestrated. Without him the whole set would disappear. It is he who arranges for their 'strokes of genius,' and he who gives them advice; in fact he has done what is regarded as a crime in me—he has *learned* something. The others are all dilettanti! Alexander Borodin—God rest him!—may have been an excellent professor of chemistry; Cui is perhaps a highly worthy professor of fortification—I have been told that his lectures on Defense at the Military College in St. Petersburg were splendid. Mussorgsky was indeed a tragic figure, a depraved, magnificent fellow, a terrific tippler. But the whole lot of them have been too little concerned with *music*: music can't be treated as a side issue. It has been a great misfortune that Russian composers from the very beginning have treated music as a side issue; that began with Glinka—our original source. He wanted to compose when he was lying on the sofa, and only then when he was in love; for the greater part of the time, however, he drank instead of working. Nevertheless he was a genius; he managed to write *A Life for the Tsar*, our first opera, without which none of us would ever have existed at all. 'It is the people who compose; we only arrange,' said Glinka, our great original source. They, the five Innovators, took note of that remark— and also of his predilection for alcohol. To tire people out with folk-music—that is the only thing worth doing; that is the only way to be linked with the people! As if the likes of us knew nothing about folk-music! Just because we haven't allowed folk-music to be our be-all and end-all, but have developed it, transformed it, and wedded it to other apparently foreign elements, we are deemed dull and conventional! Never learn anything of anybody! Never widen your horizon! *'En musique on doit être cosmopolite.'* This piece of wisdom comes from Alexander Serov, whom our friends, the Innovators, are gracious enough to recognize as one of the 'initiators' of Russian music. But that dictum no longer holds good. Now it is only the barbaric that is worthy of cultivation; only the crude, the unpolished, the ugly. Above all, it is Mussorgsky who is the real thing —who would never have come before the public at all if it hadn't been for the friendly help of Rimsky-Korsakov, so wretchedly is his music written down. Not a soul can play it. But *Boris Godunov* is *the* opera of the Russian people! Things which if done by the likes of us would be called sensational are regarded as great and beautiful and the very truth itself when done by him. When I once included bells in a score for a particular occasion, everybody smiled: 'How smartly contrived!' But *his* bells are expressive of the ancient Russian Church. Coronation processions, with cupbearers, mendicant friars, vagabond and peasant dances—everything he does is the genuine article! Murder, lamentations, screams, megalomania, apparitions—the murdered child shaking his bloody fist at the false Tsar—he is allowed to use the whole paraphernalia! I am not allowed to use them; I am a 'traditionalist,' like the brothers Rubinstein. It is only an old gentleman in Hamburg who still takes me for an Asiatic. They are better instructed here in Paris: César Cui has enlightened them. The genuine Russians are Borodin, Cui, Balakirev, Rimsky-Korsakov, and Mussorgsky—the Great Brotherhood, who jointly launched the Manifesto of the New Russian music. Maybe they are a lot of geniuses, and Mussorgsky may be the greatest. God rest his poor soul! He suffered much, the uncontrollable fellow! Perhaps he really was the nearest to our people. *I* don't belong anywhere; I am made to feel by everybody that I don't belong anywhere."

He had plenty of time to ruminate on all these things, because he had canceled all his engagements for this evening, being upset by the newspaper criticisms and exhausted and enervated and disgusted by the endless social round. He wanted to be alone. After dinner he had abandoned his hotel, which was situated near the Madeleine. He had strolled aimlessly along the great boulevards and finally had hailed a cab and asked to be driven to Montmartre. He was passing the Cirque Medrano and was stimulated to go in. The performance had already begun. "How good it smells here!" he thought as the attendant opened the door of his box. He had always loved the pungent smell of the menagerie—it aroused sensations of danger, curiosity, and excitement.

A comely lady in a stiff pink ballet skirt, with a high silver top hat on her fair curly hair, was dancing on the back of a white horse, who played his part by tripping daintily round the arena. The lady scattered kisses, and threw out little exclamations in English, half-joyous, half-fearful. Near by was a fat clown, with a dreadful violet false nose jutting out of his broad chalk-white face; it was impossible to tell whether he was trying to flee from the white horse or, contrariwise, trying to overtake it. In any case, he behaved with most comical clumsiness, constantly tumbling down, and seeming always to be in danger of shedding his broad red trousers—this aroused particularly hearty laughter; crude jokes were shouted from the gallery; the clown, his gaping red mouth distorted in a shameless-ashamed grin, got entangled in his braces, stumbled, and then, to the delight of the gallery, nearly stripped himself naked, but at the last minute managed to rescue the slipping nether garment.

After the bareback rider came the performing bears; then three tightrope dancers in white tights; then a female lion-tamer dressed as a Scottish soldier in plaid kilts, who fired a revolver in the air and rent the atmosphere with cries which sounded much more terrifying than the sullen growling of the intimidated beasts; then a great equestrian turn—and throughout, the clowns. Peter Ilych was thoroughly amused. He laughed heartily at the comedians; he got excited when the tightrope dancers performed daring steps, and admired with all his heart the clumsy artistic skill of the dancing bears. Most of all he enjoyed the audience and the enthusiasm and wit of their interjections. "It is really charming here," thought Peter Ilych. "At last I am glad to be in Paris." He forgot the duchesses, the odious critics and the five "Innovators." During the interval he drank several brandies at the buffet. The noise and bustle all around did not disturb him. He observed the paterfamilias with his little regiment of boys and girls, always alert to see that his progeny were properly reassembled after they had split up in a disorderly fashion; the cocottes who winked so eagerly from under their gaily trimmed hats; the dandies of the boulevards with their gleaming black moustaches, exaggeratedly high stiff collars, slim hips, and too pointed shoes. He loved listening to the Paris slang, the rapid, pointed speech, the resounding laughter. He was happy to be here.

He was attracted by a pretty girl, and then by the young man she was talking to. Dark, passionate eyes shone out of her pale, strained, but uncommonly attractive face. She wore a very simple tight-fitting dress of black silk, beneath the smooth surface of which the lines of her young breasts were clearly visible; in accordance with the prevailing fashion, the back part of the garment was over-elaborate. The young man with whom she was chatting and laughing had his back to Peter Ilych. His hair was soft, dull blond, and cropped short at the back. The young man did not wear an overcoat; his checked suit was made of English material, fitting close to the figure, rather shabby but not without a certain conscious chic. The girl broke into a silvery laugh which echoed through the whole foyer. As she did so, she let her head fall back; her pale face, with its large, dark, made-up mouth and long eyes, lay exposed, very charming and pathetically overstrained for all its mirthfulness, to the hard light of the gas lamps. The young man answered her laugh with his own, which sounded rough and tender but some-what mocking. What did it remind Peter Ilych of? He closed his eyes for a few moments in order to look inside himself and dis-cover what this laughter reminded him of. When he opened his eyes again, the young man had gripped hold of the pretty girl's arm; clinging close to one another, still laughing and chattering, they threaded their way through the crowd, with unhurrying but sure steps, towards the exit.

Peter Ilych thought: "I must follow them. I must go after them, along the Boulevard Clichy. I must observe them, how they go laughing as they stroll along; they are both so young; they press through the crowd with such sure steps. I must certainly find out what the young man's laugh reminds me of."

He dashed to the cloakroom, hurriedly demanded his fur coat, left a large tip; throwing the coat carelessly over his shoul-ders, he ran to the exit. He thought to himself eagerly as he ran: "Shall I be in time to find them? Or have I lost them al-ready?"

There were a great many people walking on the Boulevard Clichy at this time of night. On the pavement, brilliantly illu-minated by the gas lamps, prostitutes rubbed shoulders with respectable middle-class women, pimps with army officers, shop girls with Arabs and Negroes. The promenaders were impeded by the people streaming into cafés which spread themselves across the pavement; every café had its own atmosphere of noises and smells. Ragged lads offered newspapers and peanuts for sale, their half-mournful, half aggressive cries mingled with the sound of dance music in the cafés. At the corner of Boulevard Clichy, where it joins Place Pigalle, stood a haggard old man, his face eaten with leprosy. With a blackish lipless mouth he sang very softly and murmurously a ballad whose contents—when one grasped them—were terrible and moving. Averting his head, Peter Ilych dropped a gold coin into the withered hand. Both pity and disgust worked in him at the sight of the old man. Nevertheless, he was terrified by all beggars and was quite convinced that they brought him ill luck.

The two charming young people had been swallowed up by the crowd—the beautiful girl and the young man with the dangerous laugh. This made Peter Ilych very sad. "They've gone," he thought, and weighed down by depression, his steps became slow and heavy. "They attracted me; that is why the earth has swallowed them up. But no! Of course the earth hasn't swallowed them up; they've gone into one of these dark houses, clinging close together. They are making love in one of these dark houses. . . ."

The noisy, artificially illuminated night was mild. There was a feeling of spring in the moist air. Peter Ilych was warm from walking; he found the fur coat, which hung heavily over his shoulders, excessive. He was startled by a little Negress, who sprang in front of him and in a whimpering voice asked him to buy some matches. She had weary, anxiously staring eyes and a dark crown of crisp curly hair. As Peter Ilych bent down to put a coin in the child's blackish hand, the palm of which seemed somehow pathetically pale, as if it had been bleached, the Negro mother waddled up to them, appearing like a great shadow behind her begging daughter. The words of blessing she bestowed upon the gentleman who was giving alms to her daughter sounded as bitter as curses. The woman was *enceinte;* her body was enormously swollen beneath the gay patterned cotton skirt. Her face appeared to be almost as terrifyingly wide as her body. It could hardly be called a human face at all; it was a great, shapeless expanse, out of which her eyes glowed, and from which from time to time her teeth gleamed.

Stepping backwards, Peter Ilych escaped from the pregnant Negress; but he could not keep his eyes off her. "That will bring me terribly bad luck," he thought, staring as if bewitched at the shapeless creature. "Pregnant women always bring me bad luck, and such a one as this is bound to! What a poor miserable wretch she is! What a miserable wretch am I that I should have had to look at her!" At last he gathered up enough strength to turn his back on her. Holding his fur coat across his chest with both hands, he bounded away from her with heavy, awkward movements. The sound of a waltz came through the half-open door of a café. Peter Ilych went in.

He ordered a double brandy at the counter, drank it quickly and asked for another. The girl behind the counter tried to start a conversation with him, saying something about spring, which would not keep one waiting very much longer. She was a voluptuous brunette with the shadow of a moustache above her lip, and she had a strong southern French accent. Peter Ilych did not answer; the girl shrugged her shoulders. Sitting on the long leather-upholstered seat under the gold-framed mirror were other girls; on the grubby marble-topped tables in front of them stood coffee cups or glasses containing a greenish liquid. "That must be absinthe," thought Peter Ilych; "I should like to have one too. But I suppose the earth has swallowed up those two delightful children."

Next to him at the counter stood a wild-looking fellow, lethargic and motionless, wearing a velvet jacket; he stared with inflamed eyes at the glass of greenish liquid in front of him. Next to this hapless-looking young man—"no doubt he is a painter," thought Peter Ilych compassionately, "perhaps a very gifted portrait painter, pursued by ill-luck, like so many others in this country"—but concealed by him from Peter Ilych, stood somebody else. Suddenly Peter Ilych heard his harsh, tenderly mocking laugh: he recognized it; long ago he had heard it, and also only a short while ago. It was Apukhtin's laugh. Peter Ilych was alarmed.

So the young man who belonged to the girl he had seen in the Cirque Medrano was here too, and he had a laugh like Apukhtin's. Peter Ilych took a few steps past the wild fellow in the velvet jacket, and took up a position next to the young man. He was alarmed by his own boldness as he spoke to him.

"You are here, then," said Peter Ilych.

The young man turned an astonished face towards him. "Yes," he said, in a voice that was not particularly gracious, and he scrutinized the gentleman in the fur coat. "Why not?"

"I saw you in the Cirque Medrano," said Peter Ilych, whose forehead turned dark red under the harsh scrutiny of the young man. "You had a very beautiful girl with you."

"Did you like her?" The young man grinned understandingly. "It can be arranged. . . ."

Peter Ilych was not used to this way of speaking. What had he let himself in for? So this was just a little pimp, offering his girl for sale? He ought to have turned away and left the fellow. But Peter Ilych said: "I followed you, but you disappeared on the boulevard."

"Whom did you follow?" asked the young man and examined this strange old man with his keen, narrow, gray-green eyes. "My girl friend?"

Perhaps the girl was sitting in the café under the gold-framed mirror, with her glass of greenish liquid in front of her; perhaps the young man was keeping his eye on her, ready to let her go off with a cavalier and then towards morning meet her again and relieve her of the cash.

"I followed both of you," said Peter Ilych. "Both of you, because I liked the look of you."

"Me too?" asked the young man, not at all coquettishly, but quite objectively, with a defensive, almost evil expression on his face. Nevertheless, he had approached somewhat nearer to the foreigner in the fur coat.

To his own alarm, Peter Ilych answered: "Particularly you."

Upon which the young man said in a dry tone: "Oh, really."

Peter Ilych was silent. "Of course, he knows all about THIS," he thought. "I could ask him to come with me. He would probably become coarse, or he might say without moving a muscle: 'That can also be arranged.'" The buxom southern Frenchwoman behind the counter looked scornfully at the gray-bearded gentleman and the young man.

"You are Russian?" said the young man. His face retained its sullen expression, but he touched Tchaikovsky's arm with his own.

"How can you tell that?" asked Peter Ilych.

"I know lots of foreigners," said the young man, and his face assumed a somewhat disgusted expression, as if it were unpleasant to think about all he had experienced from foreigners. He stretched out his hand towards the glass containing the green liquid that stood in front of him; his hand was thin, sinewy, and rather dirty.

"Would you like another drink?" asked Peter Ilych, seeing that the young man had drained his glass at a gulp.

"Yes," said the young man—and with an expression of contempt, almost of hatred, said to the girl behind the counter: "Two more absinthes, Léonie, for the gentleman and me." So Peter Ilych also received some of the greenish liquid.

For a few moments they stood there in silence. Peter Ilych looked at the young man. His curly dull-blond hair was cropped short at the back and over the temples—as Peter Ilych had already noticed at the circus. Under the narrow gray-green eyes his cheekbones jutted prominently. The brow was smooth and beautiful, making the weak line of his short chin the more disappointing. His rather broad face, very youthful but already worn and no longer quite fresh, was pale and the space between his

eyelids and his fair eyebrows was a pinkish blue. The only
strong color in his face was that of his insolent, thrust-out
mouth: its dark red was in striking contrast with the pallor of
his brow and cheeks and the lifelessness of his expression. The
young man was not very tall, decidedly shorter than Peter Ilych,
and thin. His suit, which fitted close to the figure, betrayed an
acrobatically trained and flexible body. He held himself in an
attitude that was both taut and careless, his legs crossed, his
head somewhat drooping, like a runner about to start, the tired
sinewy hands encircling the glass.

"You are French?" asked Peter Ilych.

"I am Parisian," said the young man, and looked with his
pale, keen glance into his glass. "But my family doesn't belong
here; we come from some way off, from over there, from the
Balkans." He pointed with his beautiful dirty hand, as if he
wished to indicate the dark district from which his family came.
"But I have no more relations left," he added in a suddenly
and artificially woebegone tone.

"Have you a job?" inquired Peter Ilych and was at once
annoyed with himself for his naïve and clumsy question. "I
mean," he said, trying to improve matters, "have you got something to do?"

"I've done work at the circus." The young man looked into
his glass; probably he was lying. "As a matter of fact, I wanted
to be a musician; I can play the flute." He smiled tenderly, as
if he were deeply stirred by the memory of his flute-playing. No,
he was not lying.

"You wanted to be a musician," repeated Peter Ilych, looking
at him.

"But that was only a crazy idea of mine," said the young man,
the surly expression returning to his face, his voice hoarse and
ill-tempered.

"He wanted to be a musician; perhaps he has great talent.
It is quite likely—he looks as if he had. One might take charge

of him; he deserves it just as much as Sapelnikov, probably more, for he is blessed with much more charm. One might help him. . . ."

"And what do *you* do?" asked the young man. "I suppose you're an author or something like that?" The rough but tender, mocking laugh, which was like Apukhtin's, broke out: the laugh of the evil genius who had had so much power over Peter Ilych.

"One could keep him with one; one ought to help him. Perhaps something remarkable could be made of him."

As the foreigner did not answer, but seemed to have fallen into a brown study, the young man dispensed with circumlocution and asked bluntly: "Well, what about it? Are you going to take me with you?"

Peter Ilych flushed a deep red. The girl behind the counter, a dumb and scornful witness of the adventure, must have heard the question. Was she laughing? It was extremely distressing. Rather pointedly Peter Ilych said: "But it is already late." He pulled out his watch, less to discover what the hour was than to gain time, and also perhaps to assure himself that he still had with him his most beautiful possession, his good talisman.

He opened the decorated lid of the watch. At the same instant he was alarmed by the greedy look which the young man cast on the gold and platinum trinket.

Peter Ilych's hand trembled as he thrust the watch back again into his pocket. "The boy will steal my watch if I take him with me," he realized suddenly and wiped the sweat from his brow. "That is what would happen: not a friendship for life— not an educational relationship which would enable me to rescue him and turn him into a great musician. . . . Nothing at all would result from it, nothing! It is all humbug and self-deception! He would run off with my watch, and that would be the end of the great adventure; that would be the outcome of my wasted emotion.

"Even worse might happen. I have seen an unusually large

number of beggars tonight, including that terrifying pregnant woman: it all signifies ill-luck. Almost certainly it would have turned out even worse. He would have murdered me if I had shown the slightest disinclination to hand over the watch. He would have strangled me, for although he is small he is uncannily strong and agile, and very wicked; I can see that. He already hates me and his eyes are looking for the position on my throat on which, later on, he'll fasten his fingers.

"As a matter fact," thought Peter Ilych, as he hurriedly emptied his glass of the milky greenish liquid, whose aniseed flavor he found unpleasant, "as a matter of fact, it would not be such a bad death to be strangled by him. . . . The evil genius—uncannily strong and agile—pounces on you so that you lose all sense of sight and hearing; finally you recognize him for what he is, a strangling angel, who is squeezing the breath out of your body, and you slip away. . . .

"You slip away . . . oh, deliverance! But do you slip away with the approving consent of Him from Whom you received your Task? Alas, certainly not; that is more than I can hope for; for that remote Allotter of Tasks made His attitude quite clear when I challenged Him by walking into the icy water more than ten years ago, and for my pains achieved only chattering teeth and a cold in the head. And is it now to be just Apukhtin's laugh and devastating charm that are going to press the life out of me?

"Diabolical triumphs of that kind are no longer so easy to achieve, my old friend! It's no longer so easy, Apukhtin, my evil genius!" Peter Ilych was buoyed up by a feeling of boldness such as he had only once before experienced; that was at the time when the picture of his life and duty built itself up before his mind's eye with such surprising clarity that he had summoned up the strength to break off his friendship with Apukhtin, his evil genius. He went on furiously thinking: "No longer do we feel that we must surrender ourselves helplessly. Today we know what has still to be achieved and accomplished—all sorts of things such as will bring us that miserable substitute, Fame.

But you will die without fame, for all your charms, my young
friend! What was there about that short martial melody in my
friend Grieg's Sonata that I found so heartening? We must
learn how to resist."

As the curious elderly gentleman still hesitated, the young
man asked again: "What about it? Are you taking me with
you?" and was probably thinking about the handsome watch.
His narrow, pale, malicious eyes sent out a look that was both
keen and merry—an alluring, mysterious, and very dangerous
kind of merriment. Between his eyelashes and eyebrows, the
colors played on his pale skin—rosy-gray and silver, like mother-
of-pearl.

"I am tired now," said the elderly gentleman with a hypocritical smile. "I would rather go home to bed now." As the
young man's mouth twisted itself in an unpleasant grimace and
his face expressed his annoyance, the foreigner added: "But I
will see you again, my friend; please come and see me tomorrow
morning. My name is Jürgenson; I am staying at the Hôtel du
Rhin in the Place Vendôme. You have only to ask the porter for
me."

"Right," said the young man. "Tomorrow morning." And
turning suddenly and supply on his heels and facing Peter
Ilych, he added: "Give me a little money now, on account," and
he laughed his hoarse, gently mocking laugh.

The gentleman, perfectly calm, said: "With pleasure." He
took a note out of his pocket-book and gave it to the young man.
It was for a large amount, much larger than the young man had
expected; he smiled, and with his thin, grubby hand touched
the foreigner's large, white, heavy hand. The foreigner observed
the young man with his deep-blue, soft, brooding, and very sad
eyes.

He asked the girl behind the counter for the bill, paid it and
turned to go. He walked a few steps away from the young man,
turned and raised his heavy hand by way of salutation. "Fare-

well, my boy!" said the foreign gentleman; "and may you be happy!"

He stepped onto the Boulevard Clichy. The crowds had thinned; the lights in the cafés were being extinguished, and music could no longer be heard.

But Peter Ilych was not staying at the Hôtel du Rhin in the Place Vendôme, but at the Hôtel Richepanse, rue Richepanse. The rue Richepanse transected the rue St. Honoré and ran parallel with the rue Royale, and its continuation linked up the rue de Rivoli with the Madeleine.

*　　*　　*

The last stage of the tour, the stay in London, was undertaken as a duty. Tchaikovsky did not stay longer in the English capital than was absolutely necessary: four days.

He hurried home. Enough of the ceaseless procession of human faces; he gazed at them with an unhappy, brooding glance. Enough of this Art business, whether upper-middle-class, fashionable, or popular! What one needed now was Solitude; for now it was necessary to devote months and months to the Task.

Peter Ilych made notes during the stormy passage across the Channel and during the six-day railway journey. They were not notes on the opera he had been planning: the material for *Pique Dame* no longer attracted him. The operatic form seemed to him neither serious enough nor pure enough as an expression of the present period of his life, as the product and outcome of all he had learned and suffered. He would write a symphony. It should be a symphony of high defiance! It should be a symphony expressing the power to resist! It would be the very music for which he had felt himself ripe and ready when that short martial theme of his little friend Edvard Grieg had come to him as a consolation and an encouragement.

It should be the symphony of the power to resist, in which

lamentations would be conquered by an almost angry enthusiasm; the symphony of revolt, in which a manly determination
would predominate rather than melancholy. "For we are not
yet played out; there are still many things to accomplish, still
much to achieve. This time the Finale will not sound dull and
trite: it will ring out like a veritable triumph."

And in the spring and summer of the year 1888 the Symphony No. 5 in E minor, Opus 64, was written. It was born in
rapture and torment in the solitude of a small country estate
called Frolovskoe, six versts from Klin, in a wooded district; for
Peter Ilych had abandoned Maidanovo and given up the house
which only a short time ago he had liked to believe was his
home.

The Fifth Symphony was written in the face of qualms and
fears which assailed the ageing composer and crippled him with
the thought: "You are played out, dried up; nothing else can
come from you." And now behold, the symphony was big and
it was good. It was endowed with both melancholy and brilliance and withal a rapturous lightness, and, in the Finale,
with a proud and lusty exuberance held courageously under
control.

When the great score was finished, Tchaikovsky had to decide on a dedication, that "title of honor." He did not inscribe
it to any of his friends—as if the lonely bachelor wished to indicate that he did not possess any friends; he dedicated it to
M. Avé-Lallemant, first president of the Philharmonic Society
in Hamburg. He was a stranger, but it was he who had said to
Peter Ilych: "You could become a really great man," and: "You
are still young."

◇◇◇◇◇◇

THIRD MOVEMENT
Allegro molto vivace

◇◇◇◇◇◇

PETER ILYCH'S NEPHEW, Vladimir Davidov, was eighteen years of age—an overgrown, handsome youth of amiable disposition. His absent-minded smile was much like his famous uncle's; but the dark eyes were his mother's who, in turn, had them from her mother, the late Alexandra Andreyevna, *née* Assier.

If Alexandra Tchaikovsky had died under mysterious circumstances, Alexandra Davidov's ailment was no less puzzling and enigmatic. Obviously, the poor woman was in a very bad way indeed; but doctors could not agree as to the name and nature of her illness. She coughed, grew thin, wasted away. One physician was convinced that the trouble must be due to defective lungs; another declared that the cough was only a secondary symptom and traced all other troubles back to the stomach; yet another doctor attributed the trouble to the kidneys. The name of her complaint seemed to her a matter of no importance. Did she make any effort to get the better of her nameless illness? She prayed. But she remained dumb, as she lay there with folded hands, and nobody knew what proposals, wishes, or requests her heart sent to God. To the living and the healthy she divulged nothing of her dealings with her Lord. For hours she lay with folded hands, staring out of her deep-sunk eyes, which sent a dull, suffering look to Heaven. She never changed her position; she scarcely looked when a member of the family or a servant came towards her. Only when it was Vladimir, and he bent down over her, did she move her hand a little to greet him, or she smiled. Her son Vladimir was her favorite.

She scarcely troubled herself at all about the illness of her little daughter, Vera. If the doctor or her husband came with a

report of the condition of the pale-faced girl who lay suffering
in another wing of the rambling villa, a bitter and distrait expression appeared on her mother's face; indeed, she appeared
to be jealous of the young invalid. Perhaps this was because
the amount of quiet, respectful concern which a collection of
healthy people is willing to devote to the sick is limited in quantity and in intensity, and the daughter was diverting a certain
amount of attention from the mother; perhaps, however, it was
because the young creature appeared to be winging a swifter
flight to Death than she, Alexandra, who seemed to need so
much time for her silent reckoning with God. Little Vera's
illness had started later than her mother's; but agile Youth soon
overtook cautious Age, sprang briskly ahead and with nimble
feet soon left Age behind. Little Vera reached her dark and
beautiful goal while old Sasha was still tormenting herself with
elaborate prayers. Mr. Davidov closed the eyes of his little
daughter; Vladimir flung himself sobbing on the slender corpse;
the doctor stood on one side, respectful and embarrassed. When
they brought the news of the death to Alexandra as she lay in
bed, she remained bitterly silent. Then she lifted her folded
hands in prayer.

But her condition did not change; it could not be said that
she grew either better or worse. If it was true—and nobody
could tell—that she *resisted* Death, then the tenacity with which
she held him at bay was enormous, and admirable; but if she
really wished to die—and that is what her children and her
husband sometimes suspected—then Death was playing a grue-
some game with her: he came too near to her and yet kept too
far away; he beckoned to her, he tricked her, attitudinizing before her and exercising his dark seductive charm; but when she
wished to stretch out her hand to him, he drew back, a fleeting
shadow.

"I do admire Mama for being so patient," said Vladimir, at
whom she sometimes smiled. The boy was serious beyond his
years. Perhaps it was the intimate contact with his suffering

mother that had worked this change in him; at the time when Alexandra was still healthy, it was this very son, her favorite, whom she had regarded as the wildest and merriest of all. The jolly little boy had developed into an earnest young man—no less attractive, in his own way, than the chubby child had been. At school he was very much liked, and the ladies who found their way into the Davidovs' house showed that they were not unaware of his charms. Several of them started to flirt with him; he responded with adroit gallantry, threw inviting, almost tender, glances at them out of his wide-open, beautiful eyes; he kissed their hands with tender elegance; glances and kisses were accompanied for the most part by rapid, mocking speeches.

He was a good talker: the ladies, as well as the teachers and his schoolfellows, were willing to grant him that. His flexible, finely drawn mouth, his very white and healthy teeth, gave rapid utterance to words which were well chosen; and his chatter, always pleasant to hear though not always very substantial, was accompanied by a smile that was both frivolous and melancholy. It was this mixture of frivolousness and melancholy which characterized his whole nature and gave him a charm that captivated his schoolfellows, the professors, and the ladies.

His fresh, smooth, domed forehead, the thick black eyebrows surmounting the expressive dark eyes, seemed to betray a premature knowledge of the serious and bitter things of life; but the mouth, which was so ready with speech and laughter, was above all things young.

The wise clear brow was framed with dark-brown wavy hair. The small head was set on a neck that was somewhat too long, and the neck on shoulders that were too narrow and somewhat stooping. Vladimir moved on his long thin legs like an angular yet graceful page of olden time, with the somewhat hesitant but dignified gait of an ostrich. His half-serious half-mocking chatter was accompanied by awkward but elegant gestures, showing his beautiful long and slender hands to advantage. Very striking also were the small, neat, and well-set ears, which looked like a pair of delicate shells beneath the thick dark-brown hair.

Young Vladimir loved beauty and was avid of knowledge. He read a great deal, and it gave him much pleasure to discuss books with his schoolmates or with older people. He was familiar not only with Russian literature, but also with many classics and modern French and German books. He had read, either in popular Russian versions or even in the difficult original editions, many scientific works whose theories were at that time the mark of worth-while conversation. He loved to throw out names like Darwin, Marx, and Haeckel in the course of an animated conversation. He took an interest in social problems and in questions of esthetics; he chattered about Nihilists and about program music. He was not unfamiliar with art history; he could play the piano and he could draw.

He was, of course, one of Wagner's admirers. That did not prevent him from being enthusiastic over Russian music, particularly over Glinka and the five "Innovators," above all Rimsky-Korsakov; but all this was no hindrance to his regarding his famous uncle Peter Ilych Tchaikovsky as Russia's most distinguished musician and the greatest composer of his time.

During his last visit to Kamenka the famous uncle had shown his nephew Vladimir special attention and had spoiled him; everybody in the family circle had been struck by this fact. Previously, when Alexandra was still in good health and Vladimir only a jolly little boy, Peter Ilych had shown very little interest in the children, even in Vladimir. True, at times he had stroked the boy's thick curls with a certain absent-minded tenderness, saying: "Well, little Vladimir, what is going to happen to you?" But most of the time he could be seen sitting beside his dear sister Alexandra-Sasha, or walking with her. There was so much he had to tell her; their talk seemed as if it need never come to an end, and the subject of it was invariably Peter Ilych, all the troubles, needs, anxieties, adventures, and hopes that filled his rich but bitter and bewildered life. Alexandra, to whom love gave wisdom and understanding, listened attentively to her brother's confessions and complaints, his plans and schemes and emotional upheavals.

That was long ago. The time for such long talks with his sister Sasha was long since past; the invalid was no longer able, and no longer willing, to listen to other people's confessions. For now there were only two subjects that really engaged her interest, and they were closely linked with one another: her suffering and her unceasing intercourse—sometimes aggressive, sometimes gentle—with God. She received her brother, as she received everybody else except Vladimir, with that bitter aloofness which nothing could affect, neither spoken word nor caress.

Mr. Davidov had his business to attend to, and in any case was not very susceptible to the finer and gentler things in life. Two of the three sons—the eldest and the undistinguished youngest—had little attraction for their famous uncle. It was Sasha's second son, Vladimir, the clever, overgrown, melancholy-frivolous young courtier, towards whom his heart warmed.

Long talks had taken place between the famous uncle and the kind-hearted nephew when Peter Ilych had last visited Kamenka. Later on Vladimir was proud to tell how Peter Ilych had confided all his musical plans to him and had even played over to him on the piano various fragments of new melodies. Peter Ilych, for his part, encouraged his nephew—whom he used to call "Bob"—to tell him about his studies, his duties and his pleasures, while he told tales of his travels, of life in the great western cities, or stories about his own childhood. He loved talking to Vladimir-Bob about his memories; they seemed to take on a freshness, a youthful vividness from the eager receptivity of the young man, who listened with such reverential attention. The talkative Vladimir was a good listener. If the fine flexible mouth could talk, the delicate, sensitive ears could listen. The boy and the man did not confine their intercourse to long talks; they also spent time playing ball games, asking each other riddles, and in other innocent amusements.

In parting, the famous uncle embraced his good-natured young nephew for the first time and kissed him on the forehead. That was the beginning of their great friendship.

To Vladimir everything about Peter Ilych was at once puzzling and familiar. It was puzzling to him that a man still living —and, what was more, a near relation of his—could nevertheless be that awe-inspiring person about whom one read in books: one who was endowed with creative powers, who was always in contact with a mysterious spirit who conveyed melodies to him from some celestial region—melodies which the person so favored was able to pass on to a marveling humanity. What, indeed, could be more puzzling than this inexplicable, bewildering, and precious process of creation? Thus, in the eyes of young Bob, Peter Ilych appeared to be, from one point of view, an altogether wonderful stranger. On the other hand, the boy believed that he could understand his famous uncle, as a human being, completely. He quite well understood that absence of self-confidence which often suddenly transformed itself into a passionate pride; his nervousness, his restlessness, his depression. He believed that he also understood his merriment, which always seemed to have an admixture of melancholy, and which was apt to degenerate into an almost childish boisterousness. Peter Ilych's great benevolence, his joy in helping, his willingness to go out of his way to be of service to anybody, however humble and unknown to him, seemed to be in contradiction to his melancholy fear of people. This contradiction did not surprise Vladimir; on the contrary, it was because of such similarities as this that he not only knew himself to be of the same flesh and blood as his great, admired, and exciting uncle Peter Ilych, but also believed that he shared a little in his spirit. For young Vladimir had already experienced hours of depression and despair; he had known hours of anxiety, failure, hatred of mankind, and the most appalling sense of inferiority. On the other hand, he also set great store by making himself agreeable to people, in order to win their hearts by his kind and obliging manner. But none of these characteristics were so marked, or so disturbing, in young Bob as they were in the highly strung Peter Ilych. The youth and supple grace of the overgrown young courtier seemed to have the power to reconcile the contradictions of his nature, to soften the conflicts and smooth out the differences, and to transform the doubts and torments. His young mouth smiled, a melancholy or frivolous expression shone from his dark eyes; his long slender hands made little awkward gestures as he talked; and his smooth, pure brow, framed in its dark curly hair, was not disturbed or hallowed by the touch of genius.

Vladimir's life was agreeably full of all sorts of interests and activities of the kind that appealed to the son of good family at the end of the nineteenth century. But his chief interest now and most fascinating occupation was to follow and lovingly to observe everything that concerned his enigmatic and beloved uncle. It was after Peter Ilych's stay at Kamenka, which was so rich in intimate talks and was the beginning—but only the prelude—of their great friendship, that the correspondence between uncle and nephew began. The exacting young Vladimir, however, considered that Peter Ilych wrote too seldom and at too irregular intervals. The boy knew, of course, how quickly his famous uncle's time was absorbed by work and travel, by social matters and correspondence. This was the explanation of why Vladimir was at times neglected, but it was no consolation. Vladimir wanted to be utterly and completely aware of everything that concerned the life of the uncle whom he so greatly revered and so deeply loved.

He started to organize a news service and to gather information wherever he could find it. The young nephew, eager for knowledge, collected every newspaper cutting in which the name of Tchaikovsky was mentioned. The servant Alexey was instructed to write to the young gentleman at Kamenka and tell him everything he knew about his master's doings. Vladimir kept up a correspondence with the young fellow who had the good luck to go about with Peter Ilych, and also with young Volodya Napravnik, the son of the great St. Petersburg conductor, who was privileged at times to be a guest at Frolovskoe— a fact which had the double effect of arousing Bob's jealousy and at the same time of reviving his interest in his contemporary.

Thus young Vladimir practically led two lives simultaneously: his own—the quiet, gently stimulating family life of a son in Kamenka and a student in Kiev, and, in his dreams and imagination, the restless and brilliant existence of the composer who was so much courted and beset—an existence which was equally enviable and pitiable, overburdened by fame, excitement, changes, and sorrows.

Vladimir, darling of an ailing mother, clever scholar, made his first tour abroad with Peter Ilych in his imagination and in his dreams. When Tchaikovsky imagined himself quite alone, the attentive boy had been with him, in Leipzig and Hamburg, in Lübeck, in Magdeburg; in Berlin and Prague, in Paris and in London. The eager nephew—well informed by his News Service, whose information he augmented out of his fertile imagination—knew Tchaikovsky's new home in Frolovskoe long before he went there. The servant Alexey had sent him descriptions and pictures of it. He was quite familiar with the low-built wooden house and the terrace built out in front of it; he knew the trees and bushes that surrounded it; the rustic wooden benches on which one sat enjoying the shade; the flower-beds, the flat wooded landscape that could be seen from the windows of the house.

Young Vladimir had also shared in the labor which, in a period of bitter depression and triumphant exaltation, had produced the Fifth Symphony. With Peter Ilych he had despaired when inspiration had flagged, and had been entranced and proud with him when it revived; and now that the work was completed, and moreover successfully completed, he felt as contented as if it were his own.

Moreover, he had taken part in the everyday doings at Frolovskoe: the flower garden to which Peter Ilych so happily turned his attention in his leisure hours (the industrious gardener had caught a cold in the head through spending too much time digging the wet earth; and how annoyed he was when the stocks and mignonette drank too freely of the rain!); and he was familiar with the large correspondence which Peter Ilych—busy composer and busy gardener though he was—took upon himself as a schoolboy might take on an unimposed task. A considerable part of the letters still went to Madame von Meck: she received so many, and they were so full of details, that the boy in Kamenka was envious, although he was of course well aware of the peculiar role which that mysterious friend played in the life of his beloved uncle.

A good deal of time was also perforce spent, as Vladimir knew, on corresponding with His Imperial Highness the Grand Duke Constantine Constantinovich. This art-loving relative of the Tsar occupied himself with the writing of lyrics and conducted an interchange of profound opinions on questions of style, verse meters, and rhythm with the composer Tchaikovsky, whose graciously sought advice had to be given with all manner of flattery and deferential flourishes. In addition to this there was the constant correspondence with his brothers Anatol and Modest; and finally the business correspondence with his colleagues, conductors, impresarios, and theater directors, and particularly with the director of the Imperial Theater, Mr. Vsevolojsky, a very influential friend and benefactor, with whom Peter Ilych had at all costs to keep up a friendly relationship. Vladimir was understanding enough to realize how difficult and tiring all this was, and he knew that such unpleasantnesses could not possibly be avoided: success brought not only fame and glory, but also heavy obligations.

Life in Frolovskoe was tranquil; the distractions it sometimes offered were of a modest character. Vladimir, in his dreams, shared also in such innocent pleasures as were vouchsafed to his

uncle and therefore to him. For example, he had immensely enjoyed, in his dreams and in his imagination, the little party on the
estate which had been arranged to celebrate Peter Ilych's name
day. Among those present were Laroche, fat, lazy, and always
rather depressed, a comrade of his during his student days and
now one of the most esteemed music critics in the land; the publisher Jürgenson; Karl Albrecht, inventor and philosopher; and
lastly, Alexander Siloti, the unapproachable, whom Peter Ilych
could not meet again without a quickening of his heartbeat. Of
these heartbeats, it is true, the young observer in Kamenka knew
nothing, and they were, as a matter of fact, of no great significance; for the host, Peter Ilych, now felt somewhat estranged
from the very handsome but very cold young man; at the same
time he shared a moderate degree of friendly intimacy with
him, free from the sense of strain associated with the days spent
in Leipzig and Prague. On the whole, a very nice lot of men.
They played cards, made music, and related anecdotes. Vladimir
was exceedingly pleased with the way the party went.

Peter Ilych remained on at Frolovskoe throughout October;
already it was cold and dreary; there were hard frosts and no
snow; it was difficult to heat the house; Vladimir decided that it
was now rather uncomfortable, and he was pleased and contented when the return to Moscow was announced.

For the musical season had already started there—and that
brought difficulties. Peter Ilych—and Bob in Kiev—learned to
their sorrow that the subscription list for the great symphony
concerts had declined to an extremely dangerous degree. Vladimir entirely agreed that his famous uncle should from now
onwards apply himself with more enthusiasm to the Moscow
Music Society; this enterprise must undoubtedly be put on its
feet again; on no account must it be allowed to come to grief: it
represented the musical life of Russia.

To start with, Peter Ilych conducted his Fifth Symphony in
St. Petersburg, on November 5. Vladimir was extremely satisfied with the audience, which was lavish with its applause and

gifts of beautiful flowers. With the press, however, he was extremely dissatisfied; in fact he felt decidedly bitter against the press, which had taken upon itself to cavil and find fault with the things which it ought to have most admired; foremost among the critics was, of course, that odious fellow, César Cui, who actually dared to reproach the work with being clumsily orchestrated! Young Vladimir was furious about this.

Altogether, difficult times were ahead of him; for after Peter Ilych had given various concerts in Moscow and had made a visit to Prague which had not been altogether successful, he occupied himself in Frolovskoe with the *Sleeping Beauty* Ballet, commissioned by the director of the Imperial Theater, who had himself written the libretto. The lonely man, in his chilly country house, tackled the work rather peevishly. Moreover, he was tormenting himself with doubts over the value of his last work, the symphony. During his hours of depression he maintained that it was a failure, a "manufactured" work, utterly second-rate; he felt there was something "ungenuine" about it, something which did not "come from the heart." With such hypochondriac reflections and anxieties as these he brought suffering not only upon himself but also upon the boy who shared his life.

These were bitter weeks, for Peter Ilych and no less for Bob, redeemed by certain gleams of sunshine. A very pleasant gleam of sunshine, for instance, came on Christmas Eve, when Alexey laid a beautiful present for his dear master at the foot of the Christmas tree. The gift came from Peter Ilych's friend and publisher, Jürgenson; it was the fine edition of the collected works of Mozart which Breitkopf and Härtel had published. Peter Ilych and Vladimir were elated.

On other occasions Vladimir found it very strenuous and exciting to live, in accurate dreams and detailed imagination, the life of his famous uncle. After the tranquil days devoted to work in Frolovskoe came another tour. Vladimir had innumerable newspaper-cuttings to study and sort out. His lively spirit had long journeys to make from his study in Kamenka; his

nimble soul had to fly to the German towns Cologne, Frankfort-on-the-Main, Dresden, Berlin, and Hamburg, as well as to
Geneva; for in all these towns Tchaikovsky gave concerts during the February and March of 1889. A great task for the faithful imaginative heart in Kamenka, which had all sorts of things
on which to build its fancy: walks on the banks of the Alster, a
visit to the Zwinger in Dresden, an orchestral rehearsal in
Frankfort, a press conference in Cologne, a dinner in Berlin, a
conversation with Brahms—for Vladimir knew that the German
master, who was occupying the room next to Tchaikovsky's in
the hotel in Hamburg, had stayed a day longer by the river
Elbe expressly for the purpose of attending the rehearsal of
Tchaikovsky's Fifth Symphony—a very kindly gesture from so
distinguished an enemy; but the invitation which Peter Ilych
conveyed to him, that he should conduct for the Russian Music
Society, he declined with an expression of such icy astonishment that the invitation might have been to hunt polar bears in
the Arctic regions.

Old Mr. Avé-Lallemant had not been able to turn up to the
first performance of the symphony which was dedicated to him:
he was far too delicate. But he sent his good wishes and his
blessing: the blessing of this fine, gentle old man was received
also by Vladimir in Kamenka, and his heart was touched and
grateful for all the attentions shown to his uncle.

The longest letter that Peter Ilych wrote to Bob during this
tour bore the postmark of Hanover. Tchaikovsky had suc-
cumbed to his inclination to flee to some little foreign town
where he could muse on a few friends and indulge his sensation
of homesickness—or the feeling which he so called. There he
paced a dreary hotel room with heavy footsteps; gnawed at his
penholder; held conversations with himself in French; fell weeping into his chair by the writing-table and wrote to his good
nephew, telling him how he longed for him and for Russia, and
that he loved him like a son. In front of him on the writing-
table stood the brandy bottle and the ash-tray in which the

mouthpieces of his smoked-out cigarettes piled themselves. Bob, in his study in Kamenka, read the letter over and over again.

The famous uncle, who loved him like a son, had now traveled on to Paris. There once more, arising out of the question of guest performances in Moscow, he had dealings with Massenet, who showed himself more affable and better brought-up than Herr Brahms had done; he seemed to be flattered that he should have been invited to far-off Russia. From Paris Peter Ilych went to London; from London, via Marseille, Constantinople, and Tiflis, back to Moscow.

He made friends on board ship with two young Russians: one a student at Moscow University and the other a fourteen-year-old boy, Volody, the son of a famous surgeon. They spent the evening together on deck, enraptured by the picture of the stars and the moving water. On the last evening Peter Ilych took the two boys to a little restaurant in Constantinople. Here they parted. The fourteen-year-old boy and the young man went on to Odessa; Peter Ilych's passage was via Batoum. He wept when he returned to his carriage, for now once more he was alone. Peter Ilych had taken the boy Volody to his heart; he was good-looking and clever, and had the touching grace of those who are not intended to remain long in this world. What a short time the friendship had lasted: Tchaikovsky, weeping in his cabin, had the impression that he would never see the child again. When, later, he recalled this long journey, it was of the meeting with Volody that he most liked to think. It had been a long and strenuous journey, strenuous for Peter Ilych and also for Vladimir who in spirit had shared it.

The months which followed in Frolovskoe were quiet; but they were not months of recuperation. For they were crammed with work. The *Sleeping Beauty* Ballet had to be finished and orchestrated; the first production was announced to take place in St. Petersburg in the autumn.

During this tranquil summer devoted to work, young Vladimir received an abundance of letters from Frolovskoe; his uncle wrote him long and intimate reports—though nothing like so long, and perhaps not so intimate, as those he had once written, and still wrote occasionally, to his spiritual friend Madame von Meck, donor of the welcome allowance. But with the reopening of the musical season in Moscow and St. Peterśburg, Bob once more devoted himself to the service of spying and collecting newspaper-cuttings. Correspondence ceased. Peter Ilych was greatly in demand.

He did not feel at all happy in the little Moscow home which Alexey had prepared for him. He was disturbed and terrified by the quantity of visitors and the long social evenings with drink, noise, and tobacco smoke; also by the beggars in the streets, the endless meetings of the Music Society, and the dry cough of Alexey's wife, which could be heard in every corner of the little house. The spouse of the manservant who had come to him first many years ago as a very good-looking lad, suffered from consumption; now, in Tchaikovsky's home, she was being looked after on her deathbed.

Vladimir, from his post of observation, could not complain—nor did he complain—if he no longer received any letters. He knew better than anybody else how Peter Ilych was beset by all this; he knew how it upset him and absorbed his time. There was the exacting work with the Music Society, for which at this time Tchaikovsky felt himself responsible to an exaggerated and exhausting degree. Attractive guest performances had to be arranged in order to increase the number of subscribers. Massenet, following Brahms, had now declined to come; in his place came the great French conductor Colonne. Dvořák and Klindworth also came. In addition to these they had engaged the young composers Arensky, Rimsky-Korsakov, Napravnik, Altani, Alexander Siloti, and Peter Ilych.

An excitement of quite unusual magnitude—for the uncle no less than for the observant young man in his remote study —were the Jubilee celebrations in honor of Anton Rubinstein.

The chairman of the Committee of Honor, Duke George von Mecklenburg-Strelitz, had been graciously pleased to ask Tchaikovsky, as the most famous of the master's pupils, to undertake the control of the Jubilee celebrations, as well as compose a choral work, *Welcome to Anton Rubinstein*. This was flattering but extremely exhausting. The always exacting Rubinstein was anxious that as many of his symphonic works as possible should be performed during the course of the celebrations; the program became enormous. At the brilliant opening ceremony in the Festival Hall of the House of Nobility, on November 18, 1889, eight hundred persons coöperated; the choir that sang the oratorio *The Tower of Babel* was seven hundred strong. Peter Ilych did not regard himself as a match for such a terrifying undertaking: he was by no means the right man to control a vast crowd of undisciplined people. During the torture of the rehearsals his face frequently flushed a deep red, his gentle voice strained itself; the choir seemed to want to dissolve into chaos, and the unhappy conductor felt that he would expire. Nothing more frightful had ever been demanded of him, he complained afterwards in the artists' room. Vladimir, in Kamenka, suffered with the exhausted and disgusted man as if he himself had had to build the odious Tower of Babel stone by stone.

The somewhat arrogant Rubinstein showed little gratitude towards the famous pupil who had spent himself so freely on his behalf. The great man, with the striking Beethoven head, remained ungracious and peevish. He obstinately continued to treat Tchaikovsky like a subordinate. His attitude towards his colleagues had always been one of strict and dignified formality. If any of his contemporaries dared to compose he appeared to regard such audacity as a personal affront. Since Chopin and Schumann, he was in the habit of maintaining, nothing of any distinction had been written—except, of course, the works of Anton Rubinstein. But it was about these works in particular that opinions differed so widely. Not everybody had shown such good-natured respect as Peter Ilych did when he declared that the *Ocean* Symphony, *The Tower of Babel*, and the Pianoforte Concerto of Rubinstein were masterpieces. With almost meek patience Peter Ilych—in general so sensitive and easy to offend—allowed his illustrious teacher to treat him with haughty brusqueness. For him Rubinstein remained beyond question a great man, whatever injustices his conceit and obstinacy might lead him to commit. When somebody, during the Jubilee banquet, had the tactlessness to suggest to Rubinstein that he and Tchaikovsky should drink to each other and in future address each other with the familiar "thou," it was Peter Ilych who, with genuine alarm and without the least sign of pique or false modesty, energetically opposed the suggestion: with one's teacher, one's Ideal, the Great Man, one ought never to be on such familiar terms: that would be presumption and altogether opposed to good form.

*   *   *

It was young Vladimir who derived most pleasure from the performance of the *Sleeping Beauty* Ballet, although he was not permitted to be present at it. The gala "general rehearsal" —which was practically the first performance—took place on January 2, 1890, in St. Petersburg, in the presence of the highest aristocracy and the whole Court.

Brilliance streamed into the student's room in Kamenka; for Vladimir, sitting at his desk, beheld the first tier of boxes gradually fill up with officers, diplomats, and beautifully dressed women. The heart of the young fellow beat faster: the Imperial Family were entering; for them and their select retinue the whole of the stalls had been reserved. The Tsar sank coughing into his decorated *fauteuil* in the exact middle of the front row, while the dignitaries stood with uncovered heads and the elegantly decked-out women dropped deep curtseys. The clever, rebellious student, on his provincial perch, forgot everything that he had ever read or felt against the Tsar: there he was, the

All-highest, leaning back comfortably in his plush-covered seat, prepared to witness the beloved uncle's ballet. So long as His Majesty sat there and applauded the *Sleeping Beauty*, Vladimir hoped that all the saints would protect him from Nihilists, anarchists, and other evil foes.

Ah! Now the music is beginning, and with a gentle rustle, the embroidered red curtain goes up, revealing a scene flooded with light. What now followed was much more enchanting to the boy in his workroom than it was to the Tsar sitting there in his decorated *fauteuil*. The boy had read the libretto and the musical score; but his imagination did not confine itself to what his head knew: it enhanced everything extravagantly, beautified and glorified everything. The magic world which appeared before his eyes was nothing less than the wonderland which, as a musing child, he had seen when listening to fairy tales told at twilight; his darkening room was peopled by figures of enchantment.

The Princess Aurora, as young Vladimir in Kamenka saw her, was much more charming than she was as represented by the Prima Ballerina at the Imperial Theater of St. Petersburg. In his eyes the fairies who appeared at Aurora's christening were beyond a doubt genuine creatures of enchantment, endowed with marvelous grace, gentleness, and astonishing intelligence. On the other hand, he was terrified by the Wicked Fairy Karabos, who with grotesque movements pranced onto the stage for the sole purpose of cursing the Princess Aurora; and how intensely grateful he was to the Fairy Lilac, so good and energetic, because she weakened Karabos' curse and made it possible for the Prince Désiré to rescue the sleeping princess with a knightly kiss, thereby awakening and releasing her for the finale of Act II. In the third act the wedding was celebrated. The curtain fell to sounds of jubilation on a glittering array of fairies, members of the royal family, courtiers, and military officers.

The aristocracy in the first-tier boxes waited expectantly:

how had the ballet appealed to His Majesty? His Majesty
clapped, but only a few times and with a somewhat bored expression on his face. Therefore the applause from the boxes was
also cool. "It doesn't come up to the French ballet," people
whispered to one another. "His Majesty prefers the French
ballet. His Majesty reserves his judgment on the *Sleeping
Beauty*."

In the meantime, the director Vsevolojsky, the ballet master
Petipa, and the composer Tchaikovsky were presented to the
Emperor. Peter Ilych, his face a dark red, perspiring in his
evening suit, bowed low before the plush-covered *fauteuil* in the
front row. He was so worked up that he did not perceive the
Tsar's face; it swam before his misty eyes. As if through a thick
fog, he heard a nasal voice say:

"*Merci, mon cher. C'était assez joli.*"

The Tsar of all the Russias, His Imperial Majesty Alexander
III, who on March 13, 1881, had succeeded the assassinated
Alexander II, had declared that "*c'était assez joli.*" That wasn't
very much to say; it was only grudging praise. It was for this that
Peter Ilych had suffered day and night; it was for this that the
ballet master Petipa had sweated at endless rehearsals in his
indefatigable endeavor to show the ladies how they must behave
if they wanted to look like real fairies. "*C'était assez joli.*"

Peter raised himself, panting slightly, from his low bow; he
was released; the short audience was over. The dismissed composer stepped away, a timid man-of-the-world, in his somewhat
too tight evening suit.

"I shall travel," he thought. "I shall go away this very day.
Just to be somewhere else—best of all nowhere—but at any rate,
not here!"

*   *   *

Spring in Florence was lovely; this March night the air was
fragrant.

Peter Ilych had stepped out of his study onto the little bal-

cony that belonged to his suite. He had been to the opera. He
wore his camel-hair dressing-gown over his evening trousers and
stiff shirt. His patent leather shoes were somewhat too tight and
hurt him. "I ought to put my slippers on," he thought. "It would
ease my feet considerably if I got rid of these beastly evening
shoes." Nevertheless he made no attempt to abandon the balcony in order to get his house-shoes from the bedroom. On the
contrary, he remained standing there, his elbows resting on
the stone balustrade, his face in his hands. "The stars shine
more vividly here than they do at home in Russia," thought
Peter Ilych, breathing deeply. "The odors here are also much
stronger and sweeter. Probably the snow is still lying in
Frolovskoe; but in some places it will have melted, and in those
places very modest and touching little flowers will be visible. I
am about to stoop down to look at them, but a youngster is
standing by me and wants to make snowballs out of the moist,
melting snow. Why don't I always stay in Russia? I want to
touch a birchtree with my fingers: I really long to do that: it
would cool my fingers. There is nothing in the world so pleasant to the touch as a Russian birch tree in early spring. It is
perfect madness on my part to make these utterly meaningless
journeys. It is only when I'm at home that I can breathe freely.
I don't want to see any more cypresses, any more marble statues.
These odors are much too sweet and don't really please me; they
almost repel me. Moreover I don't in the least know what
flowering-bushes they come from. In Frolovskoe I know all the
plants. What a foolish notion it was to go to the opera this evening! It was not only a mistake but probably also a sin. Today I
got the news that my good Alexey's wife has died, following on
that hacking cough of hers. I cried a little when I got the news
—but I did not want to forfeit my box for *Lucia di Lammermoor*. As a punishment I had to endure this miserable production. Donizetti's music is full of all sorts of charming fancies—
but what a ridiculous libretto! The text that Modest is preparing
for me now is at least better than that. And unfortunately that

highly dramatic lady had a positively shrieking voice. She could sing—one must admit that; when Lucia went mad she had the most difficult coloratura passages to sing, and she attacked them magnificently. The audience was quite right to applaud and cry '*Da capo!*' And poor Lucia was compelled to go through the whole outbreak of madness all over again; for the second time she abandoned her wig and looked better in her own natural black hair than she had in the ridiculous blonde curls."

Peter Ilych, all alone on his balcony in the warm Italian night, laughed softly to himself as he ruminated on the evening he had spent at the opera: how comical the chorus had looked in its Scottish plaid kilts! And how grotesque the palms had seemed in an English park! He was startled by the sound of his own laughter, for it is always rather uncanny to find oneself laughing aloud in solitude. "In any case," he decided remorsefully, "it was abominable of me to go out so soon after hearing of the death of Alexey's wife. However, it seems to me that *Pique Dame* is a better opera than this *Lucia di Lammermoor.*"

Work on the opera made great strides while Peter Ilych was in Florence. He had started it in the middle of January; by the middle of March it was almost completed. Modest could hardly keep the pace; he wrote more slowly than Peter composed. Friends in St. Petersburg were rather uneasy about this quick tempo; the conductor Napravnik and fat Laroche both warned him about excessive haste. But Peter Ilych went on composing as if somebody were behind him goading him on. "Nevertheless," he wrote in high spirits to a friend, "the opera will be chic!"

He had received the commission for *Pique Dame* while he was still in Russia from the director Vsevolojsky who wished without fail to produce a Tchaikovsky opera during the coming season. For the ballet, in spite of the Tsar's lukewarm approval, and in spite of the particularly damaging newspaper criticisms, had been an outstanding box-office success. Seats for all performances had been sold out; the public adored *Sleeping Beauty.*

But all this lay far behind and belonged to a period of innocent tranquillity now past. Since then, Peter Ilych, for two feverish months of intensive work, had lived and dreamed in the
highly charged and intensely dramatic atmosphere of the Pushkin story upon which Modest had based his libretto—a somewhat rambling libretto which had to be cut in several places;
but it had not altogether failed to capture the inspiration of
Pushkin's great poem. Passions raged; there were glowing love-
passages and brilliant festival scenes, immediately succeeded
by horrors, streaming blood, despair, madness, ruin!

The passion of the poor foolhardy young man Hermann for
gambling was even stronger than his love for the maiden
Lizaveta. When Peter Ilych ruminated on what it was about
Pique Dame that had attracted him for so long, he had to admit
that it was probably just this tragic and fatal passion of the
young hero—a blinding passion for the gambling-table. For
Tchaikovsky—himself only too experienced in the squandering
of emotion—knew that it is relatively unimportant which particular illusion it is for which one sacrifices all one's feelings, pointlessly and unavailingly.

Between the young man and his sweetheart comes Liza's
grandmother, the old countess, a dreadful woman. It is she—so
believes the blinded Hermann—who knows the secret of the
three cards, which would enable one to win the great game. In
order to obtain this knowledge, if necessary by force, the obsessed
young man goes one night to the bedchamber of the old woman.
But she is so frightened that she dies before she can open her
lips to disclose the lucky formula. Hope is thus destroyed; only
despair remains. The torments of a guilty conscience now
follow, and finally madness and death. The tragedy ends in the
gambling saloon. For in the meantime the ghost of the old countess had appeared to the desperate gambler and revealed the
secret of the three infallible cards for the sake of which she had
met her death. With two of them Hermann might gain a fortune; with the third he might immeasurably increase his treas-

ure. Then, by a terrible mischance, instead of throwing onto the table the card that had been indicated, he threw down the Queen of Spades—"Pique Dame"—lost everything, and plunged a dagger into his heart.

All the emotions that could be transmuted into music combined this time to produce a wonderful effect. For once Peter Ilych himself was highly pleased and staggered by what he had achieved. The thought which took possession of him was: "For a change, the severe, Remote One is merciful to me. He has sent me some remarkable ideas—and how grateful I am to Him for them! The theme of the old countess, for instance; the motive which expresses the secret of the three cards, consisting of only three notes, three heavy notes given out pizzicato by the double-basses, like three ghostly knocks on a locked door, what a breath-taking motive that is! It startles and dismays me even to think about it! The downfall of my poor obsessed Hermann moved me to tears; and what a lot of charming and impressive things there are before that occurs. Liza playing with her friends; her lovely arioso, "It is near to midnight"; the fancy-dress ball, with the entrance of the Empress Catherine as a very effective finale; Hermann's madness and the terror aroused by the apparition! No, I am certainly not going to have to say later that all this misfired. On the contrary, I am quite convinced that this time I have succeeded uncommonly well."

He overlooked the fact that he had often before experienced a feeling of great satisfaction like this immediately after having brought a work to completion, only to fall prey shortly afterwards to exaggerated sensations of the bitterest doubt. On the contrary, he thought triumphantly: "The lonely weeks spent in this hideous and much too expensive suite of rooms which has completely ruined me financially—my God! It actually costs 27 lire a day!—these lonely weeks, when I have been weighed down by feelings of despair, have not been wasted. They might have been much worse. At least I had Nasar with me."

Nasar, Modest Tchaikovsky's young servant, had accompanied Peter Ilych to Florence, Alexey having stayed behind in Moscow on account of his wife's cough. Peter Ilych had no cause to be dissatisfied with the exchange: Nasar was a somewhat sluggish fellow, but honest, patient, and in every respect pleasant. It could not be denied that Modest was an expert where young people were concerned.

"Certainly the poor boy has suffered appallingly from homesickness the whole time," thought Peter Ilych on his balcony in the Italian night. "And he has had all my moods to contend with; but he didn't allow one to notice that anything was amiss. Every day he has shown the same lazy good humor, has always been attentive, always smiling. I am very thankful that he has been here. Without him I should not have been able to get through my work. He has been a little bit of Russia—a nice, familiar bit of home! I will take him with me now to Rome. I hope he will get some sort of amusement out of Rome. Probably I shall stay there a few weeks—but perhaps only a few days. For it is quite possible that I shall feel ill at ease in Rome. So many memories will be stirred up in me that are bitter to the taste. It is a long time since I was in Rome; last time Modest accompanied me. Since then so much time has slipped past and toppled into the abyss. Are we the same as we were then? I feel that we are completely changed: the quiet power of the passing years has transformed us into other beings. Yes, when I get to Rome I shall think day and night of what it was like when I was there before. Am I never to be released from what is past? Why does the past cling to me? Shall I never succeed in getting free? Have I no Today? What is my Today?

"What is my Today?" thought Peter Ilych, brooding on the balcony of his much too expensive hotel apartment. His young servant was sleeping two rooms away from him, snoring softly in his bed. "Am I not then strong enough to hold onto it, to enjoy it, to love it?" asked the solitary ageing man. "Do my feelings renounce the present? *What is the name of my present?*"

A big work, which had kept all his forces at high tension, was behind him; all those emotions that he had sought to resolve had been transmuted into a highly effective composition; now he felt at once exhausted and stimulated, both emptied and ready for new adventures. He turned his tired face—that gray-bearded countenance with its mouth that was too soft and its gentle brooding eyes—towards the spring night, this March night in a foreign land, with its gleaming stars and its sweet odors. His tired but eager heart asked:

"What is the name of my present?"

And out of the night there came to him the name of VLADI-MIR. Then the darkness was filled with brilliance and with a great and beautiful sound, which was wafted towards him like the sound of bells over the sleeping city of Florence.

Decide once more, you tired but eager heart! Decide once more, and this time once and for all! You have waited long enough and made yourself ready. This time you must make your own demands! Do not fail!

You have asked a question, and here is the answer. And this answer has come with such unexpected strength that it has almost deafened you. It has come like intoxication and illumination and smitten your heart with a sudden pain.

It hurts so much that with a moan and a wild gesture you press your heavy hand against your heart. At the same time your head droops and your whole face is distorted as if you had been blinded by a harsh light, a light which has illumined the darkness of the heavens and with its merciful glow has changed everything for you.

Vladimir Davidov had already been four weeks in Frolovskoe. When he arrived, at the beginning of May, there was still a little snow at the edge of the copse; but now, in these early June days, the cool spring was beginning to merge with early summer. At times Vladimir and Peter Ilych found it really hot when they went for their long walks of an afternoon, and on one occasion Vladimir had had to take off his coat.

They had been blessed weeks—blessed both for Peter Ilych and for his good nephew: long days of affectionate and stimulating intercourse, of work, of games, of witty talks, and long walks. In the mornings, while Peter Ilych composed—he was making a pianoforte arrangement of *Pique Dame* and putting down the first ideas for a sextet—Vladimir sat in the garden on that crude rustic bench which was known to him in his dreams and in his imagination. Now, beside him, on the very wood itself, rough, unpolished, natural wood, which so closely resembled the wood he had seen in his dreams, lay his thick books and notebooks. Vladimir's first examination lay behind him; he was no longer a grammar-school boy, but almost a student, and in the early autumn he would become a real student. The excited youngster, who came of good family, was interested in everything, in politics and philosophy just as much as in music and good literature, but he wished to study law; not exactly because it was a subject that particularly attracted or gripped him, but because he had to decide to specialize in some subject or other. Peter Ilych applauded what he knew was a reasonable decision on the part of his nephew. Nevertheless, he secretly hoped that young Vladimir would, in the course of his studies, change his mind and decide to become an author or a musician, rather than train himself to be a lawyer.

These weeks of good and stimulating intercourse had enabled
Peter Ilych to clarify very considerably his feelings about Bob.
They had always been of an affectionate character, but now they
had taken on an enthusiastic quality. Peter Ilych felt with emotion that during the course of the long conversations which they
exchanged morning, noon, and night, Vladimir had revealed
an abundance of cleverness, affection, wit, and depth. This
greatly pleased the famous uncle. He hoped and expected much
from Vladimir: the voluble courtier, whose awkward grace has
been referred to, might turn into something quite unusual.
"This time"—so the uncle assured his agitated heart—"this time
I am not dissipating my emotions, casting them into the void.
This is something worth while. This time it is a matter of some-
one who is *related* to me. Those earlier dealings with strangers"
—so thinks Peter Ilych enthusiastically— "were simply trials leading to the real thing—the closely related! Everything up to now
has been simply a preparation, just a long testing of the heart:
Apukhtin, and those who followed him, how strange, how
utterly strange they have been! How completely strange, too,
was the beautiful Siloti—so strange that today I can behave
towards him as towards any other esteemed colleague. How
fleeting all these adventures of the heart have been! And the
fault, rightly considered, has no doubt been mine. For my
feelings were never strong enough: I have always held them
back. They have kindled quickly to strangers, but have never
really been faithful to them. But Vladimir's look and voice often
recall my dear mother. He reminds me also of Sasha, and of my
brother Modest when he was young and handsome. He is so
nearly related to me. Vladimir, how closely you are related to
me!"

Four good weeks have gone by, but today is the last day.
Tomorrow morning Vladimir must go to Kamenka; his invalid
mother is asking for him. She will only be nursed by him, her
favorite. Peter Ilych, waking up at half-past seven in the morning, realizes with dismay: "Today is the last day. But I won't

think about it. I will treat today as if it were like any other day, and as if many more days of the same kind were going to succeed it. In twenty-five minutes' time Bob will come to wake me up. I will act as if I were still asleep: that will make the ceremony more amusing. I won't allow myself to dwell on the fact that it is for the last time."

But he went on thinking of nothing else. "What will those days be like which are no longer shared with Bob? They will be joyless days. A day without you is a weariness and a waste! My whole heart has grown so accustomed to you. You sit there on the rustic bench in front of the house, with your fat tomes and your exercise books, my clever darling! I can see you from my window. You close the book with a bang when you find it boring. You run on your long legs past my window to the kitchen. You want to find out what we are going to have for lunch. I hear you and Alexey laughing together. What will it be like when you are no longer here with me? A day without you is a weariness and a waste."

Punctually at eight o'clock Vladimir carefully opened Peter Ilych's bedroom door. On tiptoe he stepped up to the bed. Peter Ilych lay with closed eyes. The young man leaned over him and touched with his lips the domed furrowed brow, disturbing the feathery curls of the sparse, tangled gray hair. "It is eight o'clock," said Vladimir. Then Peter Ilych opened his large deep-blue and softly brooding eyes. "Is it really eight o'clock already?" he asked. Then he sighed a little and feigned astonishment—as if he had been aroused from a delicious morning sleep.

"Have you slept well, Pierre?" asked Vladimir.

Peter Ilych laughed from the depths of the pillows: "Splendidly." He touched the young man's cool, long, slender hand with the tips of his fingers. How like his mother's hands they were!—the mother whom he ought to have followed.

"How is your heart this morning?" asked Vladimir mischievously.

"Of course you want to make fun of me." Peter Ilych made an effort to look particularly hearty. "There is nothing the matter with my heart," he said.

"But yesterday evening you declared that it was practically done for," said Vladimir seriously, his fingers playing with Peter Ilych's.

"Yes," said Peter Ilych. "Yesterday it was dreadfully painful. Often it stops beating, sometimes for minutes together. But this morning it is beating quite bravely."

"I suppose you will read your Bible first, before you come out to attend to the flower-beds?" asked Vladimir, stepping away from the bedside.

"Of course," answered Peter Ilych. "I shall certainly do so."

"A mad sort of habit," smiled Vladimir. He was now standing in the middle of the room. He was already dressed for working in the garden, and over his shirt and trousers he wore a coarse blue apron. His dark hair was smoother than it usually was; he had been holding his head under cold water.

"As a matter of fact, it is a splendid habit," said Peter Ilych with dignity, now sitting up in bed; "and it is very foolish of you to believe in nothing."

They were in the habit of working in the garden for half an hour before breakfast. There was always something to sow, or weeds to pull up, something to pick or something to bury. Busying themselves with spades and rakes and watering-cans, they would break into song, the young man and the gray-bearded man. They improvised duets in the style of Italian, German, or French opera: tender or violent songs for two voices. But this morning, as they watered the flowers or pulled up weeds, it was Russian folk-songs that they sang. Vladimir, looking very slim in his blue apron, sprang about the flower-beds on his long legs, like a young colt, singing:

"To the hunt went Mr. Andrew, Mr. Andrew,
     And shot a gray duckling. . . .

All the girls are so lovely, are so lovely,
But the best in all the village, all the village,
Is the fair-haired Mariushka, Mariushka.
No one has such lovely tresses, lovely tresses. . . ."

Bob and Peter Ilych laughed a good deal over the gray duck-
ling and the long tresses of the beautiful Mariushka. But presently Peter Ilych, in his camel-hair dressing-gown, bending over
a bunch of roses, started to sing a long ballad in his deep and
rather booming voice:

"Once in Kiev, the ancient town of Kiev,
Sat Vladimir, sat the red Sun-prince;
Gave a feast, a rich and splendid feast;
Many princes and Bojars proud were there.
Bold challenging voices filled the Hall of Knights,
The welkin rang with noisy words and laughter:
See how the heroes courageously attack the food,
And all of them carouse, as valiant heroes should,
And all of them boast of bold deeds they have done."

"Just another couple of such melodies, and we have a Russian
folk-opera in the manner of the Five Innovators," laughed Vladimir.

Alexey appeared on the terrace and called his two masters, the
young and the old, to breakfast. Peter Ilych thumped Bob on
the back: "Come, Vladimir, Red Sun-prince! Let us courageously attack the food!"

Arm in arm, they went through the flower garden, over the
little gravel forecourt, and into the house.

After breakfast Bob went with his fat books and sat on the
rustic bench in the garden, while Peter worked in the music-
room. It was almost a superstition with him that in Frolovskoe
no morning should be allowed to pass without working—not
even today, although it was Bob's last morning—a circumstance,
however, about which one did not wish to think. Peter Ilych

tried to forget it by applying himself to the *Pique Dame* score. But did he succeed? He could not bear it at the piano. He got up and paced through the room, and then stood at the window. Outside he saw his Vladimir sitting on the rough-hewn wooden bench, in the shade of bushes which were stirring slightly in the breeze. The young man's left knee was elevated, the heel of his sandal propped up on the edge of the bench, one arm encircling his shin. He held his book in his right hand. His head was bent attentively and the sunlight played about his smooth forehead; on his eyelids, however, and on the soft but firm oval of the bowed face, lay the shadow.

Peter Ilych, at the window, observed Vladimir. Bob, on the rustic bench; Bob, the familiar confidant, the near-relation. "What will the days be like when you no longer share them with me? A day without you is a weariness and a waste. . . ."

Lunch was punctually at one o'clock; the days at Frolovskoe were rigidly regulated. Peter had asked the cook—a fat German woman—to prepare Bob's favorite dishes; Alexey served them with great dignity: the fish with a white sauce and mushrooms, the sweet according to an Austrian recipe. Both the young man and the ageing man ate with splendid appetite. The dining-room, which also served as lounge and sitting-room, was large and airy; the window was open and the perfume of the flowers came from the garden. Vladimir had taken off his coat, and his shirt was open at the neck.

"You must excuse me for going about in such an unconventional way," he said in a well-brought-up manner to his uncle. "But I am so delighted that summer has come."

"I am delighted too," said Peter Ilych.

Throughout the meal Vladimir talked about the sun, and how thankful he was that it was gaining strength. "I have so often been frozen," he said. "I have been coughing the whole winter, and the winter has lasted such a long time. It is splendid to have it really warm again."

After lunch came the long walk: that was a part of the program. When Peter Ilych was alone in Frolovskoe, he was in the habit of taking lots of slips of paper with him, stuffing them into all his pockets. While he was walking he made notes of all sorts of things—musical ideas, points for letters. "Tomorrow I shall have to start filling my pockets with slips of paper," he thought. But today he still had Bob.

The landscape at Frolovskoe offered very little variety: it was flat, almost a wilderness. But Peter Ilych loved the wide view across the meadows; he loved the groups of birch trees and the dark little pools at the edge of the wood. "But it is sad," he said, "that even here they have already started to chop down trees unmercifully. They will end by doing the same as they did in Maidanovo: they will ruin my lovely landscape. They want to hound me out of it."

Almost every walk began with this lament, when they came in sight of the thinning wood. Even today Peter Ilych began with it, but only half-heartedly, as if in duty bound to do so. Vladimir said: "It's a stroke of luck that the birches are still here." So they took comfort in their birches.

They went on walking for a few minutes without talking. Bob had cut himself a switch, and as he walked he drew figures with it in the sandy path. "You *have* got a serious expression," said Peter Ilych, for Vladimir was walking with bowed head. "No doubt you have been reading unpleasant things the whole morning. What were they? Your new French authors again?"

They often came into conflict over the French realists. Vladimir, fascinated by radicalism and its critical attitude to society, was enthusiastic about Zola and his school; whereas Peter Ilych took exception to their "artificial simplicity," which he considered just as bad as the "tinkling phrase-making, epithets, and antitheses of Victor Hugo."

"Life is not, of course, an easy and merry affair," he explained now, "but neither is it so slimy, so dirty-gray as these realists would have us believe. I have recently read Zola's *La Bête humaine*. How *low* that is! A crook novel decked out with obscenities! The style of these fellows consists in smearing a layer of dirt over everything. And that is why it is so easy to parody it."

"Parody it then," demanded Vladimir. "I should love to hear you do it!"

Peter Ilych laughed. "Nothing could be easier than that!" he declared. He had come to a halt in the field path. "How would a member of the Zola school describe my lonely evening meal in Frolovskoe?" he asked slyly. "Something like this." And with his face contorted by a sullen grimace, he began to declaim:

"*Une serviette de table négligement attachée à son cou, il dégustait. Tout autour, des mouches, avides, grouillantes d'un noir inquiétant, volaient. Nul bruit, sinon un claquement des machoirs énervant. Une odeur moite, fétide, écourante, lourde, répandait un je ne sais quoi d'animal, de carnacier dans l'air. Point de lumière. Un rayon de soleil couchant, pénétrant comme par hasard dans la chambre nue et basse, éclairait par-ci, par-là, tantôt la figure blême du maître engurgitant sa soupe, tantôt celle du valet, moustachue, à traits kalmouks, stupide, et rampante. On devinait un idiot servi par un idiot. Neuf heures. Un morne silence régnait. Les mouches fatiguées, somnolantes, devenues moins agitées, se dispersaient. Et là-bas, par la fenêtre, on voyait une lune grimaçante, énorme, rouge, surgir sur l'horizon embrasé. Il mangeait toujours. Puis, l'estomac bourré, la face écarlate, l'œil hagard, il se leva et sortit. . . .*"

"Very pretty! Very clever!" laughed Vladimir. "And you conveyed the atmosphere of your house marvelously!" When they continued their walk, he took Peter Ilych's arm. "You ought to write a society novel, and not always go on composing!"

"No, thank you very much!" cried Peter Ilych. "And 'society' will also be very thankful. Yes, if 'society' were really anything like the picture painted by your modern critics, then life would be an even more pitiable and viler thing than we think it is."

"Perhaps it is more pitiable and viler than you think it is," said young Vladimir seriously; he went on speaking, and Peter

Ilych, looking at his beautiful mobile mouth, listened to him willingly, although he knew quite well what was coming. He loved his eager and rapid way of speaking and the impetuous and rather awkward little gestures with which it was accompanied; and he loved the gleam that appeared in the boy's soft, golden-brown eyes. For young Bob became very excited. "In point of fact," he exclaimed, "it would be impossible to describe this society as more dismal and dirty than it is! It is a system founded on injustice; its only law is that of exploitation and oppression!"

He had certainly learned something from his thick books, French novels, and political pamphlets privately printed and circulated. He was moved and sometimes deeply affected by the extreme currents of the times, and his young head was awhirl with all sorts of passionate ideas.

If he had been put on his honor and asked seriously to declare whether he wished a fundamental change in the present system, whether he would like to see a revolution, he would probably have found himself in an embarrassing position; for he was an absolutely honest young fellow and would have had to admit that he himself—of good family, the spoiled darling of a famous uncle—had nothing to complain of. As a rule one goes only a certain distance in working against one's own interests. Young Vladimir was not an active revolutionary; he belonged to no organization. But he was influenced and often profoundly moved by revolutionary ideas, in which Nihilist and anarchist elements mingled with socialist. He believed in a progress which was mechanically determined by an inexorably conditioned causality; but at the same time, he wished to intensify and expedite the revolutionary development. This speeding-up would hasten the bloody cataclysm, the great conflagration, the abolition and destruction of the existing social order, and thus lead to a terrible, seductive goal about which they very rarely thought. The new Order that was to come occupied the young mind much less than the wild and magnificent period of chaotic disorder—that is to say, the revolution—which would precede it and bring it about.

In his bewildered, excited brain pan-Slavonic hopes and ideals came into contact with Jacobite ideals; a vague, enthusiastic patriotism with an internationalism which signified above all an enthusiasm for France. His materialism—fruits of a superficial reading of Darwin and Marx—had a lyrical exuberance about it. His somewhat confused eloquence was inspired by a mixture of burning emotion and half-understood slogans. The boy believed in the things he said; but that did not prevent him from quickly forgetting them. There were days filled with the simple daily pleasures shared with innocent comrades, when he did not bother his head with thoughts of the social order and its future. At other times his melancholy was such that it robbed him of all hope that the great problems of society would ever have an even half-satisfactory solution. Then it would appear to his deeply troubled heart that the curse laid on life could not be lifted, except by exterminating life itself, and certainly not by better organization. Then he would think: How could one even start to live one's life, what use could one make of it, if one believed that? Why must we recognize all this and feel it so deeply? Those in the vanguard, the strong ones, those who are the builders of the future, they don't recognize this. "But I belong to a class that is damned and a generation that is lost."

But such moods as these also passed; they were no more permanent than the frivolous moods or the rebellious moods. The young heart was accessible to all influences, to those which brought the light of heaven, and those which brought a perfume or a breeze; in the evening it responded to one, at noon to another, and in the morning to yet another; but his response was always immediate, strong, and always entirely honest.

Peter Ilych loved to observe the play of these emotions, the rapid change from angry remonstrance to tenderness, from tenderness to melancholy, from melancholy to frivolity, much as one might enjoy watching the play of colors on the surface of the water, reflecting the shifting clouds and changing sunshine. He was touched by the evidence of these heartfelt conflicts, proud enthusiasms, bubbling merriment, and pure melancholy, even although the problems that tormented and troubled the young heart seemed remote from him and almost matters of indifference.

For Peter Ilych, with a naïve trustfulness, believed in "Progress," as in an important and possibly great fact with which other people concerned themselves, and in which he for his part was not particularly interested. When Vladimir complained of oppression and gross injustice, Peter Ilych said diffidently: "But at least we are not living in the Middle Ages! The rack and serfdom no longer exist!" Whereupon Vladimir would only laugh bitterly. "You don't know the methods of our secret police— they are no better than the rack. And whether the worn-out and poorest people of today have a better time than serfs and slaves used to have in the past, that is a matter we need not offer an opinion on!"

"Undoubtedly there are some serious abuses," agreed Peter Ilych thoughtfully. "I am so terribly sorry for people in trouble; only to think of it makes my heart contract. The Tsar ought to know about such things; I am quite sure they never get to him. The Tsar is so far away, raised so high above all such things, that the complaints never reach him. He ought to be told, obviously: somebody ought to explain things to the Tsar."

With whimsical cunning he posed as being a degree less knowledgeable and more naïve than he really was, taking pleasure in watching young Bob's vehement reaction. And this was not slow to come. Bob pulled a scornful face, which was almost irreverent. "The Tsar!" He brought his long switch down whistling through the air, so swiftly that it made a shrill cutting sound. "He is the worst of the lot!"

"Perhaps he is distrustful," Peter conceded; "and has he no cause to be? You mustn't forget—the Nihilists murdered his predecessor, and that was undoubtedly a great sin, for it was on that very day that Alexander wanted to give the country a constitution; and the Nihilists also wanted to blow up the Winter Palace with dynamite—just think of it! The whole beautiful Winter Palace!"

"What a pity it didn't really go up in the air," said Vladimir dryly; then he smiled and showed his fine teeth. "The so-called constitution of Alexander II—I can imagine what a fine thing *that* would have been! But Alexander III has never even vouchsafed as much as that. Tyrants don't willingly give up any of their terrible power—not willingly. Oh, I could wish that Alexander III might meet the same fate as his predecessor!" cried young Vladimir with shining eyes, and there was a really cruel expression on his face. "He has already been responsible for the shedding of too much blood, and far too many appalling things have been done in his name. He must pay the price: that is exacted by the logic and justice of history."

In order to arouse the boy still further and work up the drama to an even higher pitch of excitement, Peter Ilych remarked casually in a friendly but cynical tone: "It is true that His Majesty the Emperor does not understand much about music: he prefers the worst of the Frenchmen! However, now and again he does something for a few poor Russian artists—one must not be ungrateful. He gives an income, for example, to poor Tchaikovsky. . . ." And he enjoyed catching Vladimir's scornful shrug of the shoulders and the dark flame in his eyes.

The young man went on talking and gesticulating as they walked through the meadows or the copse. What he said was not very different from what might be found in the leading articles in illegal revolutionary journals, and certainly no better; still, with every word he revealed a genuine, if naïve, indignation and a burning and quite spontaneous, if somewhat childish, abhorrence—declaiming against all the horrors of Siberia, the outrageous ambition of the Imperial policy, the corruption of the officials, the vileness of the secret police, the hypocrisy of the priests, the arrogance of the nobility and the wealthy. "And the century in which all this is possible," he concluded with bitter emphasis, *"you* call a century of progress!"

The older man listened to him, half-amused but rather staggered—amused by the display of so much rhetorical zeal, staggered by the vehement emotion which obviously inspired it, and by the appalling facts which caused the emotion and justified it.

"What dreadful things you know!" said Tchaikovsky at last. "Such things never come my way. I live so much apart, so much in myself. Indeed, it is just as well, for the sake of my work, which in the long run is the only thing that this poor creature can give to the poor old world. For you see I am already an old man and don't belong to the generation that can bring about changes on this tormented earth. It is the burden of the young, yes, Bob, of your generation—to improve conditions and put right what we old ones have put wrong."

This time he spoke very seriously. And young Bob, with a deep breath, answered with a like seriousness. "Please God we shall succeed!"

"There you are!" cried Peter Ilych laughing; "now it is you who call upon the good God!"

"That was only a manner of speaking," said Vladimir, rather annoyed. "We have got to achieve it by our own strength, or we shall never achieve it at all."

At that moment the low-built country house, with its little garden, stood before them. The long walk had come to an end.

* * *

Alexey had prepared tea on the terrace. The mail had come; between the tea glasses and the flower vases lay letters and newspapers. Peter Ilych asked Vladimir to read to him—"but only the most important things!" he exacted. "All the rest is so utterly boring—even the so-called important things are not amusing." He stretched himself comfortably on the chaise longue and looked blinking at the sun; he held his glass of tea with both hands on his propped-up knees.

"Bring me those sweet little creatures," he said to the servant in the soft pleading voice that he often used to his friends and always to his inferiors. "I am dying to press the Crown of Creation to my bosom." The Crown of Creation was five puppies who had seen the light of day in Frolovskoe a few days ago, or rather had not yet seen the light of day, for they were still blind and went dizzy when faced with the startling sunlight. Alexey brought them in in a little basket lined with soft green wool. The newly born lay asleep on the green cloth as if they were in a field; interlocked, they looked like a velvety brownish mass, blinking, sniffing, and breathing heavily.

"Aren't they enchanting?" Peter Ilych was deeply moved and highly delighted by the sight of them. "They are much more charming than flowers. Lying there, they look more beautiful than the most beautiful flower-bed." He leaned over them, and Vladimir also bent down over the basket.

"I will have at least three of them on my lap," Peter declared. "I am an old dotard and therefore I have the right. You're only going to have two at the most, young Bob." They plunged their hands into the soft brown heap. The blind, writhing creatures were lifted up; Peter Ilych laid three of them against his cheeks and neck; Vladimir took two of the others and put them on his lap. "How soft their paws are!" cried Peter Ilych. "It is delightful to hear them breathe."

Bob said: "But now we must see what is in the letters and the newspapers." He began reading aloud; holding the paper with his right hand, he stroked the silky fur of the puppies with his left.

There were letters from agents in Berlin and Paris; there was even one from an enterprising man in New York, proposing that Tchaikovsky should make a great tour through the United States.

"Will you really go to America?" asked Bob.

Peter stretched himself lazily. "Oh, I don't know yet. . . . If you come too. . . ." Bob laughed and went on opening the rest of the letters. One was from the publisher Jürgenson, one from the director of the Imperial Theater, one from the Opera House in Tiflis. "It is very charming of people to trouble themselves so zealously about me," said the flattered Peter Ilych lazily. "But at present I have no desire to go touring the world like an acrobat. I am quite satisfied here." And with an air of contentment he watched the smoke rising from his cigarette.

Vladimir left one letter unopened. "From Madame von Meck," he said, handing it to Peter Ilych, who opened it at once. It was a very long letter. In the meantime Bob opened the newspapers: Tchaikovsky subscribed to Paris and St. Petersburg journals.

"What are they doing at the Opéra in Paris?" asked Pierre, turning his attention from Nadezhda's letter.

"I was examining a speech by the German Emperor," said Vladimir. "I wonder what sort of policy this touchy young gentleman will adopt now that Bismarck has been eliminated."

"How you do trouble your head with all sorts of things, my clever darling!" smiled Peter Ilych.

"It looks to me exactly as if France wanted to bring about an alliance with us, as our treaty with Germany has not been extended," declared Vladimir, still clinging to his paper.

"Oh!" cried Peter Ilych suddenly, letting Madame von Meck's letter fall. "I believe he can see a little bit!" But he was not referring to Kaiser Wilhelm, nor to the Tsar, nor yet to the President of the Third French Republic, but to the little puppy that was crawling round his neck.

Vladimir jumped up at once; it was most important to discover whether the tiny animal really could see a little. He leaned over Peter Ilych, laying his arm over the latter's shoulder.

"It looked at me," claimed Peter. "There's not the least doubt about it; he looked at me, very expressively!" Vladimir laughed, and his laughing face was very near Peter Ilych's. The latter was startled. "What is happening?" he asked his startled heart. "Could it really be true? Was this really, really a moment of perfect happiness?"

*   *   *

Vladimir busied himself with the newspapers until dinner time; Peter Ilych dealt with correspondence. Dinner had to be taken indoors; during the latter part of the afternoon fog had risen from the marshy meadows and the atmosphere was now damp and cool. Alexey, with a dignified expression on his face, brought young Mr. Vladimir his favorite dishes.

As soon as the meal was over, Bob said: "Wouldn't it be nice to have a game of ball?"

"But it is already too dark," replied Peter Ilych. "We shouldn't see the ball." Nevertheless, they made the attempt. Peter Ilych was only too delighted to see Vladimir at play; he loved watching his awkward-graceful leaps and listening to his outbursts of laughter when the ball flew past him, and wild shouts of joy of an almost menacing hilarity. When at play, the serious youth became an unrestrained child.

Before long it became impossible to distinguish the flying rubber ball in the whitish-brown twilight. So they decided to go back into the house.

"Let us have some music," proposed Vladimir. "I want to hear Mozart as a farewell treat." It was the first time that he had mentioned his coming departure: this time he did so with a somewhat artificial casualness. Peter Ilych winced.

Alexey lit the candles on the pianoforte. They looked in the music cabinet for the score of the *Entführung aus dem Serail*. "That is the only opera we haven't been through," said Peter Ilych. They had played Mozart many evenings—many evenings of these four blessed weeks.

Vladimir sat where he always sat when Peter Ilych played to him. The large armchair in which he curled himself up was

so placed that the player, looking at the music, could also see the
face of the listener. How Peter Ilych loved to play music for
the special benefit of those small shapely ears, so sensitive and so
appreciative, which looked like delicate shells half hidden by
the thick dark hair. "You are the ears to which my music loves
most to appeal," said the player silently to his companion. The
latter, as if in answer, had a grave smile on his lips. Of what did
this remind Peter Ilych? Of the smile of the handsome stranger,
Alexander Siloti. Yes, Vladimir had a good deal in common
with him; the Siloti who had played on his feelings and prepared the way for one who united the charm of the foreigner
with the qualities of one who was his near kin and entirely trustworthy. All sorts of things crowded in on the player: Siloti's
smile; his mother's voice; the beauty of young men whom he
had known only superficially but had ardently and unsatisfy-
ingly loved; the look of his sister. So much seductive power
was concentrated in Vladimir.

Peter Ilych played. He was enthralled by the melodies of the
beloved opera; so enchanted was he that his somewhat heavy
hands attained unusual lightness of touch; they fluttered over
the keys and produced the sweetest of sounds, the subtlest and
most significant rhythms. He indicated the arias, ensembles, and
choruses in a soft husky voice.

"It is so beautiful that it is almost too beautiful," he said when
he reached the end of the first act. Vladimir had gone and sat
beside him, and, thanking him, had stroked the feathery, wavy
gray-white hair. "It is so perfect that it almost makes one sad."

"Why should the perfect make one sad?" asked young Vladimir softly. His face was as if transfigured, so deeply had he been
moved by the music.

"There is no need for you to understand that," said Peter
Ilych, looking past him in a curiously fixed stare; and, suddenly
gloomy, he added: "But it always pains me, even while it en-
chants me. Why? Because I have the impression that I shall

never never never reach such a point, never on this earth or in this lifetime. It appears to me as altogether unattainable. Often I have the feeling that its flawless loveliness is mocking me."

"Please—please don't say such things!" Vladimir caressed him with his long, cool fingers—the fingers of Peter Ilych's mother, the fingers of the strange young men. But on Tchaikovsky's face the expression of disquietude remained.

"Unattainable—unattainable!" he said gloomily, supporting his head in his hands. "That is a bit of heaven itself: what the rest of us have to sing, in our best moments, is only a *longing* for heaven, nothing more, never anything more. Perhaps it is some consolation," he added, and suddenly a malicious smile appeared on his face, "perhaps it is some small consolation that none of those now living, not a single one of my contemporaries, possesses more than this longing, and even that only in their best moments. For we are all born out of due time; we are all bewildered and we all suffer from the same sense of moral insecurity. Not a single one of us ought to pose as a 'Master,' or as a 'classic,' as one who has perfected his art, as many of them do, such as that self-satisfied German, Johannes Brahms. One is apt to become an odious creature, and in fact cut a rather comical figure in our times if one claims to have attained perfection. If Brahms is such a master, then I'm another!"

He had spoken in a kind of nervous anger, and his forehead had flushed a dark red. "If that arrogant German is a master, then I am certainly one too!" he repeated irritably. Then, striking the Mozart score with his heavy hand, he cried out: "But in comparison with that—that genius, that pure embodiment of heaven's own radiance—the rest of us are of trifling account."

Bob said: "How frightfully malicious you look! When you have that expression on your face and that vein stands out on your forehead, I could easily be quite frightened of you," and he stroked with his fingertips the vein that stood out so angrily on Tchaikovsky's brow. "But I won't let you make such a face!"

said the boy cajolingly. "Wait a minute—now I'm going to play something on your piano which will make you laugh; there is always something comic about my music-making."

"How nice of you!" said the delighted Peter Ilych, whose forehead soon became smooth under Bob's caressing fingers and coaxing words. "What are you going to perform? A waltz, perhaps? I should like to hear you play one of Johann Strauss's."

He had already vacated his place at the piano; Vladimir lowered the stool in front of the Mozart score which had received such blows from Peter Ilych. His hands made powerful movements over the keys.

"Now, old Pierre, does that comfort you?" He laughed and allowed his body to sway to the rhythm of *The Blue Danube.* "I consider that very refreshing and very consoling—if only I could play it a little better!"

But Peter Ilych, in a soft rather husky voice, bade him, "Go on playing, Bob!"

"Doesn't it hurt your ears?" Vladimir struck the keys even harder. "I am abusing your poor instrument."

"Go on playing," repeated Peter Ilych once more, and laid his hand on the young man's shoulder. Young Bob, whose cheeks had grown hot with the effort of playing, said as he bent somewhat lower over the keys:

"Do you know what I should like now? I should like to have a girl here. Then I would waltz with her and you would play for us."

Peter Ilych answered nothing. Slowly he removed his arm from Vladimir's shoulder.

"But there isn't a girl in Frolovskoe," said young Bob, while the waltz under his fingers became softer and slower.

"No," said Peter Ilych in a rough voice.

"The German cook is too bulky for my taste," laughed young Bob.

A quarter of an hour later they parted; conversation between them showed no signs of regaining its vivacity. Peter Ilych kissed the boy on his pure smooth forehead in farewell. "Thank you for everything," he said.

"It's I who have to thank you," replied Vladimir, with his grave smile.

Peter Ilych felt very tired; nevertheless, for a long time could not sleep. His head ached. "I must imagine something that will tranquillize me," thought his poor head. "I must imagine something that will bring me peace."

And he knew quite well what it was that he would imagine; for there was a dream- and wish-image which he had so many times built up before him as he slipped into the longed-for sleep.

Peter Ilych imagined that he was about to die. His powers were leaving him; the great darkness was upon him: it murmured alluringly in his ear and he had a foretaste of its sweetness on his tongue. The room in which he lay dying was narrow; through the half-opened window fell golden shafts of sunshine. But who is that sitting by the bedside? The dying man cannot, or may not, open his eyes. But even with his closed eyes he recognizes the beloved face of Vladimir. "But sit nearer to me, my child!" pleads the dying man, whose eyelids and lips are being caressed and paralyzed by the great coming darkness. "I am quite near to you," answers Vladimir's strange but familiar voice. "Are you suffering, my dear Pierre? Shall I put a compress on your forehead? You would then die more quickly and pleasantly."

Peter Ilych, passing out of life, shakes his head. "We must not be in a hurry," he murmurs; "it is so beautiful."—"There are people in the front room," says Vladimir, with the voice of his mother and the voice of the young foreigner. "Various old acquaintances—for instance, your divorced wife Antonina, and Madame Désirée Artôt-Padilla whom you might have loved, and Madame von Meck, your trustworthy friend, and one Apukhtin; there are also some journalists among them. They all want to see you. There are lots of people and they all look very inquisitive; although they all love you, they all appear to be amused by the fact that you are dying."—"I will receive nobody," mutters the dying man. "I am dying. That is the solemn fact. Only you must be with me."—"How fine, and what an honor for me," says Vladimir the beloved, the clever darling, with gentle gravity.— "—When I am dead and redeemed," Peter Ilych heard himself saying, "then, and not till then, you may allow the ladies and friends and journalists to come in, and you will be able to declare that Vladimir alone was present at the death of Peter Ilych Tchaikovsky—so highly is Vladimir esteemed. They must all be told, these journalists and ladies. A greater honor than this Peter Ilych cannot accord. And now I shall soon be dead; for I can feel myself falling. How agreeable it is! What a great joy it is!" —"Ought I not quickly to put one of the healing compresses on your forehead?" asks Vladimir, the slender watcher by the death-bed, with monotonous tenderness. But already Peter Ilych has fallen asleep.

* * *

No sooner had Vladimir departed than Peter Ilych began to hate Frolovskoe—the house, the flower garden, the rustic bench, the walk through the meadows—and to wish ardently that he were anywhere else, so long as he were not there. This hate grew as the weeks passed and he had to force himself to remain there. His stay there became more and more distasteful and caused him acute suffering. Wherever he looked and wherever he went, he missed Bob; everywhere he missed his laughter and his chatter. The days without him seemed a weariness and a waste.

All sorts of other unpleasantnesses occurred. He made very little progress with the sextet. The postman came with odious letters. The general upheaval began with harmless trifles—such as the urgent plea of a stupid lady that Peter Ilych should be present at the christening of her son and be his godfather, failing which she, the tiresome lady, would grieve till she became ill and would probably die; he was plagued by bewildering letters from agents, and by unpleasant misunderstandings and friction between himself and his colleagues; and finally by the appalling news which came to him like a thunderbolt.

Rather unceremoniously, Madame von Meck informed her friend that, having been totally ruined and reduced to a state of utter poverty, she would be unable to continue to make him the allowance of six thousand rubles a year which she had guaranteed for his lifetime.

What a heavy blow this was! Peter Ilych was so shattered by this ungracious stroke of fate that for a time he could hardly move. His great benefactress was going to stop his allowance! His surest and pleasantest source of income had failed him! He might even have to take on the responsibility of paying back something to his discreet and efficient guardian angel, for if she were really stricken with poverty it would be his duty to come to her aid—that was his very first feeling. "All sorts of problems now confront me," muttered the unhappy man. "I really cannot grapple with such matters here. In any case, I have a horror of Frolovskoe now. All these last days I have been unhappy, and now this dreadful news has come to me here. I will remain here no longer. Only to be somewhere else, anywhere; best of all, nowhere; but in any case, not here."

He went to Tiflis to conduct a concert there. He liked the town at the foot of the Caucasus with its view across the fertile but melancholy yellow plain; the tortuous old oriental alleys winding in and out, confined on the one side by the course of the river Kura and on the other by the slope of the mountains. All sorts of eastern races met and mingled here. They passed along the narrow streets, where there were a thousand different smells and a thousand different noises: tall and beautiful Georgians with their proud almond eyes and their yellowish light-brown skin; dignified and busy Jews in kaftans, beards, and side-curls; the businesslike Armenians with their fat noses and cunning expressions; the Persians, Turks, and Turcomans.

Peter Ilych lived in the Russian governmental quarter, which, with its broad streets, characterized by a cold colonial elegance, was situated on a higher level and in a purer air. But he loved to move about among the crowds of Tatars and Mongols in the oriental alleys, courtyards, and bazaars.

"I am at least as happy here as I am on the boulevards of Paris," he said to the composer Ippolitov-Ivanov, his host, conductor of the opera at Tiflis. "In Hamburg an old gentleman told me I was an Asiatic; he wasn't so very stupid, or at any rate not so stupid as the Master Brahms, who reproached me with being a Frenchman. My preferences range from the Seine to the river Kura, from grand opera to the impenetrable tinkle and clatter of these narrow streets. I like the smell of it here—all those mysterious aromatic spices. I like the nearness of Persia. . . ."

Peter answered Madame von Meck's catastrophic letter while he was at Tiflis. It was an elaborate response and began with the following phrases:

"Dear and valued Friend: The news which came to me in your last letter has greatly grieved me; not for my own sake, but for yours. That is not an empty phrase, believe me! Of course I should be lying if I were to maintain that such a drastic cutting-down of my income had no effect on my material position. But this effect need not be so considerable as perhaps you might imagine it would be. During the past few years my income has been greatly augmented, and there are signs that it will continue rapidly to increase. Therefore, if a little part of the unending burden of cares and fears which now oppress you concerns *me*, I beg you most fervently to be assured that the thought that my income is to be unexpectedly curtailed is in no sense a bitter one. . . . What upsets me is that you will be deprived of many of the amenities which have been appropriate to your mode of living. The thought of that gives me a great deal of pain. . . ."

He continued in this sympathetic tone. Refreshed and stimulated by the exotic charm of Tiflis, Peter Ilych discovered warm words in which to express his consternation over the precarious situation in which his friend found herself, and beautiful phrases to thank her for all the kindnesses she had shown him for so many years. He did not, however, allow a single syllable to creep in which might be taken as an indication that he was ready to pay back any of the money which he had received so plentifully from her. His ex-guardian angel would consider such an offer—so he told himself—in the highest degree tactless, wounding, and unbecoming; but perhaps, if he had made it, she would have accepted it in order not to upset him, and then the "unexpected curtailment" of his income would be really serious and scarcely to be borne. On the whole, Peter Ilych was very well satisfied with his long, moving, and clever letter.

A few days after he had dispatched it, some observant friends informed him of the true state of Nadezhda's affairs. She was in no sense impoverished; she had suffered no reverses; her financial position had never been more flourishing. His "spiritual friend," therefore, had lied to him when she spoke of being ruined. She simply did not want to go on paying him an income; for some reason or other, she felt she had done so long enough. So she seized hold of the very first, and most transparent, excuse that occurred to her, an excuse so crude and threadbare that its improbability could not long remain unquestioned. And then she waited cynically for the effect it would produce. She was evidently willing to wound and insult Peter Ilych brutally. Clearly, this "spiritual friendship" was at an end.

If Madame von Meck's cold announcement had left Peter Ilych dismayed and numb, the news that he had been the victim of a shameless betrayal plunged him into a whirl of anger and gloom. He had never before been so bitterly outraged—and in his long and difficult life he had suffered many injuries. This was undoubtedly the worst of them all. There was nothing left for him to do but to lie in bed and weep bitterly.

The most trustworthy of all his friends had failed him. His best friend had insulted him and struck him in the face. So she can never have really been his "best friend." It was appalling to think of! The great spiritual friendship had been an illusion. The most beautiful and disinterested kindness he had known, which had saved and beautified his life, now revealed itself as the passing whim of a rich woman. Nadezhda had pretended to love and honor Peter Ilych—and alas, he had taken the pretense seriously. What a miserable and grotesque mistake! Madame von Meck had never really loved him—that was now quite clear. Probably the pleasant income she had allowed him had, during the last few years, been paid unwillingly. No doubt she had been making fun of him because he, in his naïveté, had trustingly accepted so much money from her. There she sat in her mansion, the malicious, neurasthenic old woman, chuckling over that stupid fellow, Peter Ilych, who had accepted from her something that she had only given in malice. If only he could repay all that she had persuaded him to accept from her! But this, of course, was not to be thought of; if he did that he would be reduced to beggary; he would have to pawn his piano and carpet, fur coat and watch. The beautiful watch, however, the talisman which was by far his most lovely possession—*that* he would cling to in the face of whatever calamity might come upon him.

What a long time Peter Ilych had allowed himself to be taken in by Nadezhda! With what tender delicacy had he avoided looking directly at her when she was pointed out to him on the Corso in Florence; she had been as unaffected by his reverential glance as if she had been a dainty fairy who might at any moment disappear in a silver mist. But actually she was a witch; her body was as hard as her heart. One ought to fix her with a stare and then give her a good shaking; no doubt she would emit a shrill giggle and defend herself with her broomstick—the old witch!

"Ah, Nadezhda! Nadezhda!" thought the weeping man, for whom the beauty of Tiflis no longer had any charm. "Why have you done this to me? You were much more to me than a 'spiritual friend,' to whom I confided everything, with whom in our correspondence I discussed everything: you were actually my wife; I counted on you as if you were really my wife. And now you have betrayed me, deceived me, and scandalously made fun of me! A mocking laugh is all that remains of our spiritual friendship. You have succeeded in transforming every kindness you have ever done me into a means of humiliating me. Why should you have done this? Oh, Nadezhda, I brood and brood and try to make out what could possibly have caused you to behave like this towards me. Have wicked people been lying to you about me? Or even told you truths about me that repelled you? Have you been told about THIS? But you pretended that you loved my music, and you ought to have been able to understand my life also—not an easy life, nor a very merry one, believe me! Or perhaps you were annoyed because I did not voluntarily give up long ago the pleasant allowance—as latterly I *could* have done, if it had been necessary. But actually I could not have made ends meet without it; there are so many calls on my money. That woman Antonina has to get her monthly check, although she has now a lover and even a child by him; Vladimir and my brother Modest depend on me for support; living is expensive; recently in Florence I was in a desperate position. How, then, could I have willingly given up the six thousand rubles? Oh, you inscrutable von Meck! Do you suffer no torment at the thought of the humiliation and unspeakable distress you have brought upon me? Are you torturing yourself as well as me? Hadn't we enough to bear without this?"

His tears were now less bitter. He began to consider the best way of coping with the situation. "I shall write to her as if nothing had happened," he decided after his long brooding. "I shall not let her know that I am aware of the shameless and malicious way in which she has lied to me. I shall write in all innocence —that will be the decentest and also the most cunning thing to do. In that way I may do something to tone down the ugliness of this painful situation. I can't suddenly break off a correspondence which has been going on for years at the moment when I cease to receive money from her. That would be disgraceful, low-down!"

Peter Ilych clenched his teeth and concocted a new letter to Madame von Meck, the contents of which were noncommittal and the tone inoffensive. Madame von Meck did not answer. Then he went as far as he could by writing a second time. The unfaithful spiritual friend, however, remained dumb. All his tactful efforts to smooth away the difficulties of a painful situation were met by a complete and inexplicable silence.

All was over: the "lasting friendship" had come to a sudden end. She was forcing him to regard her as an enemy at the moment when she no longer sent him money. Through her hostile silence she was compelling him to appear guilty of common ingratitude. This was the epilogue which she designed to a spiritual romance which had endured for thirteen years. "One is in the position of an abandoned mistress!" thought the outraged Peter Ilych. "What a deplorable finale!"

When would things be different? The upshot of every relationship was distressing and banal. Why should he expect the memory of Nadezhda to be sweeter than the memory of Antonina or Désirée? All of them left a bitter taste behind them— a taste that was like wormwood on the tongue.

"But this time I allowed myself to be more trusting than ever before. That is why the Remote One wishes to show me that there is nothing at all in which one can put one's trust. Well, He has certainly succeeded in forcing this dreadful knowledge upon me. He may be well content, the Inscrutable One! He does not smile on my account, nor does He weep. Unmoved, He observes my perplexities, my pitiable defeat, my miserable shame. He is just and He waits. What does He want of me? Why does He chastise me so? What wouldst Thou compel me to do, Thou Inscrutable One?

"The blows He has inflicted on me have been very severe. How deep is the humiliation into which He has plunged me now, poisoning my spiritual friendship by bringing it to a cheap and banal end! There must be a meaning behind all this: I feel it in my poor wounded heart, which grows more and more sensitive under the hard knocks which it receives. They are intended to mellow me; they are intended to ripen me—but for what? For what? What is to be the ultimate test, Thou Hidden One? What is to be the last adventure, Thou Inscrutable One?"

◇◇◇◇◇◇◇◇◇◇◇◇◇

THE MUCH-LOVED and beautiful city of Tiflis on the river Kura fêted its famous guest, the composer Tchaikovsky. Only once before in his life had Peter Ilych been the object of such a great and spontaneous expression of appreciation: this triumph in Tiflis was characterized by the same exuberance and brilliance as that victorious festival in Prague. On that occasion, a Slav nation which felt itself to be oppressed had found an outlet in the welcome it accorded to the Russian composer, who had taken on the character of an ambassador from the great empire whose roots were linked with its own. Today, this eastern city, this Georgian capital whose enchanting oriental alleys Peter Ilych found more attractive than the boulevards of Paris, received him with a warmth such as Moscow and St. Petersburg never showed him.

The great Tchaikovsky concert on October 20, 1890, organized by the Tiflis section of the Russian Musical Society, terminated with a remarkable ovation for the composer. After the concert the Artists' Union gave a banquet. An enormous amount was eaten, drunk, and spoken. It seemed as if the fine speeches and moving toasts would never come to an end; no sooner did one orator sit down than another sprang to his feet, swaying a little, and proclaimed—generally with a somewhat thick tongue—the genius, the kindliness, and the general magnificence of little brother Peter Ilych. It was a wonderful feast lasting until the early hours of the morning. Young people decked Peter Ilych's gray head with flowers; a large rose was poised above the heated and dark red brow of the hero of the hour. His dress-tie had come undone; one of the buttons of his stiff shirt had come unfastened; ashes had fallen onto the revers of his coat from the cigarette that hung from his lips. In this manner he presided, in an armchair decorated with wreaths, over an assembly of noisy, singing, laughing people: somewhat exalted, somewhat undignified, and somewhat ridiculous in the midst of his triumph.

While an oriental gentleman lauded the great composer in a slightly confused speech, Peter Ilych tried to collect his hazy thoughts. "All this is enormously gratifying," he told himself. "Unfortunately, however, it gives me a headache; what a head I shall have in the morning! I must take some bicarbonate of soda as soon as I get home. It is madness to drink so much! Nevertheless I should very much like the detestable, faithless, and infamous von Meck, my treacherous guardian angel, to see me now. At the very moment when she saw fit to humiliate me, I am being fêted—with flowers, wreaths, flattery, and all sorts of pomp; it is like a story from the Arabian Nights. But what does all this brilliance and lavish expenditure of admiration mean to me? Merely the little fact that I can convert all my sufferings and humiliations into music. Yes, Nadezhda, I know the secret; I am in the know; I can transmute everything. It is a sort of alchemy, a wizard's trick; it is not at all difficult, and it amuses me greatly. Yes, out of the great offenses which you have committed against me, my dear infamous Nadezhda, I will conjure up melodies. Keep a look-out for them; you will see how nice they will sound; and they will bring me more fame, and once more I shall be decked with laurel wreaths and honored as a great artist. Nobody and nothing can do me any harm, for I have the wizard's trick. . . . What an idiot I must look in this wreath, and my suit is splashed with wine and ashes—a sticky mixture! . . ."

A few days later the composer was seen off at the station by a great number of admirers, very vivacious but also in a state of sentimentality at the thought of saying good-bye. Among those who gathered together on the platform were the representatives of the musical societies, conductors, singers, music students and journalists, female admirers, and idlers who were there by chance because nothing could keep them from joining any crowd they happened to see. Peter Ilych stood at the open window of his compartment and made his farewells. "Good-bye, my friends," he said in a soft voice which won people to him: "you have been very good to me; I shall never forget it." He was answered by waving hands, cries of admiration, cheers and tears.

"Happy journey, Peter Ilych! Create more beautiful works! Think of us sometimes, great little brother!"

The occasion was marked by great emotional enthusiasm.

Peter Ilych, wearing a gray traveling cap pressed back from his high forehead, his long cigarette between his soft, too-red lips, looked pensively at the many strange faces in front of him. He allowed his soft, deep-blue, brooding eyes to rest for a time on the dark, defiant, reserved face of a somewhat exotic-looking young man. "I wonder who that is?" he thought as the cries of good-bye and good luck rose from the crowd like the noise of a conflagration. "Perhaps he is a very ambitious young composer, to whom I am a sort of model; maybe he knows every note I have written, and loves all my works. . . ." But the dark defiant young man was merely one of the crowd-joining loafers; he didn't even know who the gray-bearded gentleman at the carriage window was, nor why people were making so much fuss about taking their leave of him.

"Good-bye, my friends!" said Peter Ilych once more, and looked at the young oriental. The train began to move. Peter Ilych spread out his arms in a wide emotional gesture of farewell. Hysteria seized the ladies on the platform. Two female music students broke into shrill cries; one of them, her face distorted, tore her handkerchief into a number of pieces and flung them into the air. A number of persons ran after the moving train as if they could not tear themselves away from their darling at the carriage window; they stayed the course for some hundreds of meters, and then had to return. The collection of faces was wiped out; they existed no longer. The moving scenes of farewell had slipped into the abyss of the past, from which they would only return when transformed into the tender, clinging substance of memory.

Peter Ilych, somewhat exhausted, fell back into the carriage.

He was traveling towards Kiev. He wished to pay a visit to his sick sister in Kamenka: this was the official explanation of the journey. But what was his real intention? The months without Vladimir had been wretched. Peter Ilych had decided to take Bob, now a student, to Moscow and St. Petersburg with him.

The journey to Kiev was long. Peter Ilych had plenty of time to drink a large number of French cognacs, to smoke a hundred and twenty cigarettes with long mouthpieces; to read two detective tales and some stories by a new and very talented Russian author named Chekov; to make the first notes for some *Hamlet* music which he had promised the actor, Lucien Guitry, to compose for his benefit performance, the working-out of which was giving him no delight whatever; to brood miserably over the fact that the sextet—his last composition—had totally failed and was doubtless a depressing symptom of his decline, and signified the beginning of his impotence as a creator; that Madame von Meck had behaved like a fool and a villain; that all agents wanted to cheat him; that his right arm hurt him and that in all probability he would never be able to conduct again; that he would cancel the concerts in Mainz, Frankfort-on-the-Main, and Budapest which the Berlin concert agent Wolff had organized for him; that he would never travel again, but would live in the country, indeed in Frolovskoe, with Bob, the good Alexey, and the puppies.

He was very happy when the long journey at last came to an end. The little upholstered railway carriage had been like a prison, in which he had been incarcerated with all his fears and anxieties, with endless cigarettes and endless bottles of cognac; but at last, at long last, he saw the towers and gilded domes of the pious and dignified city of Kiev between the hills. Bells were always ringing as one entered Kiev, and that made it very solemn and moving. Solemn and moving also was the consciousness that presently he would be seeing again the beloved face of Vladimir, the clever boy who was his own kith and kin.

A disappointment awaited him. It was not Bob who had come with the carriage from Kamenka to meet the famous uncle at the station in Kiev, but his elder brother, the Davidovs' first-born, a sturdy young man with a large moustache.

"Where is Bob?" asked Peter Ilych, looking round him with a helpless searching glance that did not conceal his dismay.

"Mama did not want Vladi to leave her today," explained the sturdy young man, who wore wellington boots, breeches, and a leather jacket; Peter Ilych thought he looked like an estate agent. "Mama is rather bad; she wanted Vladi to look after her. So you must do with me, Uncle Peter."

It seemed to Peter Ilych as if his hearty young nephew had a somewhat malicious expression and looked positively cheeky when he said this.

Alexandra received her brother in a darkened room. She lay motionless in bed, on her back, her thin hands folded over her difficultly heaving bosom. "How sharp her face has become!" thought the brother as he bent down to kiss her. "I hardly recognize it. But the eyes I still recognize. And how narrow and pinched her lips are!"

On Sasha's face was that expression of bitterness and absent-mindedness with which she received every visitor; for each of them interrupted the intimate dialogue, so querulous and so tender, so arrogant and unyielding, which all day long went on between her and God.

"How are you, my dear Sasha?" asked her brother, and he thought: "Ah, how differently she used to receive me! What have the passage of time and this mysterious illness done to her?"

"It is always the same," answered Alexandra, without stirring; "and it will never come to an end."

"You will soon be well," said Peter Ilych in a timid attempt to comfort her.

To this she made no rejoinder, or rather responded only with a twisted smile.

"Have you got a really good doctor?" asked her brother, standing by her bedside in perplexity.

She replied: "I no longer have a doctor." Then her body was shaken by a dry cough. She had to sit up. Peter Ilych supported her back.

"Thank you," she managed to say, and her voice had a softer tone. She looked at Peter Ilych. Yes, her dark eyes had retained their beauty, deep-set as they were in their shadowy sockets: they were the eyes of their beloved mother, the eyes of Vladimir, her child.

"Poor Sasha!" said Peter Ilych, and for a moment he forgot to employ the hypocritical and euphemistic tact which usually prevails in the sickroom.

Sasha looked at him; her glance was scrutinizing and friendly, but severe. While her dark critical eyes rested on his face and she lay lost in thought, she slowly raised her wasted hand. "My dear," she said, shaking her head as if to chide him for some trivial offense; "you haven't got younger either. Pierre, old Pierre—how time has passed! . . . You look like an old man."

He tried to smile; but his face resisted the attempt, for he found the present moment not only difficult but extremely moving. He wanted it to seem as if he were here and now meeting his sister Alexandra-Sasha, the daughter of their beloved mother, the mother of his beloved Vladimir, for the first time after a long interval. Had she not been the confidante of his troubles, his needs and doubts during his restless youth? He had run to her for comfort—but what a long time ago that was, Pierre, old Pierre! How time has passed! In the meantime he had drifted away from his sister and had rarely seen her. And now suddenly they were together again, Sasha and Pierre, who knew so much about each other, whose hearts were so heavy with common memories. One must make the most of this reunion. Sasha was ill; she was sparing with her strength. Who could say how much effort these few minutes were costing her? Very soon she would probably fall back and continue her silent and unceasing dialogue, her mysterious and obstinate altercation with the exacting Aloof One.

"Do you sometimes think about our mother?" she asked, keeping her scrutinizing gaze on his face.

"Every day I think about her," replied her brother softly.

"I shall be seeing her soon." Sasha lay quiet; she had turned her glance away from her brother and was looking at the quilt. Her eyes were brilliant. "I could give her a message from you," she said, and smiled slightly as if she had made a little joke.

"Do you really believe that people meet each other again?" Peter asked in a husky voice.

She smiled in a sly and rather haughty manner, like one who is in the possession of important and exact information but will not, for mysterious reasons, divulge it. "Oh," she said, and her head swayed to and fro excitedly on the pillow. "That isn't so simple. . . . Of course people will certainly meet again. . . . But in another manner . . . do you understand? In a manner quite different from what we imagine; entirely different." She became silent, and her face took on a comfortable expression that was almost crafty.

As he failed to answer, Alexandra said suddenly, in a changed voice, remarkably dry and detached:

"You have come to take Vladimir away from me."

Peter Ilych could not prevent himself from turning red. "What makes you think that?" he exclaimed softly. She nodded at him. "Oh, all right, all right!" she exclaimed with uncanny cheerfulness.

"Vladimir is grown up." In his embarrassment Peter Ilych

had stood up and had begun to pace through the room. "He can't remain in Kamenka for ever."

"Of course not, of course not," agreed Sasha, who remained motionless on her back. "He ought to see something of the world, and I am sure you will help him to do that. I don't grudge it him. In fact, you have come just at the right moment. Everything has its meaning and hangs together. For I can now do without him."

"Nobody had any intention of taking him away from you," repeated Peter Ilych, breathing heavily.

"In fact I can do without him today," said his sister, once more with gentle obstinacy. "I have got as far as that . . . I've reached that point. . . ." Then she was silent. Her thin face and pinched lips once again assumed that expression of dreadful reserve.

Peter had remained standing at the bedside. "I will be good to him," he promised suddenly, his head drooping.

Was there not something mocking about her smile? "Let us hope that *he* will be good to *you*," she said, pityingly but not without malice. She had spoken similarly when he—a long time ago, Pierre!—had come to her complainingly about Apukhtin or one of the others. "But don't forget that he is young," she went on, "whereas we are old people." Then she was silent. Nor had the brother anything more to say.

"Go now, dear!" were her first words after a long pause. "You want to see the boy. And now I am tired."

The expression on her face, lying there on the pillows, showed that she had withdrawn further away from him: it was detached and proud.

He leaned down over her pale thin hand. "Forgive me if I have tired you too much!" he pleaded. Her only answer was to lower her eyelids. He went slowly to the door.

In the little antechamber that led to the sickroom sat Vladimir upright and alone, on a slender chair. As Peter Ilych left his sister's room, carefully closing the door behind him, Vladimir got up. Pierre, Sasha's brother, went up to Bob and embraced him.

"How did you find Mama?" asked young Bob. "How is she today?"

"I have been talking to your mother for a long time," said Peter Ilych, whose heavy hand lay upon Vladimir's dark soft curly hair. "We have talked about you too."

"Ought I to go to her?" asked Vladimir quickly.

"No, she wants to be alone."

"I hope she is sleeping," said Vladimir, her son.

"She has no objection to your coming with me to Petersburg," said Peter Ilych.

Vladimir opened wide his fine golden-dark eyes. "To Petersburg," he repeated, drawing a deep breath. What visions did his young, lustrous eyes see as they gazed out of his pale face? Life with his famous uncle; music, beautiful women, political battles, discussions, vice, and luxury; the capital whose charm and excitements he knew only in dreams and imagination. "So I shall *really* go there now. . . ." he said with a blissful, almost stupefied smile.

Thus young Vladimir, with his uncle, left the country house in Kamenka near Kiev, where his poor mother, lying motionless on her back, obstinately suffering, carried on her silent duologue with the austere Remote One until it should reach its appointed end.

Young Vladimir spent the winter in St. Petersburg, sometimes accompanying Peter Ilych to Moscow and Frolovskoe. So at last he was *really* there! He found life in great cities, in close contact with his beloved uncle, no whit less delightful, no whit less exciting in its surprising and colorful reality, than it had been in the dreams he had dreamed so frequently by night and the fantasies he had painted by day. The whole of the winter was a festival and a thrilling, if strenuous, adventure. With the enthusiasm and the voracious appetite of youth, he devoted as much ardor to the pursuit of pleasure as he had to the solving of problems. Elegant night-clubs, where tipsy officers flung champagne bottles against the wall and French singing-girls flung their legs in the air, excited him scarcely less than the secret political meetings in which, not without a shudder and rather to his own astonishment, he took part.

The young man seemed to live in a state of perpetual intoxication—quite stupified by the passionate discussions with his comrades on God and the world; by the great evenings at the opera and at concerts; by the intensely stimulating conversations with Peter Ilych; by the glances, gestures, and perfumes of women. The winter passed like an all too beautiful dream, every day full to the brim of impressions, experiences, surprises, and periods of tender or violent happiness. How long the winters had seemed in Kamenka! The days here were, it is true, richer in experiences, but how the weeks and the months seemed to fly past! Already they had reached March 1891.

Peter Ilych had been to Frolovskoe, for once by himself; for he needed a period of intensive work: there were the first notes for a ballet and for a one-act opera which had been commissioned by the director of the Imperial Opera House. He intended now to spend only a couple of days in St. Petersburg; then he would travel, going via Berlin to Paris, and then on to Le Havre, where he would embark for America. After a great struggle and a long correspondence, he had finally decided to venture on the great American tour. "It will be dreadful. And the Americans only want to make fun of me. It is undoubtedly due to a misunderstanding on their part that they should have asked me to go at all and should have offered me so much money. They imagine that I represent the new Russian music. This all comes from their not having read the wise utterances of Mr. César Cui. The gentlemen in New York are certainly unaware that I am no genuine Slav, but the ignoble bastard of a Parisian ballet manufacturer, a German sentimentalist, and a wild Asiatic. . . . However, I need the money," he concluded, with a harsh laugh.

He had arranged a little party in his suite at the Hotel Rossija, an intimate farewell party for Bob and his friends, on the occasion of his departure for the great American tour. The young people came from the opera—a few students, a few musicians, a few military students, wearing evening dress or uniforms. Champagne and caviar were handed round by the servant Alexey and a waiter from the hotel. For a fleeting moment Peter Ilych, as he observed Alexey open another bottle of champagne, thought: "Good Heavens! What sort of bill will they hand me in the morning? . . . This winter with Bob has been the costliest time of my life. . . . Perhaps also the most beautiful. . . . The fat profits from *Pique Dame*—what became of them? All gone, all gone! Jürgenson paid me an advance of five thousand rubles—how many kopeks are left? If I don't bring back with me a nice little heap of dollars from America, then once more I shall be a ruined man, and I shall have to put everything in pawn: fur coat, watch. . . ."

One of the young people had opened the window. "It is so smoky in here," he said, "and outside there is already a hint of March. Spring is most beautiful of all when it is just about to begin."

The speaker was the young Count Lütke, a tall, elegant young fellow wearing a monocle on his good-looking but rather empty oval-shaped face. He and his brother, who also made one of the company, were the smartest and liveliest of Vladimir's good friends. They had horses and carriages, ran up real debts, and kept real mistresses; were received at Court and belonged to the gilded youth of the capital. At the bottom of his heart Vladimir was very proud of his contact with them, even though he somewhat despised their complete lack of spirituality and their frivolous way of living.

Suddenly they all began to talk about spring in St. Petersburg, how beautiful it was, and how moving it was when it started. All of them loved the city in which they lived and had been young in. "Ah," said one of them, a dreamy boy in an ill-fitting evening suit made by an inferior tailor, "ah, the white nights will soon be coming, and round about midnight we shall be able to go walking on the Neva Prospect; sky and water will shine with the same glow, and we shall smell the perfume of herbs and strange flowers. . . . And who is that coming this way? Such a slender maiden! Nastenka!"

On the faces of all the young people appeared a somewhat emotional smile of delight. For every one of them had read the marvelous story to which the young dreamer in the cheap suit was alluding: Dostoevsky's fantastic love story about the White Nights. A knowledge of this book was one of the things which the young people took for granted; even the elegant brothers Lütke had to behave as if they knew all about it; even they thought it worth while to betray a certain interest in melancholy and daring moods, in the strange, ecstatic, hypersensitive, hopeless emotions of those aloof creatures who said of themselves that they were "not real human beings but rather a sort of intermediate type." They lived in enchanted out-of-the-way corners of St. Petersburg. "A different, mysterious sun shines there. In these corners, Nastenka, it is as if one lived an altogether different kind of life." But in these corners—or rather particularly there—one senses the oncoming of the Russian spring, so bitter-sweet, so modest, so tenderly seductive . . . the spring which magically transforms the cool white city of St. Petersburg and endows it with the utmost charm, as if a plain, insignificant and colorless girl should suddenly blossom into beauty: life and color and beauty have come to her overnight; blood tints the pale, flaccid cheeks. True, it is a short-lived delight; it does not last; one stretches out one's hand to it—and it is gone!

"Nowhere else is this painful spring-magic captured as it is in the White Nights," said the dreamer, who did not belong to the gilded youth and who certainly regarded himself as one of those deeply thoughtful, eloquent, rapturous, foolish-tragic Dostoevsky oddities.

"I quite fell in love with Nastenka when I read the little book for the first time," confessed Vladimir, whose narrow face, with its mobile mouth, surmounted by a mop of hair, looked particularly soft and childlike over the stiff high collar of his evening suit; he also appeared to be tired. "Yes, I knew exactly what had happened and how sweet it had been. The atmosphere of night on the canal-bank, where as a rule one never meets a living soul at this time—well, Nastenka appeared to me, and soon she was telling me the story of her unhappy childhood: the story of the grandmother with whom she had to pass her days sewing, and of the handsome young man who went with her to the opera and declared he loved her, who then vanished, leaving her waiting for him. . . ." Vladimir, greatly moved, became silent.

One of his young friends said smiling: "Our little Bob is in love with all the Nastenkas in St. Petersburg. He always turns red when a woman looks at him, and if she goes so far as to smile at him, he could sink into the ground for embarrassment and delight."

"And look at him blushing now because we are talking about it," exclaimed one of the Counts Lütke, amused.

"Do you like the women of St. Petersburg?" asked Peter Ilych in a soft husky voice. "Do you like them better than the women of Frolovskoe?"

Everybody laughed as if it were a comical idea even to think about the ladies of Frolovskoe. A young man in cadet's uniform cried out: "Does he like the women of St. Petersburg indeed! He's to be seen with one of them everywhere—a girl of good family, very elegant and expensive!"

Vladimir, blushing a deeper red, made violent signs to him to be silent. "Leave off, leave off," he said, and added almost angrily: "The spring has made you talkative."

"Winter is hardly over, and already we have the moods of May." Peter Ilych, the speaker, smiled wistfully. "You are all so eager to get rid of the winter, you already imagine you've done with it; nevertheless, it has been a very good winter." He looked at Vladimir, almost pleadingly.

"It has been a marvelous winter," declared Vladimir and looked Peter Ilych full in the face.

"A wonderful season!" agreed one of the two Lütkes with the self-complacency of a connoisseur.

"And it's also had lots of excitements!" Vladimir laughed and Peter Ilych laughed softly with him.

They suddenly began to talk among themselves of the events of the season that lay behind them. They had all been present at some of the chief of them: for instance, the great first night of *Pique Dame* at the beginning of December, which was a social event of the first order and had been a roaring success; the production of *Hamlet*, Lucien Guitry's benefit performance at the Michaels Theater, with Tchaikovsky's music; and the elegant concert of the Patriotic Women's Union, at which Tchaikovsky, rather overshadowed by the famous singers, the brothers Reszke, and the even more famous Madame Melba, had to conduct the Third Suite before a dull and snobbish audience.

In these musical and social festivities they had all taken part, either furnished with free tickets procured by Peter Ilych, or in their own box, as was the case with the Lütke brothers. A smaller, more intimate circle, Vladimir and his best friends, had also witnessed certain unofficial events that took place behind the scenes: for example, Tchaikovsky's frenzy when *Pique Dame* was withdrawn after the thirteenth performance—an absolute scandal, he maintained, since the theater was always sold out when the opera was performed. At the time, Peter Ilych, with his persecution mania, contended that the Tsar himself was responsible for this glaring injustice which had been done to him, the composer Tchaikovsky! "The Tsar despises me!" Peter Ilych had shouted, his face darkly flushed, stamping with both feet, his eyes full of tears. "The Tsar has always despised me; he expressed himself very scornfully even about *Sleeping*

Beauty. He despises all Russian music; one only sees His Majesty in the theater when there are French or Italian guest performers. Oh, yes, when the Melba or the Patti is going to sing, then you'll find the Imperial box occupied!"

Vladimir and a couple of his most intimate friends, in addition to the dismayed director Vsevolojsky, had heard and seen this completely unrestrained and almost seditious outbreak on Tchaikovsky's part. It was an appalling scene; the whole of the musical and fashionable world of St. Petersburg had talked about it, and it was numbered among the most piquant events of the season.

The young Count Lütke mimicked the director Vsevolojsky; how in his dismay he had rushed to Count Voronzov, and Count Voronzov had rushed to Count Obolensky to discuss the ticklish matter with him; and then how Count Voronzov had gone back to the director Vsevolojsky with the welcome reassurance that Count Obolensky at the last Court ball had brought round the conversation in the Most Exalted Circle to the *compositeur* Tchaikovsky; the *compositeur* Tchaikovsky might be assured that the Imperial Box was most graciously interested in everything he might write. Great things were expected of his *Nutcracker* ballet, as well as of his one-act opera *Iolanthe,* and the opinion had been expressed that *"ce sera le clou de l'hiver prochain."* The Count Voronzov then, employing the utmost delicacy and tact, had charged the director Vsevolojsky to approach Tchaikovsky: *"Dîtes-lui qu'on l'apprécie énormement. Tous les dimanches on demande à l'orchestre des airs de son ballet et on a souvent parlé de la* Pique Dame *en faisant un grand éloge."* The director Vsevolojsky had wound up the whole incident by speaking in a fatherly manner of Peter Ilych's "remarkable and unhappy character." "Why do you torment yourself with such fancies, *mon cher?"* the friendly patron had asked.

The young Count Lütke was able to imitate the manner of speech of all these fine gentlemen in a very amusing way, so that

Peter Ilych and all the young people were highly entertained. But Tchaikovsky became serious when the *Nutcracker* ballet and the short opera were mentioned.

"I am not at all happy about this commission from the director," he said. "I am an old and played-out man, and nevertheless I am practically the only Russian composer who figures in the programs of the Moscow and St Petersburg opera houses; apart from me, only foreigners are included. My colleagues, who aren't performed at all, must complain bitterly; as for me, I get angry when my opera is withdrawn after the thirteenth performance. I sometimes fear they must hate me. I am an obstacle in their path and prevent them from getting on."

All the young people, and especially Vladimir, denied this with vehemence. What was there surprising about the fact that he, the most distinguished and most popular of Russian musicians, should dominate the program of the great opera house? Nobody could object to that. Moreover, was he not beloved by all musicians, who recognized him as the most delightful and helpful of comrades?

Peter Ilych, however, remained thoughtful and cast down. "It is charming of you to say all that," he said, his head bent meditatively, "but I know only too well that there are innumerable people who hate and despise me. They consider that I pander to the taste of the general public, and thereby stand in the way of more serious and more difficult composers."

After a long pause, he went on, somewhat irrelevantly: "But now I am off to America—I wonder why?" As his fingers toyed with his cigarette, he thought: "I wonder why? For the sake of fame? Or really only for the sake of the money? Or in order to leave Bob alone with his expensive girl of good family? I did not even know of her existence. He went very red when that tactless cadet mentioned her. Perhaps he is secretly engaged to her. How little I know about him, although we live together! I look on him as if he were my property, and all the time he is remote from me. My property, yet infinitely remote. . . . How slender he looks in his evening clothes! A short time ago I heard him cough; he must take great care of his health. . . ."

The sadness that suddenly seemed to emanate from the silent Peter Ilych made the young people ill-at-ease. The conversation flagged. The dreamer in the cheap suit sat down at the piano and began to play. He played a sweet little melody decorated with limpid runs. The young man had a good technique and a particularly pleasant touch.

"I suppose that is by Rubinstein?" asked one of the two Lütkes in a rather tinny voice.

"Of course not," said Vladimir on the defensive. "It is by Chopin."

Peter Ilych stood at the door leading to his bedroom. He opened it cautiously.

"Do you want to go?" asked Vladimir, who sat near the door. He was now looking really rather tired and ill. With his finger-tips he stroked Peter Ilych's hand which hung at his side. He coughed as he did this. "Life in a great city is not good for him," thought Tchaikovsky. "This winter was too much for his very delicate health; he undertook too much and taxed his strength. Perhaps I was not doing him a kindness in making such a life possible for him." And he said:

"Don't let me interfere with any of you. I am tired. Moreover, I can't bear Chopin. He makes me ill. Enjoy yourself, my dear, with your friends. There are some more bottles of champagne in the tub."

*   *   *

America is a long way away. The great journey begins with the too-well-known stretch from St. Petersburg to Berlin.

There is the noise of the train wheels, always telling the same story, a worn-out story that one has known for so many years but has never really understood; it always keeps its secret and remains a monotonous mystery. Evening descends on the barren landscape. The attendant comes into the compartment to prepare the bed. One ought to go to sleep, but one's head aches.

"Why did I get into this train? Where is it taking me to? Simply away from my Vladimir. Why do I call him *my* Vladimir? He has his girl, a very expensive girl, of good family! My property, but infinitely remote from me. Ah, things were different between him and me when he was a big boy in Kamenka and my guest in Frolovskoe and he devoted himself to me, and in his childlike way collected information about my life. It was I who brought him to the great cities. He scarcely has any need of me now. Now he has the girls.

"I will stay one day in Berlin. In all the hotel rooms one finds letter paper. I will put a sheet of white paper in front of me and cover it with black signs, so that my Bob may read it and know something about my doings. He must know and feel how terribly I miss him. I will write on the letter paper that I shall find in the Berlin hotel: 'Bob, I adore you! Do you remember how I said to you once that the happiness I derived from your presence was much less great than the suffering I experienced in your absence? Far away from you, with the prospect of having to spend so many days, so many weeks, so many months, without you . . . in the face of this eternity, I realize for the first time how great is my love for you.' I will write all that to him; he must know it and feel it. My Vladimir coughs too much. He looked very thin in his evening suit; one must watch his health. He should have a quite remarkable future—as a poet or as a musician. But perhaps he will not live long. His sister Vera died young. God is in the habit of taking His most delightful children early. No, I won't allow myself to think like this. Bob must live a long time. Bob is my heir. . . . I have no ideas for the *Nutcracker*. I'm played out, I'm done for. Bob loves all the Nastenkas in St. Petersburg; he turned red when they spoke about them. . . ."

Modest Tchaikovsky met his brother at the Gare du Nord in Paris. Peter Ilych embraced and kissed him rather casually.

Good Modest had looked forward to this meeting with all his heart; and now he could not help noticing that his elder brother was not in a very good mood, nor feeling very friendly. When Modest saw that Peter Ilych's face was flushed a deep red and that the veins stood out on his forehead he was alarmed.

"Did you have a pleasant journey?" asked the younger brother in a timid voice.

"Yes, thank you," said Peter Ilych. "Why, you already look quite Parisian."

Modest had grown an imperial beard and a long, pointed moustache. He wore his coat open, carried a walking-stick; his stand-up collar was very high and he wore his hat on the back of his head. This smart city get-up, carefully modeled on the fashions of the boulevards, was in amusing contrast with his gentle, good-natured face—the soft Tchaikovsky face with its sensuous mouth, deep-set eyes, and domed brow; it might have belonged to an undistinguished son of Peter Ilych.

"One acclimatizes oneself as best one can," said Modest, with the indolent coyness that was characteristic of him.

"I don't understand how anybody could willingly stay so long in foreign parts," said Peter Ilych irritably. "I am tormented by homesickness if I have to be away from Russia for a week."

"But it is so beautiful in Paris," poor Modest ventured to assert. "And after all, you yourself have lived a great deal in foreign parts."

"That was quite another matter," declared Peter Ilych contentiously. "It could never have been called 'willingly'; either I was ill or I had to travel for business reasons."

Both brothers knew that this was a lie; but Modest thought it undesirable to say so.

"You literary people seem entirely devoid of any patriotic feelings," observed the high-strung Peter Ilych severely. Modest shook his head in denial.

"Good Heavens!" he exclaimed. "How strange you are today!" They had taken a fiacre. During the drive to the Hôtel Richepanse Peter Ilych was nervous and taciturn.

"What are you working on?" he asked his younger brother almost threateningly, after a long pause.

"But you know," said Modest, "my play . . . it is nearly finished. I have read extracts out of it to a few friends here, and they said that this time it really is quite good."

"We must talk about our new libretto also." Peter Ilych stared in front of him with somewhat glassy eyes. He had certainly drunk too much on the journey. "I don't suppose I shall be able to spend much time with you. I have a great deal to do."

He saw how poor Modest crumpled up. At the same time Peter Ilych's heart gave him a twinge of remorse. "Why do I hurt him so?" he asked himself, suddenly horrified. "He can't help it if I am suffering, and every minute is a torment to me! . . ." Peter Ilych loved his brother Modest; he had looked after him like a father; followed his development and his literary career ambitiously and tenderly; regarded him as his nearest, truest, and most trustworthy of friends, now that he had lost Nadezhda and was seeing less of the loyal but prosaic Anatol. When he caused Modest pain, as he was now doing, he inflicted even greater pain on himself.

During the turbulent days in Paris which followed, Modest suffered as greatly as Peter Ilych. The latter was almost unintermittently on the go. Once more he paid visits to duchesses and music critics, for on March 24 his great concert was to take place. There were interviews with the conductor Colonne and the publisher Maquart. There were receptions, rehearsals, press conferences. Peter Ilych, wearing a black suit, with a white flower in his buttonhole, always in a state of tension, always with an undercurrent of irritation in his voice, spent his days partly in the carriage that conveyed him from the Champs Elysées to the grand boulevards, from Montmartre to the Faubourg St. Germain, and partly in antechambers, salons, concert halls, foyers, expensive restaurants, and theater boxes. Good

Modest, who had looked forward with so much pleasure to his great brother's visit, had to be satisfied if he was allowed to spend a few hours of an evening in his company. In the Hôtel Richepanse they came across the pianist Sophie Menter, who was giving concerts in Paris; the ambitious young Sapelnikov; and the violinist Jules Conus, who had studied at the Moscow Conservatory and was now playing in the Colonne orchestra. These were the most agreeable, most peaceful moments during these restless days. Sapelnikov, who could not allow half an hour to pass without music, improvised parodies on the pianoforte. The sound of Madame Sophie's laughter and chatter echoed through all the reception rooms in the hotel. She strewed her handkerchiefs, scent bottles, powder boxes, and purses all over chairs and carpets; she had always lost or forgotten something and would wring her hands in despair over her own absent-mindedness. She would amuse herself and the company by her indefatigable imitations of the dialect of the peasants in the Tyrol, where she had a summer residence; she would tell anecdotes designed to demonstrate the raciness and humor of these folk, but to her own boundless dismay the point would generally elude her before she reached the end of the story. As compensation for the vanished point, she would then, amid much laughter, issue an invitation: Peter Ilych must without fail come without delay to see her at her country house, Schloss Itter.

Peter Ilych left Paris as soon as the concert had taken place. It had been a much greater success than the two Tchaikovsky evenings at the Châtelet had been two years ago. He hoped to be able to find a remote little foreign town where, knowing no one, he could work and recuperate. This time the place to which he fled was not called Magdeburg, nor Hanover, but Rouen. But hotel rooms are the same everywhere. Peter Ilych spread out his notes for the *Nutcracker* on a dusty, shaky writing-table—a bad example of the Biedermeier period such as might be found equally well in Odessa, or Lübeck, or San Remo.

He made an effort to compose, but the ballet repelled him. "Why should an old fool like me try to invent melodies for a girl in a ballet skirt to prance about the stage to?" he thought angrily. "Is that my job? My talent—if I ever had anything worthy of the name—will degenerate into undignified and despicable potboiling. In any case I can't possibly have this damned ballet, as well as the opera, ready for the date specified. I will write to the director and tell him that I'll deliver the thing for the '92–'93 season. Is it worth doing at all? If I am destined to write anything more that deserves to be called music, it will have to be something entirely different, with a quite other direction. . . . Perhaps I have still a great avowal to make; maybe I still have a confession to make to the world. . . ."

Instead of working, he drank cognac and wrote letters to Vladimir. Two days later Modest arrived in Rouen. Peter was somewhat astonished by this unexpected visit; he had the impression that Modest had come with some special mission. The younger brother had a very solemn face and made evasive answers when Peter Ilych asked him what he had on his mind. "Oh, it's nothing particular," declared Modest with some embarrassment.

"Do you need money?" inquired Peter Ilych.

"No, no," said Modest.

"Can't you get on with your work?"

"Oh, it's going on all right," said Modest; "I can't complain. Besides, I am going back to Russia today."

"So at last you have become homesick?" Peter Ilych put the question with a certain satisfaction.

"Yes," said Modest. "I have become homesick."

And there the matter was left. The timid brother left Rouen without having revealed his depressing secret, the shadow of which was so clearly visible on his honest, good-humored face. A few days later, almost in a state of panic, Peter Ilych followed him to Paris, only to find, on inquiry at the Hôtel Richepanse, that Monsieur Modest Tchaikovsky had left for Russia two days earlier. "Why was he suddenly in such a hurry?" thought the perplexed Peter Ilych. He now began to miss Modest very much and became remorseful because he had been so impatient and irritable with him during the past few weeks. Without his excellent brother he found himself feeling lonely in Paris. In a dejected mood he sauntered down towards the boulevards. In the neighborhood of the Opéra there was a reading-room where Russian newspapers were to be found. Tchaikovsky was in the habit of sometimes spending an hour there. "This morning is dreary," he thought now; "what shall I do? I will read the newspapers. There may be some amusing gossip from Petersburg to cheer me up."

The reading-room was full of people. The only available Russian paper was in the possession of a fat asthmatic lady of ripe age. Peter Ilych had to be patient; he turned over the pages of a couple of Paris humorous papers and was annoyed by the foolish and primitive pretexts employed by the purveyors of this kind of merchandise to seduce their readers with the naked breasts of women and undraped thighs in fanciful positions. At last, breathing heavily, the asthmatic lady rose. With a smart movement, Peter Ilych grabbed the Moscow journal, for which an unshaven student had been lying in ambush. The paper was several days old. "I shan't learn anything new from this, nothing amusing," thought Peter Ilych peevishly. At that moment his eyes fell on a large announcement framed in black: "Death in Kamenka near Kiev: Mrs. Alexandra Ilyinisha Davidov."

Sasha was dead. Vladimir's mother was dead. His sister, with whom he had shared thousands of common memories, was dead. She had taken all her memories with her. She had gone to the mother whom all obedient children ought to follow, whom all children ought to obey all the time: that was a lesson which both Sasha and Pierre had learned from Fanny.

Peter Ilych sat motionless in the overcrowded Paris reading room. Next to him sat a group of French gentlemen excitedly discussing some political scandal. Through the half-open door came the noise of the Place de l'Opéra. With eyes that no longer saw, Peter Ilych stared at the Moscow journal for which the unshaven student lay in ambush.

This, then, was the secret that had been tormenting Modest, to reveal which he had come to Rouen. He had not found it in his heart to break his doleful news. No doubt he thought that if he had done so it would have meant the abandonment of the American tour. "Perhaps I *will* give it up. I ought to go back to Kamenka to comfort Bob. Bob will cry. I have never seen Bob's face wet with tears. If I went to Kamenka now I should find it drenched with tears. Strange that *I* can't weep."

Slowly Peter Ilych got up. Shaking his head, he walked through the reading-room and out through the door. His lips moved like those of an old man babbling to himself. "Strange, strange," he muttered. People looked at him and smiled. The unshaven Russian student had pounced on the Moscow journal.

Should he telegraph canceling the American tour? The temptation to do so was great, but Peter Ilych did not give way to it. He needed the dollars: he had already banked too much on these additional earnings. How would he be able to go on supporting Modest and Vladimir if he threw away lightly such great financial possibilities as this? Nevertheless he had in honesty to admit to himself that these reasonable considerations were not the sole reason why he decided to carry out his program, which was to travel to Le Havre and there embark on April 8 in the French ship *La Bretagne* to New York. The prospect of this excursion into the New World, this complete change of surroundings, charmed him as much as it scared him. He was seized by the thought: "Perhaps I shall breathe more freely on the other side of the great ocean. Perhaps I shall be quite another man in the land where, so people say, the possibilities are boundless. It must be a marvelous country, vibrant with youth and strength; I might find that invigorating. I am curious to see what sort of reception they will give me over there. Will they immediately recognize that their invitation was founded on a misunderstanding? Undoubtedly it has transpired in the meantime what I really am: that is to say, neither a great composer nor even a genuine Russian, but an entirely second-rate creature composed of the most diverse of base elements. Of course they know all about it over there. But maybe they will have the kindness not to let me feel this from the beginning. . . ."

The invigoration which Peter Ilych expected from his stay in America was certainly not afforded him by the journey thither. The *Bretagne* was a large and handsome steamer, as comfortable as a good hotel; but Peter Ilych found the time he spent in his cabin, in the smoking-room, in the dining-room, and on deck altogether intolerable. The sea both bored and alarmed him. It was with complete dismay that he saw the coast recede, grow indistinct, shrivel into a gray streak, fade, and finally disappear. He discovered that the desert of flat unending stretches of water and the monotony of the surrounding horizon had for him nothing of the powerful appeal possessed by the sea when viewed from land with the breakers beating against the shore.

For the first few days of the journey the sea was calm; but now the waves began to rise and the ship to roll. Peter Ilych, however, to his own astonishment, was not seasick; but he was alarmed. The ship *La Bretagne,* elegantly and comfortably furnished though it was, was nevertheless only a cockleshell helplessly placed in this terrifying infinity of agitated waters. Might not the waves at any moment rise a little higher and reach a disastrous point when they would be out of control? The elegant hotel-ship would then be rent asunder and shattered. It was not beyond the powers of the Far-off Inscrutable One, Whose purposes and plans we cannot know or foresee, to allow such a thing to happen.

The ship *La Bretagne* would go down: Peter Ilych quite seriously faced this possibility. The waves looked to him exactly as if they intended presently to pour destructively into the smoking-room, the dining-room, and the carpeted lounge. And then one would be drowned. Very well—and what next? Had one not time and time again called ardently on Death, the dark friend? Had one not turned to him for the sweetest comfort of all? Well, he was probably quite near. And now one was afraid. The inconsistency of human nature is scandalous and ridiculous!

Peter Ilych could not endure it in the swaying dining-saloon: it seemed to him incongruous and absurd to consume a menu of eight courses, while in the storm that raged and roared in the outer darkness the waves were preparing to swallow at a gulp the cook, the kitchen-boys, and the stewards, the plates and dishes and the people who ate from them. Furthermore, he found the fellow-passengers with whom he usually sat at table particularly unbearable. They included a Canadian bishop who had come from Rome, where he had been blessed by the Pope; his secretary; and a German-American married couple from Chicago with two young daughters. The conversation turned on an unfortunate fellow-traveler who the previous day had jumped into the sea from the deck of the second class and had been drowned. The excitement on board had been enormous; the sirens had screeched, the ship had stopped, the lifeboat had been lowered—but the suicide had disappeared. They found a note in his cabin, covered with almost illegible signs, out of which the following words in German were finally deciphered: "I am innocent . . . the boy weeps . . ." It meant nothing. The unhappy fellow was probably out of his mind.

This melancholy accident had occupied the minds of all souls on board the *Bretagne* for the past twenty-four hours and still provided a topic of conversation for the Canadian bishop and the German-American family.

"God have mercy on his soul!" said the churchman. "The unfortunate man has committed the worst sin, in fact the unforgivable sin. Of all the deadly sins self-slaughter is regarded by God with greatest anger."

The lady from Chicago ventured to wonder whether the fact

that the man was mentally deranged might not be considered an extenuating circumstance; but the bishop would not hear of this: he felt it his duty to say frankly that in these frivolous times people spoke too readily of mental derangement when dealing with things that were essentially of a wicked, sinful character. The secretary nodded in agreement; the lady from Chicago did not venture to speak again; the paterfamilias—proprietor of several slaughter-houses—cleared his throat solemnly, while one of the girls said in a high shrill voice: "If the man was really mad, one would have noticed it before. Madmen always have a queer expression on their faces."

Peter Ilych, rising, asked permission to retire: he felt ill, which, in view of the rough sea, everybody understood. He stamped through the dining-saloon, whose floor rose and fell, went up the companionway to the deck. What hatred he now felt for the bishop, his secretary, and the married couple from Chicago, not to mention their daughters! What compassion, on the other hand, for the unfortunate who had been able to find no way out of his difficulties save to plunge into the sea—what brotherly sympathy with him! The absurd note: "I am innocent . . . the boy weeps . . ." seemed to him to paraphrase a secret to which neither the bishop nor the slaughter-house owner possessed the key, and a problem to whose nature he, Peter Ilych, was no stranger.

Peter Ilych's mind was so much taken up with the unfortunate fellow-human from the second class, on whose soul—according to the Canadian bishop's judgment—God would have no mercy, that he even forgot his fear of the sea and of being wrecked. He walked up and down the promenade deck, which at this hour was empty of people.

What was the song the waves sang to him? Perhaps it was the same as he had heard in the rumble of the railway train. "I know now what it meant," he thinks as he paces the dark deck. "It is the song of vanished faces. It is the song of those who have been obliterated, have slipped away, drifted away, and disappeared, beyond my reach. How many have already gone from me and transformed themselves into shadows, or live a life in which I have no share and play no part! Has not Désirée's face vanished as certainly as Sasha's? Is not the loathsome face of that woman, Antonina, who is still alive somewhere, as remote as the face of dear Fanny who is long since dead? Has not Apukhtin disappeared from my life as surely as Nikolay Rubinstein or my poor Kotek? Once Apukhtin, my evil genius, tried to play his game of seduction all over again by resurrecting himself in the form of that extraordinarily attractive boy who stood next to me in the foyer of the Cirque Medrano and later on at the bar. But even that face, which had a particular power of attraction for me, I let slip away. Faces that have meant so much to me slip away . . . for instance, that of dear Edvard Grieg, who stimulated and invigorated me with his brave, defiant music—gone! The face of Siloti, the beautiful stranger, shining with the cold light of ambition; the nervous, tormented face of my friend Bülow, the face of Nikisch, the face of Busoni! And why have I never seen Brodsky again; was he not my good friend? And Volody, the boy with whom I had dinner in Constantinople; and the little singer in Florence. . . . My life crumbles in episodes and fragments; it is devoured and tormented by the past. Gone; completely vanished into the abyss, the face of my unknown soul-friend, the faithless, cruel Nadezhda! And nearest of all to me at this moment is the face of my mother, the austere and lovable, admonishing and alluring! I move among shadows. I am surrounded only by the dead. How old am I? I must be age-old; I must be the oldest of men. *Monsieur, votre maladie est inguérissable, mais on peut vivre avec elle jusqu'à cent ans.* . . . Who among the living has remained near to me? Vladimir, my dear child. But did not even his features appear in the procession of vanished faces, in the cycle of shadows? Alas, that the most familiar face of all should already seem half-estranged! Already my little Vladimir seeks the society of others whom he will love, and his love for them will be differ-

ent from his love for an old man like me. But I must not pursue
this thought to its conclusion; it is a thought that leads to despair; I should collapse under it; I should totter and fall into the
sea—the terrifying sea into which my poor desperate brother, the
'Innocent' one, jumped—the abyss out of which the Song of
Lost Faces rises."

Peter Ilych decided to visit his friends in the second class:
that would give another turn to his thoughts. In the railway
train between Rouen and Le Havre he had become acquainted
with a Paris clerk who was emigrating to America. He was a
jolly, enterprising fellow and Peter Ilych took pleasure in his
society. Furthermore, in the second class there were also six
young ladies very gay to behold: these were the "Six Butterflies," who were on their way to New York accompanied by their
manager; there they would sing, prance about, and show their
legs at a great variety theater. This society was much more
congenial to Peter Ilych than that of the Canadian bishop and
the slaughter-house proprietor and his family.

He found the six merry ladies and the jolly clerk gathered in
the manager's small smoke-filled cabin. One of the butterflies
was singing an indecent ditty to a guitar accompaniment; the
the clerk smacked his lips with enjoyment, while the manager
remained calm and detached; indeed, he even had comments
to make on the diction of the pretty little thing entrusted to his
care.

Peter Ilych was greeted with loud rejoicing, and at once had
to order drinks. As he thereupon secured two bottles of cognac,
several of the butterflies planted kisses on his nose and cheeks,
while the clerk declared hilariously that the old Russian uncle
was a great sport. The pretty little thing with the faulty technique sang another song, the obscene point of which was perfectly obvious. Peter Ilych asked if the ladies and gentlemen
had no fear of the ship's going down. They all laughed; but
out of politeness the clerk admitted that the sea was this evening "en effet un peu grosse." Presently they played cards. With

incredible rapidity Peter Ilych lost several hundred francs to the clerk and the manager.

As he had drunk a good deal, he now began to pour out his heart to the clerk. He explained that he felt lonely and was terribly homesick, and that he had a great terror of the strange country, America. The clerk looked at him sympathetically. *"Eh bien, mon vieux,"* he said finally, *"à votre age c'est assez naturel!"* Peter Ilych remembered that he would shortly be having a birthday. How old would he be? Fifty-one years. The clerk looked at him as at a hoary graybeard.

The manager said: "Chin up, old boy!" and poured him out a glass of cognac. One of the butterflies, playfully comforting him, caressed and kissed the old Russian uncle on the face and on the pate. On Tchaikovsky's domelike brow the rouge of her lips left an impression like a bloody stain.

* * *

His journey continues. The sea calms down; the *Bretagne* does not go to the bottom. A few days later she enters New York Harbor. Several ladies and gentlemen come on board the French steamer in order to greet the composer Tchaikovsky, one of the glories of the Old World. The president of the Music Hall Company of New York, Morris Reno, in the name of musical America welcomes the composer to the shores of the United States; slim, pretty, smiling Mrs. Reno, as representative of the women's clubs, hands him a gigantic bouquet of red roses. The journalists inquire what Mrs. Tchaikovsky's first impressions of America are; Peter Ilych assures them that he has brought no Mrs. Tchaikovsky with him, upon which a certain disappointment is expressed on the faces of the newspapermen. The bewildered celebrity is then put in a cab by Mr. and Mrs. Reno and taken to the Hotel Normandie at Thirty-eighth Street and Broadway.

The strong, youthful, rapidly developing New World receives the bearer of European fame, the latter-day classic, with enthusiastic curiosity. The New York public knows that Peter Ilych has come to conduct at the ceremonies on the occasion of opening the new Carnegie Hall, on May 5, 1891. Everything that has to do with the inauguration of that much-discussed "temple of music"—financed mostly by the fabulously rich Andrew Carnegie—appeals to the newspaper-reading masses and therefore makes "good copy." Besides, Tchaikovsky's work is famous in this country—better known here in New York, perhaps, and more whole-heartedly appreciated, than in Paris, Berlin, or Vienna.

The composer's photograph, that of an ageing man with a rounded, whitish gray beard, high forehead, a too-soft mouth, appears on the front pages. But the subject himself is now expected to supply material to go with it, and journalists besiege the Hotel Normandie. Both impressed and disappointed, they have to depart. They find no way of approach to this veiled life, and not even the least sensitive of them can be unaware of the melancholy that weighs him down. The baffled reporters say to one another: Unfortunately our famous visitor has nothing dramatic in his life; there's nothing of a sensational character to get hold of . . . and as they leave him and saunter towards Broadway, they have no inkling of the state of tension in which this monotonous existence of his runs its course, nor of the tragic Task which rules it, nor of its impressive magnitude. However, the ignorance and misunderstanding are mutual. Peter Ilych, who brings a ready-made conception of his hosts' country, is scarcely more able to appreciate the pathos of the New World, its courage, its great charm, its zest for life, than the young newspapermen on Broadway are able to appreciate the spiritual and human qualities of the Russian composer.

The famous visitor is caught up in the current of New York life; it showers honors and loving tributes upon him; he is overwhelmed by its noise, by its somewhat crude sentiment, its hospitality of truly Russian-Asiatic dimensions. He is hardly ever allowed an hour's peace, and when he chances to have a few moments to himself in his hotel he spends them in weeping: he sheds tears of exhaustion, of homesickness, of perplexity —for the phenomenon of his fame never ceases to puzzle and frighten him; it disgusts even while it flatters him, and even, to his own amazement, pleases him.

This journey to America seems to him like some marvelous and grotesque interlude in a life that appears to be rushing with ever-increasing tempo towards some dark and mysterious end. At night, when he returns to the hotel, fatigued by fêting and junketing, he tries to pull himself together and take stock, in order that he may come to the point of writing a full and lucid letter to Modest or Vladimir. But he finds that the impressions in his tired head are all muddled and confused. . . . Mr. Reno had given a great dinner, which had lasted from half-past seven till eleven o'clock; all the gentlemen had been presented with boutonnieres of lilies-of-the-valley, and all the ladies with roses; such things did not happen even in the finest Moscow and St. Petersburg houses. In addition to this, every guest had received a photograph of the composer in whose honor all this splendor had been arranged. With the ices were served little sweetmeats on which motives from the works of the guest of honor were beautifully inscribed, a charming attention which pleased both the composer and his admirers. The small, gray-haired man who was particularly attentive to the Russian guest was Andrew Carnegie; though he possessed countless millions of dollars, he was affable and even amusing; moreover he appeared to be a great lover of music, and particularly of Russian music. A very powerful and important little gentleman, but a good sort: everybody referred to him as a philanthropist and patron. It was considered good form among these enormously rich gentlemen of the New World to play the role of philanthropists and patrons of art; it was a sort of "indulgence" which they paid to society in return for the vast sums which they made out of society. Peter Ilych heard astonishing things about the charming, good-natured, music-loving little Carnegie; for instance, that he tried to compel the workers whom he employed in his enormous business to visit the libraries he had benevolently established in their interest. In order that they should have nothing left over with which to buy naughty intoxicating drinks, he paid them quite remarkably low wages; thus they were forced to fill up their spare time with reading instead of drinking. With the money he saved on wages he was able to build yet more libraries and still have a trifle over for himself. A very original fellow! He did not talk to Peter Ilych about money matters, but about Russian choirs, which he wanted to have brought to America. . . . Various people were particularly attentive to Tchaikovsky, for instance, Mr. Ferdinand Mayer, joint proprietor of the firm of pianoforte manufacturers, Knabe and Mayer, who showed the Russian visitor many of the sights of New York: the palaces on Fifth Avenue and the new thirteen-story buildings on Broadway, which rose to heaven, remarkably bare and terrifying, cheek by jowl with buildings of one and two stories and half-demolished houses; Brooklyn Bridge; the cellar of the Mint; the roof gardens from which one had such fine views; and the Athletic Club with its swimming-pool and gymnasium with the most up-to-date equipment. He also invited him to dinner, with oysters and champagne, at Delmonico's famous and expensive restaurant. Peter Ilych could not help asking himself why Mr. Mayer lavished these attentions upon him. A few days later it transpired that the hospitable gentleman was desirous of having Tchaikovsky's good opinion of the pianofortes of Messrs. Knabe and Mayer; these had to be appraised as the best in the world—hence the sight-seeing trips and the expensive meals: nothing is given for nothing; everything has to be paid for; everything has its price.

One ought to be businesslike and decide to stay here for a few years; one would quickly earn a lot of money and be able to subsidize Vladimir and Modest in really fine style, and in due course pay back to Madame von Meck all that she had once pressed upon one. The pianist Adele Aus der Ohe, for instance, who had come here penniless four years ago, had already amassed a fortune of some quarter of a million dollars from her nationwide tours—the indefatigable lady! Yes, this was the proper course for those who had such strength at their disposal as this pianist had, a tough and tender creature. But Peter Ilych found that already the demands which these few days made upon him were almost more than he could take; to cope with the situation, at least once a day one had to give way unrestrainedly to tears.

In addition to the strenuous sight-seeing and the even more exhausting social obligations, there were rehearsals at Carnegie Hall. Not that Tchaikovsky's *Coronation* March—the only piece he was to conduct on the occasion of the gala concert— required a great deal of preparation; but it would have been impolite not to attend the rehearsals of his colleague, Walter Damrosch—especially since it had been his (Damrosch's) idea to invite Peter Ilych Tchaikovsky.

The opening concert on May 5 turned out to be quite a glamorous and colossal affair. "All New York" was there—including little Mr. Carnegie, John D. Rockefeller, Secretary of State James G. Blaine (Walter Damrosch's father-in-law), Henry Clay Frick, and more than five thousand other more or less distinguished personalities. There were endless speeches— the dullest one delivered by Bishop Henry C. Potter—followed by Beethoven's *Leonore* Overture No. 3. Conductor Damrosch —he was only twenty-nine and by no means unattractive, as Peter Ilych did not fail to notice—was given a cordial reception, while the one granted to the composer-conductor Tchaikovsky was polite rather than enthusiastic. His *Coronation* March, however, obviously made an impression: Peter Ilych had to return to the platform twice to acknowledge the applause.

The climax of the program was Berlioz' *Te Deum*, a novelty for the American public. Peter Ilych found it rather on the boring side, but maybe that was just because he was tired and

irritated. The next day, he had to read in the papers that the
Te Deum was a great work of art, in contrast to his March,
which was described as "pleasant but undistinguished." As for
his personality, it hurt his vanity to find himself depicted as a
"rather stout gentleman, approximately sixty years old, good-
natured and a little clumsy." He was offended: they made him
ten years older than he actually was!

He had to conduct concerts in Baltimore and Philadelphia;
and he visited Niagara Falls. On May 16, the Metropolitan
Club in Washington gave a dinner for him, followed by a reception at the Russian Embassy. Then he had to stand some more
hectic days in New York.

Homesickness was at its most poignant when he heard Russian spoken. At such moments the longing to hear a familiar
voice—in fact, Vladimir's voice—afflicted him like a sudden
illness. ("Why have I gone so far away from you? A day without you is a weariness and a waste.")

A certain mysteriousness clung about some of the Russians
who called on their famous compatriot at the Hotel Normandie
—they seemed to be almost as furtive and suspicious as the
sinister refugees in Clarens. Maybe they were preparing, or
had even already taken a share in, certain assassinations—
Nihilists and anarchists! Peter Ilych did not feel altogether comfortable in their society, but was nevertheless very friendly to
them and even gave them money when they asked for it; partly
because he was interested in and moved by their hard and
unusual life, but partly also because he knew that these exiles
had many views and sympathies in common with young Vladimir—that they fought and suffered for convictions which the
boy so enthusiastically proclaimed.

Tchaikovsky could not help thinking of Vladimir and his
revolutionary utterances when he witnessed a workers' demonstration on Broadway: a very long procession—five thousand
strong, so he was told; they carried red flags and banners bearing slogans such as: "Comrades, we are slaves in free America!

We will not work more than eight hours!" "I ought to ask little Carnegie if there are grounds for these complaints," thought Peter Ilych, who was much impressed. "Even in free America, it looks as if everything were not as it should be. Probably my clever Bob is right and this century of progress has still some ugly and barbarous features."

However, he forgot to broach the subject to little Carnegie—who would certainly have been competent to express an opinion—although he had an opportunity of doing so at the great farewell banquet which the millionaire gave in honor of the composer, in the course of which he referred to him publicly as "the uncrowned king of music." This feast was the last which that marvelous but grotesque interlude—the American tour—had to offer Peter Ilych. He still had a series of farewell visits to pay. On his return from these fatiguing journeys he always found interviewers and female autograph-hunters awaiting him in the hall of his hotel. One of the ladies handed him a somewhat bulky plaster replica of the Statue of Liberty as a farewell gift. "But they wouldn't let the thing cross the Russian frontier," said the exhausted Peter Ilych, attempting a joke. Another admirer, with a murderous gesture, thrust a small, hard bunch of roses in the middle of his face and hurt one of his eyes; as she did so the aggressive lady shouted in an angry, piercing voice: "Long live the master!" as she did everything in her power to bring about his untimely end. Peter Ilych stood in the middle of the hotel hall, his swollen eye streaming, surrounded by newspaper men, ladies, and photographers; and suddenly he was reminded of Johannes Brahms and his Amazon-like adorer, Miss Brown. "What grotesque figures the 'Masters' cut in these times!" he thought, dabbing his wounded eye with his handkerchief. "Scorn is inflicted on us as payment and penance for our fame."

Tchaikovsky made the return voyage in a German steamer, the *Fürst Bismarck*, which was making the journey from New York to Hamburg for the first time. Peter Ilych tried to work on the way back; he made notes for a new symphony—the Sixth. But he felt depleted; the rhythms and harmonies which ran through his overworked brain were not those he sought or believed in. No, with such themes as these he could not content himself; something different had to be created and brought to perfection; the Task demanded something else—a complete outpouring, an all-embracing confession had to be made, a great lamentation had to be sounded; what was hidden must be revealed. This ultimate goal must be reached and he was still far off, still very far off. . . .

◇◇◇◇◇◇

FOURTH MOVEMENT
Adagio lamentoso

◇◇◇◇◇◇

R ICH IN QUALITIES and events; endowed with enormous perceptions and powers; burdened with problems and unfulfilled aspirations; dismal and brilliant; earthbound, yet rich in daring speculations; brutal, yet gifted with ethical sensibility; pathetically inadequate in all technical knowledge; dipping with ill-informed ingenuity into the future; rich in contradictions, defeats, and triumphs; rich in mental-moral impulses, and repulsive in its avarice, materialism, pseudo-morality, and hypocritical hollowness; courageous in self-criticism; the physiognomy and the surface of the globe fantastically changed—thus the great nineteenth century takes its place in history.

The century bestowed fame lavishly. Its prizes were showered extravagantly on a host of its children: history records the names of those whose triumphs gave unity to the epoch. The century exhibited itself in all its fine qualities and most ambitious claims through a regiment of great personalities and groups of talented individuals. Great men of action, philosophers, and men of artistic achievement represented the problems and triumphs of the epoch in all its splendor.

These bearers of imperishable glory, Europe's latter-day classics, present themselves to us as enigmatic giants. Every one of them, for all his stature and power, had some shortcoming, his vulnerable spot, so that the glance we give these dubious great ones is composed as much of pity as of awe; it is a sight that cannot but stir one's deep emotions.

We have allowed our awed and pitying glance to rest on one of these figures. He is not one of the greatest of his race—far from it. But we surmise, indeed we know, that he belongs to the company of the elect. We discovered that he was endowed with their creative power and weighed down by their sadness.

Our awed and pitying glance cannot get its fill of his melancholy, nor of the noble defiance with which he overcomes it and transmutes it into art. How we love the spectacle of his pathetic struggles! For this difficult son of the waning century and contributor to its culture is always struggling: against the devastating pain of the loneliness to which his most individual and personal characteristics condemn him; against the torment of doubt with which he regards his own talent—a talent composed of many contradictory elements—and which leads him to judge and often to condemn his own achievement. He fights; he arouses opposition; he will not give way—therefore he is a hero. He feels that he is vowed to a higher mission—therefore he is humble and religious. Every day he is confronted with the temptation to yield, to desist from striving, to lay down his tools. But always, after a profound and bitter internal conflict, he pulls himself violently together and starts again. He behaves like one who has some mysterious and very exact message to deliver and may not give way to fatigue so long as a single word, a single note of this message remains locked in his breast. He goes on and on. It is the message that drives him on. The traveler sees landscapes change and faces change; but he remains alone with his message. He leaves one station after another behind him.

At which station do we find him now?

We find him on his way from the New World back to the Old—on his way home. The New York press has bidden him a cordial and respectful farewell. One paper, the *Herald,* has informed its readers that Peter Ilych ranks with the most illustrious figures of his epoch: "Bismarck, to head the list, of course; Edison, Tolstoy, Sarah Bernhardt, Ibsen, Herbert Spencer, Dvořák, and Tchaikovsky."

He does not feel like an Olympian, however, as he is sitting there in his stateroom, trying to work on a new symphony. His journey will not be long—the newly constructed *Fürst Bismarck* crosses the Atlantic in six days and fourteen hours!—which is a comforting little thought. But even one week seems an eternity to the lonely, neurotic tourist. And then there will be other journeys, more weeks of anguish and solitude.

Places and faces change. They appear and disappear. Peter Ilych gazes on them and after them, with his soft brooding glance. One station after another he leaves behind him. His life shall be without peace: such is the merciless law. His pilgrimage continues, always more swiftly, towards some obscure goal, towards some mysterious fulfilment.

There is one peaceful point in the monotony of unrest and the torment of hurry: Vladimir. Whether Bob, the good and much-loved nephew, has spent the day with his uncle or not, at night, before composing himself for sleep, Peter Ilych conjures up the slender figure and familiar face. It is Bob's voice that talks or sings to him until he achieves the longed-for sleep. This sleep is not induced and coveted merely as repose for a night, but as Repose its very self, as the ultimate peace, as the final rest, as Death.

It is the recurring duty of the overgrown yet graceful youth to accompany the ageing man and soothe him into the sleep of death. And during this process the countenance of the boy, who is somewhat aloof and yet is his kin, is gradually transformed and takes on the lines of another face—the most familiar and most beloved of all. The figure by the bedside, who chatters in a drowsy voice, melts into another figure: a woman's motherly figure. It has the grace of the Knight, the gentleness and the severity of the Mother. Vladimir and the Mother have become one. The beauty of the mother and the charm of the boy are combined in a slender form that is no longer womanish, and no longer masculine. She beckons to him to follow her. She admonishes and pleads. One must obey one's mother; all good children learn that. It would be a dire sin obstinately to resist her admonishing and her pleading. A day without you is an offense. The mother and Vladimir are combined in a mystical union of love which is both tender and austere. . . .

Needless to say, the good nephew had no suspicion of the extremely odd games which his honored benefactor, great friend, and beloved uncle played with his countenance and his voice. How should he know that he, as a motherly angel of death, floated nightly into his uncle's bedroom? Doubtless, if he had known, he would have been alarmed, perhaps, even frightened. But the artful Peter Ilych divulges nothing. With the greatest of care he separates young Bob who day in day out provides such exhilarating companionship from the mysterious slender figure with the double countenance who rises up nightly a quarter of an hour before sleep. For this second Vladimir, this knight of Death, he feels a rapturous, overpowering love mingled with awe and indeed with fear; for the living, breathing Bob, however, he feels the most natural and grateful tenderness.

He feels grateful to him every hour of the day, for Bob brings the buoyancy and vigor of youth into the gloomy existence of the ageing man. He brings his passionate interests, his love of pleasure, his thirst for knowledge, his eager criticism of things as they are, his gaiety, his fine youthful seriousness. With his head full of fervent thoughts and his luggage full of new books, the tall young man comes to Maidanovo, accompanied by one of his friends, Count Lütke or young Napravnik. The young people fill the house with their laughter and their discussions. Once again there are games and long walks. Once more Alexey has to provide his young master's favorite dishes. Vladimir decides that it is even more beautiful in Maidanovo than it had been in Frolovskoe. For Tchaikovsky, who remains nowhere long, has sold the property in Frolovskoe because the ruthless cutting down of the forest has upset and embittered him, and he has moved back into his old house in Maidanovo near Klin, halfway between Moscow and St. Petersburg, where indeed for a long time there had been no forest to boast of.

Is it possible for him, who made a point of storing up memories—only to cringe before them and allow them to wound him

—to be happy in a place where every stick and stone reminds him of a life that is past and gone? He was in fact happy here when Bob and his friends came to stay with him. Immediately after they went, depression and boredom set in. When his loneliness became quite insupportable, he went and joined forces with the young people in Moscow or St. Petersburg. There he spent an amusing but expensive time. The striking, indeed rather astonishing group were to be seen in all the theaters, in all the expensive restaurants of both capitals: the gray-bearded man with a noisy following of students, music pupils, and cadets; and sometimes Modest was also with them. Peter Ilych loved to be exploited by young people. The publisher Jürgenson often pulled a long face over the demands for money which the composer made, demands that were apt to mount up alarmingly at such times. If he did not soon deliver the new ballet and the one-act opera, he would be heading for a financial crisis. So Peter Ilych had willy-nilly to go back to Maidanovo in order to get down to work on the two compositions.

His antagonism to the ballet and the opera did not diminish. The torment he suffered as he worked on them was worthy of a higher and more serious purpose. If he were once again to put all his strength into a work—and in order to achieve anything at all he found that he *must* put all his strength into it—then there was only one work worthy of such devotion, only one work that possessed him body and soul: the symphony which should be final and all-embracing. He turned constantly to the notes for the symphony which he had made in the narrow, swaying cabin on the ocean-liner; and constantly he had to lay them aside, disappointed. No, they were not the Sixth Symphony. That had not yet come to birth within him: it still held back. He waited for it as for a miracle. And he turned to the work which he had to do as a duty—trifles paid for with so much suffering.

True, he sometimes turned out charming things—greatly to his own astonishment—he had to admit this. The *"Valse des*

fleurs" from the *Nutcracker* Suite, for instance—wasn't that an
enchanting inspiration, a very pretty and attractive piece of
music?

Peter Ilych played the *"Valse des fleurs"* to fat Laroche who
was on a visit to Maidanovo. "But that is *superb!"* exclaimed fat
Laroche, whose heavy mind was rarely moved to such lively
expressions of praise. "What delightful things still go in and
out of that gray pate of yours, old Peter!"

Old Peter laughed inwardly. "Yes, it is a miracle," he said
at last. "I still turn out some pleasant pages. A melody like that
falls quite gratefully on the ear, doesn't it? Yes, I know; I know
it sounds quite nice; one doesn't forget it in a hurry—one goes
on humming it on one's way back from the theater. For that
very reason lots of people will raise their eyebrows in a haughty
fashion when they hear it—and not only the superior Germans,
but also the superior Russians."

"You can afford to despise the superior Germans and the
superior Russians too," said Laroche. "You're worth the whole
lot of them put together—for you have inspiration. Believe me,
my instinct did not go far astray years ago when I spotted you,
old friend." It was only rarely that Laroche put so many consecutive sentences together.

"César Cui will sneer, and Master Brahms will shrug his
shoulders," declared Tchaikovsky in a resigned voice. "Both of
them will say that it is Parisian, superficial stuff. Very well,
then; perhaps there is a bit of the Parisian in me. Is that a
crime? Is it a crime occasionally to please people with a "Waltz of
the Flowers" and give them something they can whistle on their
way home from the theater?"

"So far from being a crime, it is a great service," said Laroche
with a dignified air.

"It was not for nothing that I was discovered, so to speak, by
the great Johann Strauss, the Waltz King, and first brought
before the public," said Peter Ilych, his face lighting up with
pleasure at the memory of the Vienna master. "That was not

altogether without significance," he added after a thoughtful pause, looking pleased.

The two old friends sat a few moments without speaking. "But naturally these little jokes are not what I ought to be devoting myself to just now," said Peter Ilych at last, as if after extended deliberation he were delivering a verdict. "As you can well believe, something of a quite different order must now be accomplished."

Laroche nodded. Peter Ilych had never spoken to him about the scheme which occupied his mind—the great, all-embracing symphony that he was planning; but they had known each other so well and so long that either of them could conjecture the thoughts and intentions of the other.

"Yes, yes," said Laroche after another pause, and he nodded his heavy head in a melancholy fashion. "If only one could carry out what one has in mind! I, for instance, in all my long life, have brought nothing, absolutely nothing, to a conclusion —not a single one of the projects I had in my mind at the time we got to know each other at the Conservatory. You have had successes on and off—I, absolutely nothing. What are a few articles on music? Not worth talking about, not worth talking about! And here are we, a couple of old fogeys, sitting here and drinking vodka."

The fat fellow sat with his heavy, melancholy face on one side; his eyes, made narrow by the encircling folds of flesh, blinked wearily through the smoke of the cigarettes. "But I wonder what is making me jabber so much this evening," he added before lapsing into complete silence.

Laroche was like that. Peter Ilych knew quite well why he did not wish to have this faithful and good friend very often in his society. A crippling hopelessness emanated from him. A day started with him was a day half lost. For the portly melancholiac would say at breakfast: "I wonder why we got up? We might just as well have stayed in bed. In fact it would have been a much more reasonable thing to have done." Then he would moan about some pain or other in some part of his body; and would spend the day in an armchair in a state of lethargy.

Peter found this spectacle very disturbing. It depressed him to observe how a man of such great talent should lose hold of himself and become so completely demoralized. The habits and opinions of this friend of his youth were the more odious to him because he did not find them at all difficult to understand and because they were by no means remote from himself; indeed, fat Laroche gave way to moods against which Peter Ilych battled daily and which he daily overcame.

Moreover, the lazy colossus brought him bad luck. It was during that dark autumn week when he was staying at Maidanovo that something happened that shattered and frightened Peter Ilych.

Peter Ilych carried his beautiful watch, the most costly and by far the handsomest thing he possessed, in his pocket. Occasionally, when he went out, he would leave it on his bedside table, the more keenly to enjoy the sight of it when he returned. It was only very rarely that Laroche joined him on these long afternoon walks; as a rule he was far too lazy to undertake anything so strenuous. But today, Peter Ilych had persuaded him to join him. The silent walk had stretched itself out and it was already dark as they drew near the house. Peter Ilych went to his bedroom to change his shoes. With his first glance he sought his treasure. He uttered a low cry and fumbled with trembling fingers among bicarbonate of soda boxes, valerian bottles, photographs, and French books: the watch had vanished.

In his dismay, Peter Ilych was at once certain that it had gone for good, was lost forever. "I shall never see it again," he muttered. Then he called Alexey, Laroche, and the cook. The matter was discussed; all kinds of conjectures were made; the police were informed.

As no possible shadow of suspicion could fall on Alexey or the cook, there could only be one explanation. Somebody must have broken into the house; the thief must have come from the high road. Unfortunately Alexey had forgotten to shut the window. An agile man could no doubt easily climb the wall. True, there was no trace of anybody either on the wall, on the window-ledge, or in the room itself. Nothing was missing except the most beautiful thing of all; nothing had been moved; everything else was in order. It looked as if the burglar had had one object and one object only—to steal the watch; as if he had known exactly where it was lying, and with great dexterity had seized hold of the costly timepiece which was the aim and object of his daring expedition.

"I shall never see my lovely watch again," said Peter Ilych to the police officers, struggling hard to be calm as his eyes filled with tears.

"Rest assured, your worship, that everything humanly possible will be done to restore your property to you," answered the officer.

"Thank you," said Peter Ilych. But as soon as the sergeant of the police had gone he turned to fat Laroche and declared, weeping bitterly: "The watch is gone; I feel quite sure of it. I shall never again enjoy the sight of the Apollo and the Maid of Orleans. It is really most upsetting, terribly upsetting!"

"We will give you a new one," said Laroche, comforting him as if he were a child. "I will get contributions from all our friends and we will buy you a new one which will be even more beautiful than the old."

"But it was my talisman!" moaned Peter Ilych, unwilling to be comforted. "Its disappearance has undoubtedly some dreadful significance. It won't be long now before I come to an end too!"

"How can you be so superstitious?" said Laroche, his voice quavering; he spent half his life consulting fortune-tellers and in terror of every kind of sign and symbol. "You see, you will live another thirty years without the watch."

"Do you know what I believe, what I can't help fearing?" With a mysterious gesture Peter Ilych drew his friend nearer to him. "This thief, this burglar, was an emissary from Madame von Meck! My treacherous guardian angel wanted to rob me of the most beautiful memento I had of her. She knows, of course, that it is my talisman. She sent the thieving messenger, like a murderer!"

"Oh, but that is sheer fancy!" cried Laroche, whose face wore an expression of terror. "The police will soon lay hands on the real thief."

"Oh, the police . . ." began Peter Ilych contemptuously.

Next day the police officers presented themselves at Tchaikovsky's house with a ragged yokel whom they had captured on the high road, and, failing anybody more suspicious, had taken to be the thief. They had put the handcuffs on him and had already given him a beating; the lad had a torn and bleeding lip and swollen eye.

"The fellow won't confess," said one of the officers, shoving the boy into the room; "but we have every reason to believe that he is the criminal."

At the sight of the harried creature, who seemed to him half-witted, Peter Ilych felt sick and full of compassion.

"Release him," he bade the officer, and he beckoned to the boy to come nearer.

"Did you steal the watch?" he asked quietly, looking at the ragged fellow with his deep-blue, soft, brooding eyes.

The boy fell down on his knees before him. Remaining on his knees, he swayed backwards and forwards in a sudden ecstasy and stretched out his manacled hands. "Forgive me, sir," he cried, and the wound on his lip broke open and the blood streamed down over his mouth and chin. "Forgive me, all-gracious sir! I did do it, God help me! I am a sinner; God has rejected me; I am damned. I have committed a great sin!" As he spoke his body rocked to and fro convulsively in despair, and his wailings mingled with the clatter of the chains of the handcuffs.

The police officers put on expressions of triumph. Peter Ilych asked very quietly, "Where is the watch?" Whereupon the boy suddenly became quite quiet and stared reproachfully and in deep astonishment at Tchaikovsky. "But I haven't got it any longer," he said, with a sly, stupid grin.

"Very well," cried one of the police officers, "we'll soon find out where he's hidden the watch." He hauled to boy to his feet. "Get up!" he shouted. "No more of this play-acting."

The second officer bowed to Peter Ilych: "Tomorrow we shall be able to bring the stolen object back to your grace."

In the meantime his colleague had pushed the boy towards the door. The latter threw a pleading look over his shoulder from his swollen eye.

"Don't beat him!" called Peter Ilych to the officer. "I beg of you not to beat him."

Twenty-four hours later the officers appeared again, this time without the boy. "We haven't been able to get anything out of him," they reported, and there was an air of exhaustion on their rough faces. "The fact of the matter is that the fellow is either a madman or a particularly clever scamp. When we were about to take him into the police station, he behaved suddenly as if he had no notion of what it was all about. He denied everything and asserted that he'd never heard anything about a watch. Between whiles he told us he was a sinner before God and was going to hell. It's quite impossible to get anything reasonable out of him."

Peter Ilych begged the officers to release the boy. "I knew quite well that my watch had gone for good," he said sadly. "This poor creature probably did not steal it."

"But what shall we do with him?" asked the tired officers, whom the strenuous task of chastising the boy, coupled with the glimpse of religious ecstasy vouchsafed them by their prisoner, had exhausted and rendered almost soft.

"Here is money for him," said Tchaikovsky, who was moved

and unhappy, remembering the bleeding lip and the low forehead with its matted hair. "He must buy food and clothes for himself. Perhaps he will find work."

The officers went off with the money. They cogitated over whether they should really hand over part of the money to the boy, so that the tiresome fellow might be induced to clear out of the district.

The talisman was never recovered. Apollo and the much-loved Maid of Orleans vanished out of Tchaikovsky's life.

"I ought never to have come back to Maidanovo," said Peter Ilych to fat Laroche. "I hate everything here. The house is under a curse. Alexey must sell it, or let it, while I am touring. Later on perhaps I will settle down in Klin. . . ."

"Why, particularly, in Klin?" inquired Laroche. "It's a horrible hole!"

"I am used to the district," said Peter Ilych. "True, Klin is an ugly place; but it lies conveniently between Moscow and Petersburg. Vladimir can come and visit me. And Alexey likes it there. He can have the house when I am dead."

During the past few days he had wept a great deal, had slept very little, and composed not at all. His face looked tired, indeed haggard; his lips and his hands showed a tendency to shiver.

"What on earth have you been writing all the time since we dispatched the little thief with the bleeding mouth?" Laroche wanted to know.

"I have been making my will," answered Peter Ilych.

The friend of his youth regarded him thoughtfully with eyes elongated by the layers of fat. "Oh, indeed," he said at last. "Who is the lucky heir to be?"

"Not you," said Tchaikovsky.

*   *   *

It was the end of October: in the capitals the season was beginning. "Let's take our share in it!" Peter Ilych decided.

"Every autumn and every winter the same old farce! One imagines one is going to enhance one's reputation enormously; one torments oneself and then gets terribly depressed; the spring comes and one has achieved nothing beyond adding a bit to one's age; one has grown more tired and worn out. So let's take our share in it once more!"

He conducted in Moscow and St. Petersburg. The audience clapped; the ladies threw flowers; the critics wrote disparaging notices: these cold douches were unceasing—they even followed the first performance in Moscow of *Pique Dame*. On the other hand, a work which Peter Ilych himself regarded as particularly unsuccessful, and which at this period he was very reluctant to rehearse, was unanimously praised by all the papers. "One can count on the instinct of these people being unsound," said Tchaikovsky bitterly. "*The Voyevode* is the purest rubbish." After the first performance, in his desperation he tore the score down the middle—which no doubt afforded him great relief, but was after all only an empty gesture, for there were other copies available.

Let us take our share in it! There were concerts in Kiev and there were concerts in Warsaw; there were long dinners and admiring speeches followed by collapses in dreary hotel rooms, and finally, the writing-desk, the white paper, and the letter to Bob. "Ah, my dear, once more, like last year, like every year, I count the days, the hours, the minutes to the end of my tour. All my thoughts, dear boy, are with you; for at every moment of unhappiness, at every pang of homesickness, every time my thoughts grow gloomy, then, like a ray from the sun, comes the certainty that you are there and that at some not impossibly distant date I shall see you again. Please don't think I am exaggerating. More and more I comfort myself with this same great fact: 'Yes, all is bitterness and often it is hard to bear; but never mind! For Bob exists! Somewhere, far away, in St. Petersburg, Bob sits, drudging at his work. In a month's time I shall see him again.' "

What postmark does this letter bear? It bears the postmark of Warsaw and the date of December 29, 1891. It might just as easily have borne the postmark of Hamburg; for there our sentimental traveler experiences the same desires as he experienced in Warsaw, Kiev, or anywhere else.

In Hamburg Peter Ilych ought to have conducted his *Onegin*; but he found the German version of the text far too unfamiliar. He therefore handed over the rehearsals to the young conductor at the opera house.

"I have complete confidence in you," said Tchaikovsky. "You will make a much better job of it than I could. I am quite sure that you will do it much better than I should."

The young conductor bowed without saying anything. He looked through the thick lenses of his spectacles at the famous visitor with a keenly scrutinizing glance. Peter Ilych found himself becoming uneasy under the scrutiny of those eyes; they seemed to send out a challenge, an inexorable demand. There was something intimidating, almost breath-taking, about this young man, who was laconic to the point of rudeness, with his sharp profile and a forehead already furrowed by the passionate stress of his thinking. Of a night, in the tavern frequented by artists, he was capable of a certain amount of merriment and a somewhat condescending geniality; by day, during the rehearsals, no trace of a smile disturbed the almost angry intensity of his glowing earnestness. This remarkable young conductor— his name was Gustav Mahler—took over the direction of *Eugen Onegin*. Notwithstanding the fanatical care which he devoted to every detail of the production, these "lyrical scenes" achieved only a *succés d'estime* in Hamburg. After the first performance, Peter Ilych, in his labored but ingratiating German, with its soft singing inflection, thanked the taciturn young conductor for all the trouble he had taken over the production. The vulgar and dynamic manager of the Hamburg Opera, Pollini, stood there looking like a circus master, while the young con-

ductor and the ageing composer shook hands. Afterwards Tchaikovsky took the train for Paris.

In the Hôtel Richepanse he had expected to fix up the date
of a tour in Holland. But after a few days the unrest and tor-
tured longing which he called "homesickness" became unbearable. He was also depressed by a disagreement with Monsieur
Colonne. The latter had promised to produce *Pique Dame* at the
Opéra; but, in spite of Tchaikovsky's remonstrances, the performance never took place. Thereupon Peter Ilych decided that
Paris was no longer tolerable. He said bitterly that the French
friendliness towards Russia was limited to cheering the clown
Durov when he appeared in the Folies Bergère with his 250
trained rats. He canceled the concerts in Amsterdam and The
Hague and decided once more to return to Maidanovo, no
suitable house having been found for him in Klin. Now he
wanted to work. The necessity to work—it was almost a matter
of indifference *what* work—had suddenly grown strong within
him. Both the *Nutcracker* and *Iolanthe* were waiting to be
orchestrated.

* * *

Had the hour not yet struck when he should embark on his
last and greatest effort, the final, all-embracing work which
would be a lament and a penance, and his most candid confession, his Sixth Symphony?

. . . Time speeds on; signs indicating that he has not many
more years to count on seem to multiply. Nadezhda, his guardian angel, his only true wife, has passed away from him; the
beloved watch, his talisman, his most beautiful possession, is
gone. But the time has not yet come. . . .

The year 1892, which had begun with the distracting visits
to Warsaw, Hamburg, and Paris, went on in loneliness or in
the society of people to whom he was indifferent, or in the
company of the good nephew (familiar, yet a stranger!) upon

whom he concentrated the emotions he had once dissipated in all directions. Journeys are made, visits to Moscow or Petersburg, or to the new house in Klin, situated on the edge of the town, where the high road leads into open fields—a large, roomy house, which good Alexey has arranged nicely. The time passes in work on the definitive edition of his music. He applies himself to this task with pedantic thoroughness, for on the day of fulfilment, the day of deliverance, there must be a tidy writing-table: everything must be in its place; nothing must be left to chance. Peter Ilych, the man who feels himself and calls himself the age-old man, plunges into the task of proofreading definitive arrangements of operas, symphonies, and orchestral suites, as if he were making preparations for a long journey. He insists on doing everything himself. Even the most careful helpers— Klindworth or Siloti—do not work with sufficient accuracy to satisfy him; not the smallest mistake is allowed to pass. The work when done, however important or unimportant it may be, must be presented to the Court of Justice in a flawless state, for the verdict of the stern Judge; to achieve this is Peter Ilych's last melancholy ambition.

In the meantime life goes on and isolated events seem to attain a certain importance. The new work, the *Nutcracker* Suite, has it first performance as a concert hall composition; it is warmly received, and five out of the six numbers have to be repeated. That is in the month of March in the year 1892. The *Nutcracker* does not appear as a ballet until the winter, when it is produced together with the opera *Iolanthe*. After the dress rehearsal His Majesty the Tsar sends for the composer and receives him in his box with a few complimentary phrases in nasal French. Such are the events; added to these were a few other concerts and opera first-nights. Peter Ilych gazes at them and gazes after them, with his soft brooding glance. . . .

Although he is preparing for the hour of his fulfilment and deliverance, and lives only for that, nevertheless he worries over his health, complains of pains in the heart and stomach, swallows a good deal of bicarbonate of soda and valerian drops, and goes to Vichy to take the waters. Bob goes with him. It is splendid being able to show Bob foreign parts. In Berlin the ageing uncle takes the good-looking nephew to hear *Lohengrin;* in Paris they go together to the Louvre and to a café chantant. Young Bob is enthusiastic about everything; unfortunately, however, he cannot restrain himself from sending picture postcards from Berlin, Paris, and Vichy to a certain lady in St. Petersburg; is it the same tender and expensive maiden about whom his friends had chaffed him? Peter Ilych forbears to ask. He avoids looking at the photograph which Vladimir stands on his bedside table. He endeavors to forget the existence of the receiver of letters on the banks of the Neva. But all day long he avoids touching the hair or the hand of his favorite. There comes into his mind the memory of his own first trip abroad: the elderly engineer and his odious advances. The thought pains him.

The year of expectations goes by; summer comes and merges into autumn; autumn goes by, and it is winter again. Peter Ilych listens within himself for the note which is to be the sign of his fulfilment: the ultimate theme, the melody which will contain within itself all the melodies of all his works, just as his love for Vladimir links up and combines all the emotions of his life. But the stillness continues to prevail, listen as he may. The year is almost over when the sign comes for which he has been waiting.

Peter Ilych had at last accepted the often repeated invitation from Madame Sophie Menter, and spent a few days at her country house in the Tyrol. An entirely unsuccessful visit to Vienna lay behind him: he had arranged to give a concert under the auspices of the *Musik und Theater Austellung.* "But there is no luck for me in Vienna," declared Tchaikovsky. "My love for the beautiful city is completely unrequited. Ever since Hanslick attacked my violin concerto, Vienna has been lost territory to me."

And he told his friends at Schloss Itter how miserably things had gone with him in the Austrian capital. "Not a soul to meet me at the station. That was a good beginning," he said, while Madame Sophie, Sapelnikov, a German woman singer, and a Paris music critic made indignant faces. "That was how it began—but how do you imagine it went on? The hall in which my concert was to have taken place was a large beer-hall—a beer-hall, just think of it! It smelled of drippings and roast chicken. That was where I was expected to conduct! What a bit of luck that I had not unpacked my luggage. I hurried back to my hotel. There in the corridor, in front of my room, there was a collection of people. But they had not come to welcome me— by no means; they were expecting Maestro Pietro Mascagni, whose room was next to mine. The composer of *Cavalleria* is indeed one of the most popular men in Europe at the present moment."

Sapelnikov said something respectful about Mascagni's fame, while Sophie Menter laughed over the roast chicken and the smell of beer until the tears streamed down her cheeks, and the German singer cried: "Perform music in a beer-house! That is what I call the desecration of art!" She had, alas, almost completely lost her beautiful contralto voice, and all she could do nowadays was occasionally to sing at church concerts. She had just taken part in one at Innsbruck. The Paris critic declared scornfully that such were Teutonic customs; but Sapelnikov said: "Now then, we must not run the Germans down. I have just been given a delightful reception in Munich." He was spending with his friend and teacher, Madame Menter, the few free days between a concert in Munich and the next in Florence. He wanted her to go over his Chopin program with him. Sapelnikov spent half the day sitting at the pianoforte, appearing at meals with a harassed expression on his face, and even while he was eating he would exercise his long fingers on the table, as if he could not wait until he got back to the keyboard.

"I can't help being glad about your misfortune," declared the

Menter when she had had her fill of laughter. "I have it to thank for your coming up here at last to see me. Why, I must have invited you at least fifty times. I had almost come to believe that I should never see you here."

"But I had no idea it was so lovely here," said Peter Ilych, who, with his head somewhat aslant, was enjoying the view through the large window of the snow-covered mountains.

"Unfortunately it is so cold," complained the singer, who wore one thick woolen shawl on top of another and was knitting a third. "It is only in the summer that I find Schloss Itter really comfortable." She had a mournful, significant look on her face. Invited or not invited, the singer appeared at Sophie Menter's house at every season of the year.

The lady of the house smiled amiably, first at the singer, then at Peter Ilych, and finally over at the marble bust of Liszt. "Ah," she said, "it is when everything is under snow that I find it so particularly beautiful here. . . . And during the holidays the whole crowd comes. . . . Then it is as busy here as in the waiting-room of a large railway station between the departures of two express trains." She stretched herself out comfortably in her armchair and wrapped herself more tightly in her long silk *robe de chambre*. "Oh, those guests!" she exclaimed, laughing and shaking her head. "There are always some among them whom I don't know at all."

And she recalled, with amusement and astonishment, the liveliness of the summer visitors to Schloss Itter: the ambitious youths who suddenly appeared in the music-room, perspiring with excitement, in order to beg the great pianist to let them show what they could do; the venturesome people who undertook dangerous tours in the higher mountains and had to be rescued by native mountain guides. "It is quite fantastic!" cried Madame Menter, who could never leave her guests in peace. "What strange people there are in the world! Do you know who that is?" she asked, handing Peter Ilych a framed photograph standing on a little table under the white marble bust of Liszt.

"No," answered Peter Ilych. "But it is beautiful." He could not take his eyes from the photograph. The young man whom it depicted was unusually and disturbingly attractive. The first thing that struck one was the prominent and finely formed back of the head, on which the smooth, glossy black hair gleamed; then one observed the mournful glance of the deep-set eyes under their long lashes; then the infinite sensitiveness and nobility of the outline of the face, which the young man—melancholy but eager to please—turned to the beholder in half-profile. "But he really is very handsome," repeated Tchaikovsky. "What young oriental prince is this?"

Madame Menter laughed heartily. "He is no oriental prince," she said at last. "He comes from up north. He is a Danish author; he comes here sometimes in the summer. A fascinating creature! His name is Herman Bang."

"So that is Herman Bang," said Peter Ilych slowly, his eyes still on the picture. "I have heard of him. He comes to St. Petersburg sometimes. But I had no idea he was so handsome."

"*Mon Dieu!*" laughed the Menter. "He no longer looks like that—one must admit that. *Le pauvre*, his face has become quite yellow and wrinkled. But in spite of that he is irresistible. My goodness, how often I have been amused by him! You know, he is an impossible creature; always hung about with bracelets and other kinds of jewelry. There is a soft jingling noise when he walks through the room, and when he appears in evening dress he wears a brocade waistcoat and long white glacé gloves underneath his coatsleeves: long ladies' gloves, you understand; he is a scream! But he has retained his splendid eyes; when he looks at you they pierce you through and through with a look that seems to discover everything, absolutely everything, while he remains quite innocent. Yes, I love him; he stirs my heart, and at the same time is very amusing, and you could not imagine a better friend."

"He is very effeminate and rather malicious," said the contralto. "I always have the feeling that he is laughing at me." She assumed her most dignified expression.

"But who would dare to poke fun at you, my beloved!" cried Madame Sophie. "No, no; Bang is a good fellow!"

The French music critic had met the Danish author in Paris; Sapelnikov had known him in Prague. Each of them knew an anecdote about him. "Malicious friends maintain that he is the illegitimate son of a grand duchess and a headwaiter," smiled the Frenchman. Sophie Menter gave an imitation of Bang when he appeared on the platform and read from his own works. "He took on the role of an actor far too readily, *le pauvre!*" she exclaimed. "Most of all he liked appearing at Variety shows or at the circus; those are the milieus he adores. And yet he is a *noble* creature—do you know what I mean?— And sometimes he wears an expression of great, moving, almost terrifying seriousness, as if he saw something frightful which was concealed from the rest of us. And there is no doubt that he is a great writer; of course I understand nothing about literature, but I find his books absorbing. Have you read anything of his?"

"No," answered Peter Ilych. "But you have made me curious about his things." He looked at the photograph again.

"I'll hunt up some of his books for you," offered the Menter. "You are bound to weep over them. He is only too well informed on the most tragic things. . . ."

Somewhat abruptly, Sapelnikov asked for permission to withdraw. "I still have five hours' practice to do today," he explained hurriedly.

The mail was brought in by the Munich servant, over whose broad dialect the mistress of the house was inordinately amused. "There are letters from Russia among them," said the maid, curtseying to Tchaikovsky.

"At last!" Peter Ilych hastily opened Vladimir's letter. "Will you forgive me if I read it?" he asked the ladies. "It is so long since I heard from home."

A second letter was from Jürgenson, a third from Modest. The address on the fourth was in neat, childishly clear handwriting that seemed to Peter Ilych quite strange and yet remarkably familiar. He broke open the envelope with a certain uneasiness. As he read, his face flushed, and then turned very white. "It's not possible," he said softly, staring at the paper.

"Unpleasant news?" asked Madame Menter, while the contralto, excited and compassionate, regarded the dismayed Peter Ilych: the only joy left to her in life was to acquaint herself with the blows that fate inflicted on her fellow-creatures.

"News from the Kingdom of the Dead," said Peter Ilych, who had risen.

The letter was from his old governess, Fanny Dürbach. For twenty years he had reckoned her among the dead. But she was still living. She was living in Montbéliard near Belfort, and for the past twenty-five years had communicated with nobody. Now she had made herself known. The remote past became present again. The world of childhood rose again from the abyss of the past. Fanny, old Fanny, who had always been so good to him, was calling her pupil. She begged Peter Ilych to come to see her. "I must see you once more before I die," she wrote in her clear, childlike handwriting.

(Here was the sign. The circle is closing and time is fulfiling itself.)

"It is news from the Kingdom of the Dead," repeated Tchaikovsky.

He passed the remainder of the day in his own room. "When can I be in Montbéliard?" was the question he was turning over in his mind. "First of all I have to go to Prague for the first performance of *Pique Dame*. Then there is the concert in Basel to arrange. It certainly isn't far from Basel to the town where Fanny lives, where Fanny has lived mysteriously hidden away all this time."

He lay down on the bed—a French state-bed, richly carved, with a blue silk canopy, probably the gift of one of Madame

Menter's admirers in Paris. Over the bed hung a commonplace oil painting, depicting in shrill, sickly colors the bay of Naples and Vesuvius in eruption. The furnishings of this beautiful house were a curious mixture of styles.

Peter Ilych turned over the pages of the book by the Danish author, which Madame Menter had had sent to him. His eyes fell on the following passage:

> "It is said that he who looks on Jehovah dies. But I say: if a single creature were to see another creature to the very depths of his soul, he would die. And if it were conceivable that a man should see himself to the very depths of his soul, he would have no hesitation in laying his head uncomplainingly on the block and accepting his inevitable punishment."

Peter Ilych shut the book, stood up, and strode about the room. "Why have I never met this homeless northerner? We should have understood each other. The man who wrote that terrible passage is my brother. Brothers should know one another. Why do they pass one another by? I ought to have met him; that would have been right and proper. But now it is too late."

He had remained standing by the window. What was he seeking in this noble landscape, which stretched out before him, scene on scene, like some great theatrical décor? The white peaks of the mountains were colored orange and blood-red by the rays of the sinking sun, and the furrowed fields and valleys lay in black and deep-blue shadow. He who is accustomed to the broad and barren plains, over which he can walk briskly or saunter, or rest at will and find healing, recoils from the merciless beauty of the scene before him. The broad and barren plain, which he loves because it is his home, is gentle and mild. But this merciless beauty hurts. The lonely man at the window closes his eyes in the presence of such great, wild beauty.

*   *   *

The year draws to its close; already it has almost slipped away and dropped into the abyss of the past. Its last day brings its most significant adventure—the excursion into the Kingdom of the Dead.

The little town of Montbéliard has not many more than five thousand inhabitants; it has winding alleys and a venerable castle where once the Count von Mömpelgard resided, when there were still counts of that name: they belonged to the kingdom of Württemberg.

The narrow streets of Montbéliard are deserted; they seem to have fallen asleep, with their turrets and balconies and their frozen fountains. It is cold. The inhabitants of the little town do not venture out into the streets. Perhaps some of the old ladies who sit at the windows, concealed by the looped-up plush curtains, observe the stranger in the long fur coat and round cap who has come from the station and is making his way up the tile-paved high street.

Peter Ilych had asked a frozen boy for the house in which Mademoiselle Dürbach lived. The excited child was now trotting ahead of him. Every child in the little town knows the house of the maiden lady who has lived here more than sixty years. It is true that once she went to work for a time in far-off Russia, but that was ages ago. The lady had taught three generations of Montbéliarders a little music, a little mathematics, grammar, and deportment. In order to reach her house one had to bear round to the left of the high street; then one would find a steep alley in front of one; one climbed up this, leaving the drugstore and the post office behind one. This brought one to the oldest part of the town, where there is a perfect maze of courts, so narrow that it would be impossible for three people to walk abreast in them. A stranger would certainly lose himself here. But the eager little guide, with his frozen blue face and patched trousers-seat, knows the way. One more corner, and then a gateway, and then a courtyard, and then the house. The boy receives his reward from the strange gentleman in the long fur coat, and goes off. Peter Ilych tugs at the heavy old-fashioned bell-pull; it responds with a surprisingly high-pitched pealing. The silvery note has not ceased to reverberate before one hears steps inside the little house; somebody is coming downstairs. The door is opened.

But surely this is a dream!

Fanny, who appears in the frame of the door, is unchanged! That is her face, just as it always was; those are the familiar eyes; she has the same flat figure and friendly face, and her hair has retained its ash-blonde color—or is it now gray? Peter Ilych cannot tell because his eyes are clouded by tears. All he sees is the Fanny he has known from the beginning. The passage of time no longer comes into the reckoning; time has passed without touching that quiet visage; as he looks at it, the past becomes the present.

"So there you are, Pierre dear," says Fanny Dürbach, and it is as if she were seeing her little pupil on his return from an excursion to the next village: for the first time he has been allowed to stand on his own feet and has been allowed out without the protection of his governess; now he has found his way back to her and she says to him, in a soft tranquil voice: "So there you are, Pierre dear."

Pierre, the gray-haired pupil with the furrowed features, mounts the steep, narrow, and rather dark staircase, followed by Fanny. With head lowered, he treads rather carefully because his eyes are misty; she, however, holds herself very erect in her simple gray dress—isn't it the very dress she wore years ago in Votinsk?—and for all her sixty years, she has remained slim, whereas the gray-haired pupil has put on weight. She opens the door to her room. There stands the little work-table at which she used to sit and crochet and correct the pupils' exercise-books. The same smell prevails in her room now as Pierre remembers so well to have pervaded her room in Votinsk: a smell telling of overscrupulous cleanliness, freshly washed linen, and a little lavender.

The odor makes Pierre close his eyes. It is certainly a dream.
Can forty-five years really have passed, with all their bitterness
wiped out, banished?

"Have you still got the lovely music box?" asks Pierre. And
already he hears its sweet tune—had some magician set it working?

No; it was an old lady, who now steps quietly up to Fanny
and her gray-haired pupil: it is Mademoiselle Dürbach the elder,
Fanny's sister. The two dear old ladies had planned this little
surprise with the music box as a welcome to their guest; the
elder sister had remained upstairs with the express purpose of
setting the works going when he entered.

The beloved melody from *Don Giovanni* is played to its end,
while Pierre, Fanny, and the elder sister remain standing. It
is still the most beautiful of all melodies; its perfection is almost
wounding: it is the eternal ideal, the unattainable, a piece of
heaven itself.

"I expect you still have the pictures of Joan of Arc also," said
Pierre softly. But before he is shown them, he has to greet
Fanny's sister, which he does very warmly; then he must drink
a glass of bilberry wine and consume at least two crackers. The
old ladies apologize for not offering him a hot meal, "But our
housekeeping will not run to it," explains Fanny. She and her
sister stand side by side holding hands. In this room these two
have spent their lives together. How tranquilly each year has
passed, multiplying into decades! And what has Pierre done
during all these years? With what adventures has he filled them?
And what remains of the adventures?

Miss Fanny says out loud what the gray-haired pupil has
been thinking. "Yes, it has been very peaceful all this time. But
what have you been doing with yourself?" There is a gentle
reproach in her voice. Pierre blushes and doesn't know what
to answer. Then Fanny adds: "But I've been very proud of you,
my dear. People have shown me your picture in the newspapers.
What a great man you have become!" She says this with a

smile, as if she were not quite in earnest but were trying to offer some consolation to a discouraged pupil. What did fame signify in this little room? A miserable substitute—the sign of the pariah! What validity had it, what worth? Had it not spent itself with the passage of time, during which he had struggled and suffered?

As one in a dream, Pierre answers the questions which Fanny puts to him. He tells her what has become of his brothers Nikolay and Hippolyte, where they live and whether they have any children. He tells her about Sasha and her slow, painful death. Fanny does not inquire after the twins Anatol and Modest; she had never known them; but she does speak about their mother. She produces some letters of hers out of an old box. Pierre sees his mother's handwriting. His eyes have a rapturous gleam in them as he looks at the familiar characters on the yellowish paper.

"Your dear *Maman* wrote this letter on her deathbed," says Fanny Dürbach. "Look, already her hand was trembling."

Memories rise from the old lady's box as if from a wizard's casket. Here are toys which used to belong to little Pierre: a doll, a colored glass ball. Here are the French poems which he had inscribed so beautifully with curls and tails on stiff paper. Here is the poem to the Maid of Orleans; here are others that Pierre had forgotten, but which now, as he reads them again, with their awkwardness and mistakes, bring back forgotten places and forgotten times—oh, what a magical return to the past and reliving of past events! It is like going home. . . . The poem reads as follows:

MORT D'UN OISEAU

Elle dort dans une place, sans tombeau,
Elle n'est point comme un homme dans la terre endormie.
Cependant, elle n'est point rien du tout pour Dieu.
Elle Lui est quelque chose, sa vie n'est pas perdue.
Pauvre petit, n'aie pas peur!

Les enfants te mettront dans la terre froide.
Ils t'orneront de fleurs,
Ils te feront un tombeau.
Oh, le bon Dieu ne l'a point oubliée!
Oh, toi, petit oiseau, tu ne peux pas te souvenir de lieu. . . .

What has happened to Pierre? Is this a small room in a little town called Montbéliard, and is he old and gray, and is this the last day of the year 1892? Another world has been conjured up from the magic casket, spreading itself out before him and taking form, to the incantation of a child's lament for a dead bird. This town is called Votinsk. Little Pierre is lying on the thick carpet in front of the sofa from which his beautiful mother has just risen. His mother has silently left the room, but Fanny has stayed behind. She is sitting with her work in the armchair by the window. She observes her little Pierre who with a huge lead pencil is tracing words and designs on a piece of stiff paper: *"Mort d'un oiseau."* "Didn't you hear, little Pierre?" says Fanny's familiar voice. "Your mother says you must leave off writing; you are to go out into the garden and play with Hippolyte. If you are not obedient, you shan't hear the music box. People have to obey their mothers, you know."

*   *   *

◇◇◇◇◇◇◇◇◇◇◇◇◇

THE CUSTOMS of the city of Odessa are somewhat crude, but very hearty and well-meaning. When the people there wish to fête and honor a beloved visitor, they are likely to break all bounds.

Peter Ilych was a great favorite in Odessa. He himself did not quite know why they were so passionately enthusiastic about him there; but he almost paid for it with his own body. For one of the crude but hearty customs of the city of Odessa is the "tossing" of the person fêted; that is to say, two rows of strong men stand opposite one another and join hands, and the beloved guest is required to stretch himself on the elastic ladder of human hands. Then the fun begins. The guest is tossed high into the air to the accompaniment of a roar of cheers; down he comes on the elastic ladder, and up he bounds again. This exquisite piece of foolery is repeated at least seven times—an old tradition demands this—and causes the audience and the participators enormous joy—with the exception of the guest who has been tossed up, perhaps.

We must record that Peter Ilych's face wore a terrified expression while he underwent this piece of local buffoonery. The first time he bounded into the air he allowed a low moan to escape him; then he clenched his teeth and remained silent, but his eyes opened wider and wider in dismay. The men who had tossed him up, as well as those who had looked on, shouted "Hurrah!" for this was also part of the ceremony. Among the spectators were Madame Sophie Menter and Sapelnikov, who were going to take part in the Tchaikovsky concerts in Odessa. Madame Sophie laughed till the tears came, over what her old friend was undergoing. "Oh, dear, isn't it a splendid joke!" she cried over and over again and had to borrow Sapelnikov's handkerchief, for she had lost her own and had to dry the tears that were making furrows down her powdered cheeks. "What a priceless spectacle!" Sapelnikov, who seemed also to be enormously amused, had a secret longing to be "tossed" also; it might hurt you and cause you some anxiety, but as it was one of the ceremonies imposed by fame, he would have loved it to happen to him—for he loved fame and all it brought in its train.

During these days in Odessa the ambitious young man had many other occasions for being jealous of the enormous popularity of his great friend, who was venerated as the "savior of his fatherland." The festivals in Prague, Tiflis, and New York paled into insignificance beside the overwhelming triumph of Odessa. Tchaikovsky, the gray-bearded and tired old man, was for some days the real hero of the great seaport; the children in the streets cheered him; the newspapers daily devoted whole pages to him; the whole orchestra rose to its feet to honor him when he mounted the rostrum for the first rehearsal, and after the first performance of *Pique Dame*—that was on January 19, 1893 —it seemed as if the ovations would never come to an end; the cries of approval from the galleries almost sounded like howls of anger; old gentlemen waved large handkerchiefs meaninglessly; women stampeded the master to kiss his hands. The admiration for the "Russian Beethoven," for their wonderful guest, never to be enough loved or enough praised, spread like hysteria through all strata of the community; every society wanted to organize a banquet in his honor, every rich family wanted to give a reception for him.

For such a passionate display of emotion Peter Ilych was in no way prepared. What a lot of friends he had made in this great city, all through this trick of his—this magic trick which enabled him to transmute suffering into music!

He was touched and a little alarmed by the intense interest in him as a person which was manifested all around him. Nevertheless, the only thought that persisted with him was how to get back home to his work. For it was his work alone that really occupied his heart and mind—a work that would be the greatest, probably the last, and certainly the most important of all his works. Time had come full circle; the signs had revealed themselves; the hour for the great confession had struck.

When our awed and compassionate glance falls on the picture of Tchaikovsky painted by the artist Kuznetsov during these fête days in Odessa, we do not see a vain, self-satisfied, and triumphant hero, but rather the tragic, introspective face of one rendered dumb by the noise and clamor of the world. Our glance does not fall on the Peter Ilych who suffered the crude and hearty ceremony of "tossing" in Odessa, but upon him in whose mind the Sixth Symphony is already complete. All four movements came to him simultaneously; all motives were present at the same time: when did this happen? When was the miracle consummated for which he had waited so long and in vain? Perhaps in Montbéliard, in that little room which smelled of clean linen and lavender? Was this the place of conception? And were two old spinsters, the sisters Dürbach, the witnesses of the greatest moment in the life of Peter Ilych Tchaikovsky? The last day of the passing year had been a day of crisis and of conception.

Rather shattered and tired out by the adventures that had befallen him in the port of Odessa, the lonely man whom Kuznetsov had painted went back to Klin, to the dreary house in the dreary town. Now there was only work before him, and sometimes of an evening a letter to write to Bob on the progress of the symphony, the "program symphony" whose program should remain a riddle to everybody. But will Vladimir—the student in Petersburg, friend of the girls and of lively arguments and of gay nights—guess the hidden meaning? The Sixth Symphony will be dedicated to him; his name will be inscribed on the Great Confession which Peter Ilych wishes to make to the world and to a tribunal beyond the world. What will the boy make of his resounding confession? Will he be strong enough to bear the weight of such mighty homage? Will he

not be alarmed by the panic-stricken despair of the middle movement and by the suffering expressed by the slow Finale? What
will Bob, the boy, make of this last and most important gift of
his famous uncle and great friend?

And is it really intended for young Bob? Is it not rather dedicated to the *other* Vladimir, the one who appears of a night and
sings the great cradle song—the youth with the features of the
mother?

Tchaikovsky receives him, this Knight of Death who is
beyond sex, every night in his spacious and somewhat bare
bedroom in Klin. He listens to his chatter, follows him when he
beckons, and allows him to sing and rock him to health-giving
sleep, so that next morning he awakens at eight o'clock and
turns to his daily task with a certain melancholy freshness.

Over the pianoforte hangs the portrait of his favorite nephew;
thus Peter Ilych does not pass the whole day working alone; he
has before him the familiar image of the well-loved young
man, alert and intelligent, already rather high-strung; his face
already too thin, with his wavy hair, his dark eyes under the
smooth brow, the expressive, tender mouth. Without this picture
the working day would be a weariness and a waste. For Peter
Ilych, at this time intoxicated by melody, loves him as one
remote, as one near, as the son of his sister, the grandchild of
his mother, as his heir, as the Angel of Death, as the giver of life
—loves him with a passionate intensity that wounds the heart,
with a love such as he has never known before in his life. There
is no longer any question of separating his love for his work and
his love for Vladimir: they are united in one mighty stream and
fill with ecstasy these lonely, and yet not lonely, days and these
inspired weeks.

Every diversion from outside is regarded as an interference,
a cause for annoyance. Nevertheless the world comes with its
demands and requests; it applies itself with particular zeal to
one who has at the present time no interest in it. So far as the

demands and requests of the world are concerned, Peter Ilych was always weak, and indeed he believed that he owed it to his fame to give way to them.

Thus he broke into his great work once more in order to go to Moscow to conduct the *Hamlet* Fantasy and the *Nutcracker* Suite. He also went to Kharkov, where he was richly honored; and at Eastertide he arrived in St. Petersburg. There he paid a visit to a hospital to see his old friend Apukhtin, whom he had not met for many years. The man whom he had formerly found so admirable and desirable was now hideously deformed by dropsy. His yellowish face was sunken, but his limbs were bloated.

"I see that you look at me with horror," said the sick man hoarsely, scrutinizing his visitor with a malicious, distrustful glance. "Yes, I must make a disgusting impression. Just look at my feet!" With appalling exhibitionism—for his character was compounded of a typical mixture of sadism and foolish vanity—he drew back the bedclothes to show the bluish white swollen legs. "They look charming, don't they?" He screwed up his blackening lips in a grin. "Everything is poisoned," he said, patting his deformed limbs. "Everything poisoned—do you understand? The whole of my blood. I've got to die!" he cried out suddenly, clutching at the sheet. "My blood is decomposing. I'm going to pieces!"

"That's true," answered Tchaikovsky, with surprising hardness. "Our time has come."

"*You* can say that," barked the sick man, "because you can get about and enjoy yourself and are still in good health. It is *my* blood that is decomposing, not yours." He shouted, his face distorted with fury, as if he would arraign destiny for its base injustice towards him.

"Calm down!" said Peter Ilych. "My day is also near."

"But I should have liked so much to live longer," whispered Apukhtin, stretching his hands over the counterpane. "Life is beautiful; life has so much charm—I only realize that now. And probably one has missed all the best things. There must be many more surprises . . . if only one could go on living! . . ."

Peter Ilych remained silent. With an unmoved, almost malicious look he regarded this hideous, life-hungry, dying man. This had been the seductive evil genius of his youth; it was this man who had made him party to the mysteries of lust; by him he had been inspired, for his sake he had suffered. "Oh, transitoriness! Oh, empty and macabre end of all earthly things! Why am I sitting here?" thought Tchaikovsky, while the sick man stared at the white wall in front of him as if already he saw the fearful shadow of death. "If I want to see my charming, dangerous Apukhtin again, the beloved with the moist lips and the tender-mocking smile, it is better to look for that corrupt young man at the Cirque Medrano. This mass of moaning and decaying flesh lying on the bed is no longer he. . . . Is my life now to consist only of horrible or touching reunions and farewell visits? First it was the overfat Désirée; then the dying Sasha; then the blessed Fanny; and now this. . . . But I shall remain no longer in this hospital; it smells too unpleasantly of carbolic or something of the kind. I want to go out into the sunshine! . . ."

A few hours after his visit to the distorted favorite of years gone by, Peter Ilych was presiding over a merry table in an elegant Petersburg café. His guests were Vladimir, Modest, and several young people who were in the habit of calling themselves Tchaikovsky's Fourth Suite because they followed the Master everywhere and allowed him to pay for them. Among them were the Count Lütke, a young Baron Buxhövden— fair, broad-shouldered, slender-hipped, narrow-waisted, with the grace and strength of an athlete of antiquity, and young Conradine, also very pleasant to look at, pupil and protégé of Modest, who busied himself not only with literary matters but also with pedagogic interests. His little comedy *Prejudice* had been accepted and would receive its first performance shortly at the

Moscow Little Theater. In the meantime the playwright supervised the studies of the attractive boy of good family—which provided him with a welcome addition to his income and moreover gave him pleasure.

Today they were celebrating some examination for which Bob had been sitting; in addition, once more Peter Ilych was on the eve of another journey. On the occasion of the fiftieth anniversary of the foundation of the Cambridge University Musical Society, the great English university had offered him a doctor's degree *honoris causa*. This he had to receive personally: it was part of the sacrifice which fame demanded.

Towards the end of the party in the elegant café they all became very wild and boisterous. It went so far that Count Lütke jumped on to the table and with a thick tongue recited verses, while little Conradine got so drunk that he would certainly have tumbled off his chair if he had not been held fast by his mentor, Modest.

During the journey home in an open carriage Peter Ilych assured the young Baron Buxhövden time after time that he was far too handsome for this miserable age and for this drab, bourgeois century. The flattered young man held erect his athletic head, crowned with its thick blond hair, displaying his straight nose, firm lips, and luminous eyes. He remained silent, his broad hands on his knees; only a proud smile betrayed that he had taken in the lavish compliments paid him by the famous composer and appreciated them. Suddenly Peter Ilych interrupted his own eloquence and shouted almost angrily: "But what am I talking about? What has all this to do with me? Vladimir is sitting here." Whereupon, with a wild extravagant movement of his body he turned towards his nephew. The latter was at that moment joking with a little prostitute who had followed the slowly running carriage a few steps. "Till tomorrow evening, then, in front of the opera house!" said Vladimir to the girl, in a voice whose greedy, caressing tone was something new and frightening for Peter Ilych. "The dear boy is quite obsessed by all the Nastenkas in St. Petersburg. . . ." Tchaikovsky's head sank and he sat suddenly motionless in the midst of the young people.

And now once more, yet again, a journey had to be made.

The capitals were looking bright, for it was May. Berlin, where the desperate Peter Ilych—who had nothing in his head save Vladimir and the Symphony—spent one day, displayed itself in sumptuous beauty as if she wished to proclaim in resounding tones: "Behold, ye strangers, and rejoice: I, the imperial capital of the mighty, rapidly developing, victorious, and universally venerated land—I, residence of the splendid young Kaiser, prince of peace and gifted friend of the sciences, arts, services, and industries—I, majestic capital though I am, can also be charming!" Unter den Linden was clad in green; the ladies in light dresses promenaded, carrying sunshades; in the Tiergarten the great flower-beds rayed out in precisely measured patterns. Here Peter Ilych wandered for two whole hours, till, to the somewhat annoyed surprise of the passers-by decked in spring array, he began uncontrollably to weep—perhaps remembering other tears which he had shed here . . . how long ago? This time he could not leave off sobbing. At last he returned to his hotel and wrote to Bob: "Never in my life have I suffered and wept so much. It is quite pathological. . . ."

If it had been so deplorable in Berlin, what would it be like in England, where he would have to endure concerts, dinners, and the ceremonies connected with the investiture of the doctorate?

The London season surpassed in elegance, brilliance, and luxury anything that Peter Ilych had yet seen in the capitals of two continents. The splendor of equipages and horses during the hour of the promenade in Regent Street and Hyde Park put in the shade anything that the Champs Elysées, Nice, or Florence had to offer. Once more the ageing man, whose heart was full of the melodies of his own requiem, found himself forced into the society of the nobility and high finance and made to play his part in their exclusive and expensive rites. During his stay in London, Peter Ilych—who every night conjured up the figure of the motherly-boyish Angel of Death—was booked up for every lunch and every dinner; duchesses and financiers pursued him; every evening he had either to attend or to take part in some gala musical performance or other. The recipients of the doctor's degree of Cambridge University were reckoned among the most attractive lions of the season. Edvard Grieg had also been invited to Cambridge, but owing to illness was not able to put in an appearance; the two most distinguished names among the foreign visitors were therefore Saint-Saëns and Tchaikovsky, for the German, Max Bruch, did not cut a very good figure in worldly society.

On the day of the great ceremony—June 13, 1893—Peter Ilych, as he stood looking at himself in the glass, garbed in his long silk robe, half white, half red, with broad sleeves and his gold-fringed cap, could not help laughing. He addressed his splendid image in the mirror laughingly: "So you have progressed as far as this, have you, old Pierre? You disguise yourself in this grotesque and wonderful get-up! For this you have endured all the sufferings of the past thirty years: this comical hat with its gold rim is the world's gratitude. Nobody can say now that the world is ungrateful. . . ."

The ceremony itself, which was treated with the greatest seriousness by all taking part in it; the long procession through the town; the ceremonial investiture in the Senate House—in all these things he showed an intense interest and a curiosity not unmixed with horror: was it not like a solemn procession of specters? The ornate robes and grave visages, beards and paunches, Latin orations and chiming bells dissolved into a sort of phantasmagoria. He stood in a dignified attitude among the other recipients—there was even a maharajah among them —and could not help thinking: "This is certainly a significant moment. (The bells chime; the people press towards the doors; the Vice-Chancellor extols the merits of the composer Tchaikovsky in well-built Latin phrases.) Unfortunately I can't help thinking all this rather horrible and ridiculous. The Parade of Fame—here we have it once more, and this time with the utmost display. Once again it is spread out before me, and once again I must play my part. In Odessa, the nationalistic friendliness which was so rough that all my limbs ached after it; here, the beautiful rites of fame, which make a ghostlike impression on me. . . . It would be very unfortunate if I suddenly burst out laughing; the Vice-Chancellor would certainly be shocked; people would think I'd gone mad. . . . I have an enormous desire to laugh . . . !"

After the impressive ceremony had taken place, there was a breakfast given by the Vice-Chancellor, to which all the new doctors, wearing their dignified and theatrical costumes, were invited as dignitaries of the university. Breakfast was followed by a garden party, attended by innumerable fine people from London. Peter Ilych walked among the bushes and flower-beds arm in arm with Saint-Saëns, who was an old acquaintance of his. Long ago the two composers had worked together at the Conservatory in Moscow.

"Well, here we are promenading in our comical dressing-gowns," said Peter Ilych cheerfully, looking across the magnificent lawns. "I wish Grieg were with us; it would give me great pleasure to see the dear fellow at these solemn ceremonies."

"Grieg would undoubtedly trip over his robe," laughed the composer of *Samson and Delilah,* and the composer of *Eugen Onegin* laughed with him. The two of them yielded by degrees to a mood of almost childish unrestraint. They spoke of times long since left behind them. Then they had been young.

"Do you still remember how we danced a ballet together?" exclaimed Tchaikovsky. "Nobody was allowed to see us except Nikolay Rubinstein, who accompanied our graceful antics on the piano. How coquettishly you skipped about as Galatea! But I wasn't at all bad as Pygmalion. We were a charming couple!" They laughed aloud at their memories, these two doctors *honoris causa,* these two dignified gentlemen, decked out in their long, white and red robes, strolling happily in the beautiful university gardens.

"You could jump quite high," laughed Saint-Saëns, the author of *Materialism and Music* and *Harmony and Melody.* "But I had far more charm." Saint-Saëns, like Tchaikovsky, had gone gray; his scanty hair grew far back on his high, receding forehead. His arched nose, which towered above his long hanging moustache and short, neatly cut beard, broke into creases when he laughed.

"You have no grounds for being so conceited," said Peter Ilych, not without severity. "It was you who ruined the final position by stumbling clumsily."

"I only stumbled because you came down on my foot," said Saint-Saëns, attempting to justify himself.

Thus debating which of them was guilty twenty years ago of stumbling and ruining a final position, they drew nearer to the rest of the company.

*   *   *

Tchaikovsky, favorite of the London season and doctor *honoris causa* of Cambridge University, returned to Russia with all possible speed. He was met at the station in St. Petersburg by Vladimir and Modest, both with very grave faces.

"Many sad things have happened while you have been away, *mon pauvre* Pierre," said Modest. Karl Albrecht, friend of his youth, Nikolay Rubinstein's right-hand man, inventor and philosopher, had died. Shilovsky had also died—Constantine Shilovsky, almost as attractive as his unforgettable brother, Vladimir; the talented Constantine who had helped in arranging the *Eugen Onegin* libretto.

Peter Ilych, who had shed so many tears in so many cities of the world, did not weep when he heard this news. He remained completely calm; he did not even make any inquiries about the circumstances in which his old friends had passed away. His

wide-open deep-blue eyes had a remarkably hard, almost triumphant expression. All he said was: "Is Apukhtin also dead?"

"Not yet," answered Modest; "but he is nearing the end."

Peter Ilych was silent. With a sudden strong movement he
gripped young Vladimir's arm. "And how are you, my dear?"
he asked hoarsely, his large, worn face close to the young face
of his favorite. Vladimir was quite startled by his uncle's rough
voice.

"Very well, thank you," he said hastily, and then added with
artificial calmness: "It was only yesterday that I took another
idiotic exam. . . . It is ridiculous: I do nothing but take examinations. . . . But perhaps this evening one might be allowed
to relax a little and go out—Lütke and Buxhövden wanted to
come too. . . ."

"I am going straight on to Klin," decided Peter Ilych and
stared at the beloved face; there was a hard gleam in his eyes.
"Now I must work."

Alexey had prepared the modest house in Klin for his master's return. The garden fence had been given a new coat of
paint; and over the entrance was a shield bearing the words:
"Welcome to the doctor" surmounted by a large wreath of
many-colored flowers.

"How charmingly you have arranged everything, dear old
Alexey," cried Tchaikovsky, whose wide-open, staring eyes
seemed to see nothing.

Later, during dinner, Peter suddenly asked the servant who
had been his comrade for so many years: "How do you think
your wife is getting on up there?"

The good fellow went first white and then red.

"But, sir . . ." he brought out at last. "But Peter Ilych! How
can you talk like that? We mustn't be sinful. What can we
know of that place where my sainted Natalie is now reposing?
I know for sure that she is in heaven, for she was a good woman

and had a lot to put up with, with her cough. But what do we know about such things? . . ."

Peter Ilych, his napkin on his lap, his full wine glass on the table in front of him, said with grim high spirits: "Does the place where your Natalie is seem so strange to you, my old Alexey? It doesn't seem strange to me. So many of my friends have gone there. They make the strange place seem quite familiar. Already I feel quite at home there. Where our friends are we must surely be *comme tout à fait chez nous*. . . ." He seemed to laugh inside himself in a rather uncanny fashion. The servant withdrew with a somewhat scared expression.

That evening, before retiring to bed, his master said to him: "Now I don't intend to leave this beautiful home again till the symphony is completed . . . until my last symphony is completed; do you hear that, Alexey?"

"Of course I hear, Peter Ilych," said the good fellow.

And then Peter Ilych worked. With the portrait of Vladimir, the beloved face, in front of him, he passed his days at the pianoforte and the evenings, solitary as the days, pacing about the room, opening a book, writing a line, ruminating, whistling to himself, or declaiming.

The late spring gave way to a glowing summer. In Klin it was very hot. Peter Ilych did not once leave the district and only rarely the house. The symphony grew. "The master must have a little distraction," said good Alexey. "Perhaps it would be a good thing if young Mr. Vladimir came and paid us a visit."

But the master would tolerate no distraction, no visit—not even from Vladimir, before whose picture all the work was accomplished and whose motherly-youthlike appearance transfigured the quarter of an hour which came before sleep. The beloved form, with his mother's features, floated past the iron frame of the bed, beckoning. "Follow me!" cried the familiar voice eagerly. And then Peter Ilych answered "Soon! It will soon be finished. A few more weeks and the work will be done, and the true purpose of my life, after long travail, accomplished. Wait just a little longer, my dear! Have just a little patience, dearest mother!"

When Apukhtin died in St. Petersburg, Peter Ilych did not go to his funeral. He remained in Klin and worked. "We shall soon reach the end. The work is growing. Let us hope that the world will not be startled by its terrible frankness; it is at any rate a stroke of luck that the world will not be able to understand it. The world will be disconcerted by the tone-picture compact of all the things that ever stirred, wounded, or blessed that poor mortal, Peter Ilych Tchaikovsky. But He, the Remote One, He will comprehend it completely and will nod His approval. In the long last movement he who is tired unto death will sing his own requiem; for his heart craves for that dark region where so many of his loved ones have already gone. There he will see once more faces which had vanished. Will he be welcomed by those memories that he has so carefully preserved and cherished? Does love go on over there, in that longed-for region?" When Peter Ilych asks himself these questions, he cannot help smiling rather arrogantly, as his sister Sasha, Vladimir's mother, had laughed on her bed of suffering. "What had such questions to do with him, and of what value was the answer to them? Here was one whose task it had been to express the meaning of his life in musical sound—that, and that only, had ever been his duty, his great Task. When the Task has been carried out, then comes deliverance. Maybe some transformation will take place; ask no questions, heart! Leave words and explanation alone! What do words signify? Be true to the Task set you by the Highest Tribunal of all! Lose no time, lest you should not be ready! What does it matter to you whether deliverance awaits you, or transformation? Be certain of one thing: your worn-out heart will fall to pieces. Have no doubt about that: you will be allowed to take repose. What is the distinction between transformation and deliverance? How would it be possible for you, with your finite understanding, to grasp such distinctions?

Make haste! The glowing summer is burning itself out, and the fourth movement has not yet been orchestrated."

It is a hot August day in the fields. The earth is gray and cracked; not a breath of air brings freshness, and the inhabitants of the little town of Klin go lazily and reluctantly to work. On this day Peter Ilych Tchaikovsky puts the finishing touches to the score. The work is finished. He can now write the dedication: "Symphony No. 6. For Vladimir Lyovich Davidov."

*   *   *

Life did not by any means come to a standstill while the solitary man in Klin worked on his great confession; on the contrary, it made strides in matters great and small.

Young Bob had finished his law studies. Concurrently, Modest—pedagogue and dramatist—had brought the education of his protégé to such a point that Conradi's parents regarded their son as now ready to become a student on his own. Good Modest had gone to Moscow, where his play *Prejudice* was produced, meeting with a not unfriendly reception from press and public. Modest returned to St. Petersburg; there he rented a home jointly with his nephew Vladimir Davidov. Peter Ilych had to pay the bill for the furniture; it cost a good deal. "But you must have it nice," he declared, and went in search of beautiful Persian carpets, lampshades, quilts, flower vases. He appeared to take the utmost interest in the equipment of the home. Moreover, he took part in all sorts of events—true, in a rather remarkable fashion: there was a certain numbness about his expression as he went about attending to business and making purchases.

His face somewhat rigid, and with an absent-minded look in his eyes, he discussed the subject of a new libretto with Modest. Something based on George Eliot's *Scenes from Clerical Life* was considered. "But it isn't quite right," said Peter Ilych with a lifeless smile. With His Highness the Grand Duke Constantine Constantinovich he discussed a composition which His

Highness had been so gracious as to propose to him: a posthumous work by the poet Apukhtin—a Requiem.

"All things considered, your Highness," said Tchaikovsky finally, "I would rather not do it. The text is good. But I can't write two requiems."

"What do you mean—*two* requiems?" asked the art-loving relative of the Tsar.

"Your Highness doesn't know my last symphony yet," said the composer. "If I now tried to do a musical setting of my friend Apukhtin's poem, I should be bound to repeat myself."

"Is your latest symphony a requiem, then?" inquired the Grand Duke.

"Yes," said the composer.

A few more weeks were to elapse before the rehearsals on the symphony would be started. Peter Ilych went traveling. He visited his brother Anatol whom he had not seen for a long time. "I have come to say good-bye," said Peter Ilych.

"Where are you going?" asked Anatol.

"Probably to America again," answered Peter Ilych, somewhat distrait, and he laughed a little. "Yes, they have made a magnificent offer."

He traveled further, to Klin, where he arranged his papers, and with Alexey's help put the house in scrupulous order. "Is the master going traveling again?" asked the good Alexey.

"Perhaps to America again," answered his master.

In Moscow he lived in a hotel. He spent a few days locked in his room. Then he began to take long solitary walks through the city. Once he remained standing for minutes together in the broad square in front of the Kremlin.

"Is not this square incomparable?" he said to a passer-by. The latter nodded; and the old man continued: "Thirty years ago I stood in front of the wall of the Kremlin and of our most Holy Church, quite enchanted. Do you know, at that time I could have wept for rapture? Well, I could weep again now. What a splendid city it is!" The passer-by thus addressed, half indignant, half touched, left him standing there. Peter Ilych, entering the church, was greeted by the smell of incense in a golden brown twilight.

He remained motionless in front of an icon. This particular Virgin Mary he had often sought out as a young man and had always regarded with especial affection. Had her tilted face, with its expression of suffering in the huge eyes, become even darker than it had been then? As a matter of fact, it looked almost black; but on the cheeks and forehead, reddish patches still gleamed. The thin hands were folded in an affected pose. From under her heavy eyelids the Madonna's tender glance lost itself in the twilight of the Byzantine arches. Peter Ilych stayed for a long time in front of the holy image, lost in thought.

Equally immobile he stood, an hour later, on the bridge spanning the river Moskva. Was not this the place where he once—it must have been hundreds of years ago—caught a severe cold because he wished to deceive and provoke the Remote One? How cold the water had been—but not cold enough! Probably at that moment he had been surrounded by scornfully tittering and chaffing evil spirits. But at home Antonina had sat, the unfortunate creature, preparing a warm compress for "Peter the Great," her unsatisfactory husband. What a lot of time had passed since then! Peter Ilych stared over at the wall of the Kremlin, gilded by the evening light.

*　　　*　　　*

A few days later—on October 10—young Vladimir and Modest met their great relative at the station in St. Petersburg.

"Let us go straight to our new home," said Bob; "it is magnificent now."

"Is it?" asked Peter Ilych, and lightly touched the smooth forehead of his favorite with the tips of his fingers. "Have you made it cosy?"

"It is the last word in cosiness!" said Modest eagerly. "You must certainly come and see what a fine show the Persian carpet makes."

"And I've discovered such a beautiful writing-table!" cried Vladimir. "Very heavy, you know; made of mahogany, and not at all expensive."

When they reached the new home he admired the writing-table, the pictures, the carpet, and every separate piece of furniture which had been procured with his money.

"I am really delighted that you are so nicely set up," he said and stood there between his brother and his nephew.

"We are enormously grateful to you," said Modest.

"Only one who is permitted to give has any reason to be grateful," answered Peter Ilych seriously, but still smiling; and once more he allowed his fingertips to touch, as if in the act of blessing, Vladimir's bright young brow.

Next day the rehearsals of the Sixth Symphony started.

"The orchestra finds my new work very strange," declared Tchaikovsky afterwards to a few acquaintances with whom he was having lunch in a restaurant. "All the players looked astonished, even offended, particularly during the slow last movement. For that reason, I made the rehearsal as short as possible; I found it rather disagreeable to go on boring the gentlemen so much." After a pause he added, staring fixedly in front of him: "However, I don't suppose the general public is any more likely to know what to make of this symphony than *they* were; I suspect it will be amazed and rather repelled. . . ."

When Peter Ilych mounted the conductor's rostrum for the first performance—that was on October 16, 1893—his face was very white and there was a hard gleam in his eyes. The audience clapped respectfully. Thanks to his success abroad and in the provinces, Tchaikovsky's fame had increased even in St. Petersburg. Peter Ilych gave a jerky bow in response to the applause.

His movements when he was conducting, as one had latterly come to expect, were awkward; his gestures were those of an irritable manikin, heavy and at the same time spasmodic. His embarrassment, which he had seemed to overcome during the years when he was making so many public appearances, was again as evident as when he had conducted a work of his own— *The Woman's Shoe*—for the first time.

The audience seemed to be almost bored by the first, long-drawn-out movement, and also by the *Allegro con grazia*, whose slow rhythm they found disappointing. The wild, forward-pressing tempo of the third movement seemed to arouse a certain uneasiness in the auditorium; people fidgeted in their seats and exchanged glances of surprise. The last movement, the *Adagio lamentoso*, had the same alienating effect upon them as it had had upon the musicians at the first orchestral rehearsal.

This Finale, so full of suffering, produced an atmosphere which left no room for gratitude, no room for enthusiasm: this farewell lament, which appeared almost to come from another world, seemed to freeze the art-loving public of St. Petersburg, and many of them it passed by unaffected.

As soon as the last sound had died away, Peter Ilych strode from the platform. He did not show himself again in acknowledgment of the scanty applause.

The well-tried Pianoforte Concerto in B-flat minor met with a much friendlier reception than the surprising new symphony with its unsatisfying, indeed almost terrifying last movement. The concerto was played with bravura by the pianist Miss Adele Aus der Ohe, that efficient lady who had amassed a quarter of a million dollars in America. She also delighted the audience with Liszt's *Spanish* Rhapsody and ravished it with several gems by Mozart; it seemed as if the applause would never come to an end.

The Aus der Ohe had to appear again and again, her arms full of flowers, graceful, competent, crowned with success.

Meantime, Peter Ilych sat alone in the artists' room, upright, his head inclined to a listening attitude. What voice was he listening to with such keen and eager attention? What call was on its way to him?

Vladimir came in quietly, he took a few steps towards Peter Ilych. The latter did not appear to notice him. He stared unseeingly past him.

"It was wonderful," said the boy shyly. "But why has it such a sad ending?" He leaned against the old man and touched his gray hair.

"Because it is dedicated to you," said Peter Ilych.

"What do you mean by that?" asked young Bob, revealing his teeth in a rather anxious smile. "What do you mean, Pierre? Why must music dedicated by you to me be sad?"

"I did not mean anything," declared the old man, standing up. "I am tired. Let us go home."

Twelve hours later, at breakfast in the pretty new home, Modest said as he poured out tea: "This new symphony is something great and unusual. The audience didn't understand it. But it will be your most famous work, Peter. A special title must be found for it. Just 'Sixth Symphony' is not enough."

Peter Ilych, in his long camel-hair dressing gown, sitting at the friendly breakfast table, seemed to be feeling at his ease and in an excellent mood. He agreed that it would be good to find a special title. As they consumed their toast and cherry jam, Peter Ilych, Modest, and Vladimir cudgeled their brains for a suitable title for the Sixth Symphony.

" 'Program Symphony,' " suggested Modest. "Perhaps 'Program Symphony' would be quite a good name for it."

"Not particularly good," said young Bob.

"There's one special reason why it isn't suitable," explained Peter Ilych and laughed inwardly, "and that is that the symphony really has a program, but a secret program, whose contents and meaning nobody will ever know." Still laughing, he looked at Vladimir.

All kinds of titles were brought in review. Bob suggested "Tragic Symphony," turning red as he did so, for he himself thought the title far too pretentious.

Suddenly Modest brought his fist down on the table with such force that the tea-glasses jingled. " 'Symphonie pathétique!' " he cried. All three of them knew at once that this was the right title.

"You are the most gifted of all of us," declared Peter Ilych, smiling at him. "Whenever the *Pathetic* Symphony is performed in memory of me, 'Title by the good Modest' should be printed on the program!"

During the day Peter Ilych went about his business. He had an appointment with the director of the Imperial Theater and he received a German music critic. In the evening he went, accompanied by Modest, to a very mediocre amateur performance of Anton Rubinstein's *Maccabaeus*. On the way home he apologized to his brother for having dragged him there. "But I owed it to old Rubinstein," he said. "Duties in life are like that!" For the next evening he had invited Modest and Vladimir, the two Lütkes, and the handsome Buxhövden to the Alexander Theater. *A Burning Heart* by Ostrovsky was being performed. Throughout the whole performance the behavior of the company in Tchaikovsky's box was extremely noisy and shocking; the two Lütkes were particularly boisterous, laughing out loud in the sentimental passages. Young Bob was also in an unusually merry mood, flirting with all the pretty girls in the stalls, and this provided his friends with plenty of scope for further laughter and exuberant observations.

In the interval Peter Ilych went round to see the leading actor, Mr. Varlamov, in his dressing-room, and congratulated him heartily on his performance. "You are splendid, my friend," said Peter Ilych. "Nobody could equal you!" By way of answer Mr. Varlamov only smiled grimly: "I am particularly anxious to be finished early this evening," he went on to explain, using the charcoal pencil on his eyebrows, "because I want to take part in a spiritualist séance."

Peter Ilych was intensely amused that the actor Varlamov should dabble in spiritualism. The pair of them spent the whole of the interval discussing very excitedly such subjects as apparitions, life after death, and death in general. "No," said Tchaikovsky, who had laughed loud and long, "let's hope that we two—you, my fine Varlamov, and insignificant I—are not going to meet the old gaffer Death—that odious old snub-nose, as I am in the habit of calling him—for a very long time!"

After the performance Peter Ilych went with his lively suite to the Restaurant Leimer, which was only a few yards away from the theater. The place was fairly full; an orchestra was playing. From the tables came the sound of laughter and a jumble of conversation. The gentlemen, chatting and laughing, in their uniforms or evening clothes, bowed to the ladies, whose dresses looked gay in the dazzling lamplight. Several acquaintances greeted Tchaikovsky, while Modest went ahead with the young people to look for a free table.

A faded, elegantly set-up lady—wife of a high government official—who was waving a black ostrich-feather fan in front of her highly colored face, said shrilly to Peter Ilych: "Greetings, Master! May one congratulate you on your success?"

"Which success?" asked Peter Ilych irritably, standing there in his fur coat and suddenly feeling very hot.

"Come, come!" said the lady, threatening him playfully with upraised index finger, as if she were accusing him of something shocking. "You know quite well—the new symphony, of course! Very effective, *cher maître*—rather sad and rather noisy, but extremely effective!"

Peter Ilych tried to smile, but all he managed to achieve was a grimace. His only thought was: "How can I get rid of this person? She's a complete fool—and why does she laugh so loudly? And yet by accident she has perhaps said something that is true. Perhaps my great Confession has turned out to be too 'effective': but the stupid public didn't happen to notice it, while this foolish creature spoke as she did just to create a sensation. Perhaps the symphony *has* failed, isn't *hard* enough, not strict enough, too calculated, too sentimental—a mass of vanity— insincere, empty noise. If so, then may the Lord have mercy on my soul! Nearer to the truth than that *I* shall never get; more exactly than that I shall never express myself."

While he stood thus in his fur coat and brooded gloomily, the conductor of the little orchestra recognized him. Peter Ilych took his leave of the odious lady with the fan. At this moment the band struck up a Tchaikovsky melody: it was the *"Valse des Fleurs"* from the *Nutcracker* ballet.

Peter Ilych moved convulsively and flushed a dark red.

In a sudden fit of anger he thundered "Stop it!" and gestured violently with his arm; the thick sleeve of his fur coat made him look as clumsy as a bear about to strike with its paw. "Stop it!" he cried angrily once more.

The music ceased; the manager hurried up.

"I beg your pardon," he said slowly in a solemn nasal voice, stroking his beard, which hung like a thin reddish fabric from the edge of his shaven chin. "The players meant well. Surely the Master is a little nervous; that is of course quite understandable. May I take your coat? Your brother has already found a table."

Peter Ilych took off his coat and handed it silently to the manager, whose demeanor as he received it was at once humble and dignified, and he passed it on at once to the cloakroom boy. "We are very glad, very glad indeed, to be allowed to welcome you again," said the importunate manager, and he regarded his illustrious client with bright, eyelashless eyes, which seemed to be covered with a thin veil of filmy skin. This curious and rather repulsive creature had a long pink face, with a proudly sniffing nose; the cut of his long frockcoat was dignified, with its padded shoulders and narrow hips. "The Master has been traveling a good deal?" he asked with a somewhat offensive curiosity, the sniffing nose screwed up tightly. Yes, there was no doubt about it; the man bore an uncanny and disconcerting resemblance to a certain dreadful personage whom Peter Ilych had known long, long ago. He had the same unassailable detachment, the dignified and merciless importunity of the agent Siegfried Neugebauer.

While studying the manager's face with a kind of disgusted curiosity, Peter Ilych could not help overhearing the conversation at the table next to which he was standing. Two elderly gentlemen—both dressed in black, with ashen and mournful faces—were discussing the current cholera epidemic in St. Petersburg. "It's a rather light epidemic, this time," one of the two observed in a somewhat disappointed tone—obviously, he would have liked to see the disease spread more quickly and more violently; maybe he was an undertaker and therefore interested from a professional point of view. The other man—he had the physiognomy of a sorrowful owl, whereas his companion resembled a vulture—said encouragingly: "In my little street alone, six persons passed away last week—one of them was a shoemaker. One cannot be too careful."

Peter Ilych, standing there between the smiling manager and the two gloomy birds, closed his eyes for a moment. What voices did he hear? What images assailed his mind which was yearning for rest and darkness? His dear *Maman*—there she was, calling, alluring, summoning her mortally tired son.

"Do it!" the mother demanded, beckoning her weary son with a graceful but compelling motion of her long, lovely forefinger, just as she had been wont to do in the faraway days of childhood. "Do it, *mon petit* Pierre—it's easy! Nobody will ever know—it's such a discreet, sly way of doing it. Nor is it a sin— not really. The Remote One has forgiven me—after all, it was His concern whether the water was poisoned or not; I haven't put anything evil into the water myself . . . He will forgive you, too, *mon petit Pierre. Allons, mon fils—du courage!*"

"I want a glass of cold water."

His voice had sounded a little hoarse, but he had said it. The mother image smiled and nodded: *"C'est ça, mon petit—it's as simple as that."*

"No doubt the Master means a glass of mineral water." The manager, with a slow smile, revealed his discolored, harelike fangs.

"I said a glass of cold water," Peter Ilych said, looking the other way.

The manager observed him for a few moments with his veiled eyes; then smiled respectfully and, with a bow, withdrew.

Peter Ilych stalked through the crowded restaurant with head erect, staring eyes, and very red face.

"God, let me follow my mother! I will follow her. I wish to follow her in all things. No one will ever know; I'll fool my contemporaries and my future biographers. . . . Of course, He will know, but He will forgive me: *Maman* promised He would! The last time, He did not accept my challenge—*Why didst Thou not let me die?* But now the Task is fulfilled—even if only in an inadequate, faulty fashion. The Inscrutable One will be more lenient, more understanding now. I shall follow my mother and, by doing so, give the lie to Dr. Archambault. *Oui, ma maladie est inguérissable, monsieur le docteur;* but I know a little medicine that will shorten my suffering."

He had reached Modest's table and remained standing behind Vladimir's chair. Count Lütke was just telling a spicy story; Modest and the young people, all in high spirits, laughed uproariously. "That's a good one!" young Vladimir cried, breathless with hilarity. "You're priceless, Lütke! You're really a number!"

At this moment, the manager appeared with the glass of water. His head somewhat lowered, his ugly teeth revealed by a sweet-mocking smile, he presented the glass to Peter Ilych on a silver tray.

Vladimir, still laughing, turned to his uncle: "Why are you standing, Pierre? Why don't you sit down?"

"In a minute," answered Peter Ilych. "I want to drink a glass of mineral water first; I am thirsty."

With one hand he touched Vladimir's shoulder, with the other he put the glass to his lips. The manager observed him with a half-amused, half-regretful expression, screwing up his nose, his hands folded across his stomach in an attitude of hypocritical piety.

Peter Ilych swallowed a great gulp of water. It was lukewarm; it had a stale, flat taste that made him want to retch.

"This was the taste that my beloved mother tasted; this is the taste of the drink that leads to deliverance. The taste on my tongue, on my palate, and in my throat is the same unpleasant taste as must have dusgusted you, *chère Maman*. But you were brave and swallowed the water. People talk of disobedient children who will not take their medicine; be good, remember your mother! You must always obey your mother! So I raise the glass to my lips once more!"

Peter Ilych looked at Vladimir's soft dark curly hair.

"I heard you cough several times this evening," he said, one of his hands still on Bob's shoulder, the other holding the half-emptied glass. "You must be very careful about your health, my dear boy! I want you to become a strong man, and be very happy, and fifty-nine years old!"

"Oh, I'm very careful," said young Bob. "And I feel splendid. Have you at last finished with your mineral water?"

"Yes," answered Peter Ilych. "Now I have done with it."

He had emptied the glass.

A flower girl came by. Peter Ilych asked her for a bunch of violets. The woman had a broad face and her eyes were dull and sad. Peter Ilych noticed that she was pregnant. He shrank in horror before her distended body. Turning his face away from her, he handed her a heavy tip. The woman's lips moved in a blessing that sounded like a curse.

Peter Ilych laid the bunch of violets next to Vladimir's plate. Then he put the empty tumbler on the table, next to young Bob's champagne glass.

The decision was in the hands of the Highest Tribunal. Once before it might have availed itself of a certain icy bath in the river Moskva, when wanton provocation was countered by a cold in the head. This time it behaved differently. By next morning the illness had set in.

Peter Ilych complained that he felt seriously unwell, and Modest advised him to take castor oil. Vladimir asked if he should call Dr. Bertenson—a suggestion that Peter Ilych vigorously resisted. "I will neither take castor oil nor see Dr. Bertenson," he said; his voice sounded rough. He looked out of the window, over the heads of Vladimir and Modest. It was a clear, mild autumn day.

"I will go for a little walk," declared Pierre. "Indeed, I have an appointment with Napravnik in the opera café."

Vladimir looked at him tenderly and scrutinizingly.

"You really do look rather played out," he said, and he laid his cool delicate hand on Peter Ilych's. "You ought to take care of yourself. Don't go walking for long."

Peter Ilych, who had just lighted a cigarette, pressed it out in the ash-tray. As he slowly rose to his feet, he said in the same unusually husky voice: "There's nothing the matter with me."

He asked Nasar to bring him his coat. The young man, rather like a peasant, whom Modest had fitted out in very elegant livery, white stockings, and buckled shoes, helped him on with his coat. "Give me my scarf too," said Peter Ilych. "It is rather cold out today, or so it strikes me." As the servant handed him the woolen scarf, his master said with a sudden very gentle smile: "It was warmer in Florence. Can you still remember it, my son?"

"Of course, Peter Ilych," said young Nasar Litrov, assuming a military attitude. With a somewhat distrait but pleased expression, his master observed the sturdy young fellow, from his powdered head to his broad buckled shoes. Then he looked in his pocket for a few silver coins. "Here, my son," he said, giving the boy the money. "Buy yourself a pretty girl!" The boy bowed, grinned; in the meantime, his master had gone to the door. On the threshold he turned round again.

"I want to see the Neva once more," said Peter Ilych—whereupon Nasar's grin changed to an expression of complete bewilderment.

The sick man returned from his walk within half an hour, without even attempting to see Napravnik. He confessed to the anxious Modest that his headache and general indisposition had become somewhat worse. Nevertheless, he would not hear of a doctor's being sent for. "It is nothing," he repeated obstinately, with irritation. However, he allowed Nasar to put a warm flannel round his body. Lying on the sofa, he attended to a little correspondence—a couple of letters and a card. When he attempted to start a third letter, he was compelled to stand up. He went to the bathroom with unsteady steps. Violent diarrhœa seized him, and vomiting. When he reappeared in the sitting-room his face was white and his hands trembled. "I am going for Bertenson now," said Bob, while Modest murmured something about castor oil.

"I forbid you," said Peter Ilych in a tone that brooked no contradiction. "I feel better now. Perhaps I can sleep."

They laid him on the sofa. Modest said: "A disordered stomach can be very tiresome. Sleep well, dear old Peter!"

Vladimir arranged the pillows and coverlet.

"Thank you," said Peter Ilych, staring at the coverlet.

"We will leave you alone for two or three hours, so that you can have a good sleep," said Vladimir, his fingers touching Peter's fine white-gray hair. "Modest and I have some shopping to do. There is always something or other wanting in the house."

"Yes, my dear," answered Peter Ilych. "There is always something or other wanting. . . ."

When Modest and Vladimir came back towards eight o'clock in the evening, they were met by Nasar with a disturbed expression on his face. "The master is worse," he said, and anxiety gave words to his usually heavy tongue. "He looks very pale and I think he is feverish. He's been sick several times, and when he wanted to go to a certain place, I had to support him. He has been to a certain place very many times."

Vladimir grasped Modest's arm, gripping it tightly. Without saying a word they both ran down the corridor. Vladimir tore open the door of the sitting-room: the sofa was unoccupied. Nasar, who had remained at the street door, called out: "I put the master to bed." Whereupon Vladimir and Modest returned hurriedly down the corridor. They stood panting outside the door of the room in which Peter Ilych slept. They stepped inside, and were startled.

The face of the sick man was terribly changed. While his kindly brother and his beloved nephew had been seeing about the purchases which would make their bachelor establishment more cosy, his face had collapsed. His eyes seemed to have sunk deeper in their sockets; the half-open puffed-up mouth had taken on the same gray-white color as the disheveled beard. The mark of death was on his face. The High Tribunal had smitten it, wasted it, distorted it, and had given its answer to the audacious, desperate challenge which the mortal Peter Ilych Tchaikovsky had thrown down.

Half an hour later Doctor Bertenson arrived. Before he had had time to examine the patient, but had only glanced at him, the anxious relatives, Vladimir and Modest, could read his painful verdict in his expression. The doctor declared that the case was too serious for him to assume all responsibility, and asked to be allowed to call in his brother, Professor Leo Bertenson, as consultant. The latter arrived in his carriage fifteen minutes later. He was not known to the Tchaikovsky family and therefore his appearance now invested the situation with a solemn and depressing significance. The two learned brothers, general practitioner and specialist, engaged in a whispered consultation for some moments. They were very much alike: both were bald, both wore gleaming, gold-rimmed spectacles and square-cut black beards, and both had unusually large ears, from which black hair sprouted.

The doctors found the patient's bed defiled. The discharges now were all too frequent; Nasar no longer dared to lift the sufferer out of bed.

The examination did not last long. Vladimir and Modest had waited outside the door. The doctors came solemnly out of the sickroom.

"Is he very bad?" asked young Bob, whose fine eyes were full of tears.

The brothers Bertenson both nodded.

Then Modest had the courage to speak out what was in his mind: "Is it cholera?"

Once again the two black beards nodded in confirmation.

This was about nine o'clock on the evening of October 21, 1893.

The hardy body of the sick man fought more than three times twenty-four hours against the embrace of the dark Power for whose coming he had so eagerly prepared and which finally he had beckoned towards him. Now that it had really come, had really seized him and would not relax its hold, death no longer wore the soft seductive expression that had characterized it when night after night, in the sweet quarter of an hour just before sleep, its boyish-motherly figure had floated into his room. It no longer needed to appear seductive, so now it revealed its merciless, hideous face. None of the torments endured by the beloved mother was spared the son who was at last obeying her behest; imitating her, he suffered as she had suffered, lived through her pains, cried out as she had cried out, and shed her tears over again.

With what pain and pity does our compassionate glance now fall upon this pathetic son of men, this faithful one, who had at

last, at long last, come to the end of his tether; on our friend
and hero Peter Ilych Tchaikovsky! We see him now afflicted
with every pain, besoiled by excrement and vomiting and
shaken with convulsions. On his countenance, designed by the
austere Lord and already laid waste by Him, blackish spots are
beginning to appear; his arms and legs have also turned a blackish hue—Nasar and a hefty nurse keep on rubbing them. The
suffering Peter Ilych, his blue eyes painfully wide open in their
sunken sockets, submits in silence. But when Vladimir comes
forward to take part in such offices, he prevents him. "No, no!"
cries the sick man then. "I don't want you to touch me! I forbid
you. You might be infected. Besides, I smell horrible. . . ."

Then young Bob draws back from the sick bed, and tears
stream down his cheeks, which have grown even thinner than
usual during these terrible days.

"Go out of the room!" cries the tormented man from his bed.
"I look revolting. I don't want you to see me. Go away!"

The weeping boy is compelled to leave the room. Peter Ilych,
alone with the nurse and Nasar, racked with convulsions, in-
quires with uncanny curiosity: "Is the end of cholera always
like this? Do arms and legs always turn blue?"

The servant and the nurse do not know what to answer. "Oh,
but you haven't got the cholera," Nasar tries to say finally.
Whereupon Peter Ilych laughs quietly to himself.

"Then why do you all wear such comical coats? And why
does the room smell of disinfectants? I suppose that is simply
because my stomach is out of order? Eh?" He chuckles in such
a strange way that the servants are anxious and afraid.

"Give me a looking-glass," asks Tchaikovsky, who, after a
particularly terrible attack, has attained a few moments of calm
and comparative ease. "I am quite sure I have the dark spots on
my face, just as my mother had." And when they hand him a
mirror, hesitatingly and unwillingly, he studies with interest the
blue-black stains on his forehead and on his cheeks.

His condition changes several times during the thrice twenty-

four hours through which the bitter struggle rages. There are
short deceptive periods when he seems to be better, heavy crises,
sudden heart attacks, and agonizing moments which seem to
tear the sick man to pieces, causing him to cry out: "This is
death! Good-bye, Mody. God bless you, Bob." But still Death
holds back. Dr. Bertenson comes and gives him an injection.

Our awed glance, falling on the befouled bed whereon our
friend and hero is passing away, momentarily recovering and
again relapsing, beholds a number of white-clad figures crowd-
ing round, tiptoeing about the room and talking in subdued
voices; we witness the solemn and rather grotesque pantomime
of the kind so often produced round the bed of the dying. We
see the doctors detach themselves from the sickroom and meet
in the sitting-room for the third and the fourth long consulta-
tions—plied by Nasar with coffee and cognac, or making themselves important with enemas and injections. On the second day
of the attack, when the dark patches appeared for the first time
on Peter Ilych's face, the brothers Bertenson called in Dr. Kam-
anov. During the night he, in his turn, sent for a German
medical man, a Dr. Sanders: the two handsome black beards
are joined by a gray beard and a carefully tended blond beard.

Peter Ilych, round whom these ghostly white-clad supernu-
meraries and bearers of variegated beards displayed themselves,
passed through hours of delirium during which he recognized
nobody; he was in the grip of the wildest fantasy. At such times
he would call the hefty nurse "Désirée" or "Antonina," and
when she approached him with the enema he would call out,
"Ô toi que j'eusse aimée!" an expression which greatly disconcerted her; or "Why did I marry you, you unhappy creature?
What madness! What a scandal! And your fingernails look
worse than ever—bitten to the quick." The enema trembled in
the poor nurse's hand.

Suddenly the fever-racked man demanded of Nasar that he
should give him back his beautiful watch. "You have it!" he
declared obstinately. "I know perfectly well that you stole it,

my talisman, by far the most beautiful thing I possessed. That time in Paris, in that accursed café on the Boulevard Clichy. You were acting on instructions from my treacherous guardian angel, I know, I know perfectly well. . . . Oh, you ought not to have done that! Nadezhda and Apukhtin conspired against me; they formed themselves into a terrible league against me. Give me the watch. I must know what the time is. Time is passing; I shall miss the train; I shall be too late; they are expecting me. I have to conduct; Altani has declined. I am going to have a doctor's degree and be 'tossed'—give me the watch! Everything depends on my getting the watch back again!"

Poor Nasar, in his anxiety and helplessness, handed the delirious man a huge and hideous alarm clock which stood on the bedside table. "Here is your beautiful watch, Peter Ilych," said the peasant, made cunning by pity and despair.

Peter Ilych pressed the cheap clock to him. "I have it back again!" Great tears ran down his cheeks. "Oh, Nadezhda, Nadezhda, friend of my soul, I knew that you would forgive me. What a wicked game you have played with me all this time! You have done us both wrong, *ma femme!* But now is the hour of reconciliation: you have forgiven me for THIS and for all my other sins! The talisman is here again. We all belong to one another again—the talisman, you, and I. And when I have been released, you will not go on living much longer, my beloved friend!"

In his delirium he attached many names to young Vladimir. He called him "Dear Kotek," and "My handsome Siloti," and also "Poor Sasha." He declared: "I begot you! You are my son and heir. All that I have done wrongly, you will put right. You will be a great man; I give you all my fame—it was only for your sake that I sought it, *mon prince!* Come here!" cried the sufferer in his ecstasy, rising in the bed and stretching out his arms to the boy. "Come here and let me bless you!" The nurse, assisted by Professor Bertenson, had to force him back again. The spectacle of this delirium alarmed and shattered Vladimir so much that he could not bear it. Shaken by a fit of weeping, young Bob collapsed into a chair. Moreover, for forty-eight hours he had slept not at all and eaten practically nothing. And now the dying man cried out to him from his bed: "Show me your face, my angel of death! Hide yourself no longer, for the hour has come."

Bob could bear it no longer; it was too appalling. Shaken with weeping, his white face distorted, the boy rushed with long strides out of the dreadful sick chamber. But Peter Ilych raved in his bed, with arms wide-outstretched, as if he longed to hug Death to him as a bride. In a wild and confused ecstasy, which froze the blood of all those who heard him, he called Death his mother, his mother his son, his son his beloved, his beloved the black angel; in his delirium he seemed bent on bringing about this ghastly incestuous union.

After some minutes he became calmer; he was heard to pray to the saintly Fanny in Montbéliard, which might have shocked his hearers, but which, after the excesses that had gone before, seemed almost reassuring.

After the last and cruelest attack the dying man remained in a state of exhaustion, from which he never recovered. He dozed a little, and when he awoke he was once more clear in his head, but very tired.

He recognized Alexey, who had come from Klin, and his brother Nikolay, a nervous and somewhat cantankerous old man who had come all the way to St. Petersburg in response to Modest's alarming telegram. Peter Ilych greeted both of them with an exhausted smile.

It was about noon on October 24 that Dr. Bertenson decided that the sick man must have a warm bath "in order to stimulate the action of the kidneys," he said. Peter Ilych submitted without resistance to being undressed and carried to the bath. As he sat in the warm water he smiled, with his eyes closed. "Quite pleasant," he whispered, and smiled. "Pleasantly warm. . . ."

My mother also died after they'd put her in warm water. . . .
That is as it should be. . . ."

The peaceful face, with its closed eyes, above the white, hair-
covered body, had taken on an expression of moving dignity and
great beauty. A sort of radiance came from his brow. All strain
had been released; he seemed free at last from convulsions and
torment.

The heartbeat was very weak. After a very few moments the
almost unconscious man had to be lifted out of the water. The
expression of perfect contentment and assuagement remained
on his features. Full consciousness never returned.

In the meantime the room of him who was dying, taking his
leave, passing over, had become full of people, as if for a festive
occasion. The brothers Lütke, in a solemn mood not unmixed
with curiosity, had arrived, elegantly clad in dark suits; with
them came the handsome Buxhövden and a young 'cellist from
the Conservatory who had been a protégé of Peter Ilych and
who now wept quietly to himself for the loss of his influential
patron. The young people sat stiffly, close to one another, on
chairs that had been brought in from the dining-room. Behind
them stood the old and the young servants—Alexey and Nasar—
both of them trying to stifle their sobs. Close to the bed were
Vladimir and Modest, who had retreated inside himself, while
the elder brother, Nikolay, the three doctors, and the nurse
were eagerly prepared for anything that might be required of
them.

Towards the evening, when the brothers Lütke, the handsome Buxhövden, and the young 'cellist had already begun to
be rather weary, the arrival of a priest from the Isaacs Cathedral
brought about a change in the sickroom, in which the only
sound for several hours had been the soft, regular groans of the
dying man and the occasional whispering of the doctors and
servants. The priest, with his fine beard, colorful vestments, and
jingling holy vessels, joined the melancholy and silent company.

It is true that after muttering a few short prayers he soon retired, for it would not have been seemly to administer the last Sacrament to one who was practically unconscious. This pious distraction and slight diversion was therefore soon over.

The brothers Lütke began to feel uncomfortable on their hard chairs. The handsome Buxhövden stretched his long athletic body and kept on looking at his watch and yawning. Peter Ilych did not move. He lay quiet, with his eyes closed. The regular rattle in his throat had a soporific rhythm; indeed a few hours later several of those present, including one of the Lütkes, Buxhövden, and Dr. Sanders, had fallen asleep.

After midnight—the condition of the patient seemed unchanged—Nasar had prepared a little meal, and Nikolay, with a careful fluttering gesture, had invited everybody to the dining-room. Lütke and Buxhövden, who had both snored a little, raised themselves out of their collapsed positions; they put on an expression of dismay, for they believed that the end of Peter Ilych Tchaikovsky had come. When they heard that it was only a matter of a little snack, they rose, much relieved.

Nikolay Ilych, nervous and dignified, presided over the improvised meal. There was tea, vodka, some ham, boiled eggs, and preserves. Most of the guests showed a really gratifying appetite; some, it is true, did not come in this category—Modest, for instance, who was still shaken with sobs; as for the silent and gloomy Nasar, he stared at the eaters with fierce disapproval.

Buxhövden had prepared a ham sandwich for his friend Vladimir and in a low voice tried to persuade him to eat it. "You must think of your health, Vlady!" he said. "Eat at any rate half of it—please. You owe that to your uncle. You are already a pitiable sight!" And indeed the fine and sensitive oval of Bob's face had become terribly haggard during these days; the dark eyes lay deep in their sockets, and beads of sweat stood on the pale skin; he had not shaved and the growth of his beard gave his face a wild, tragic expression.

"Just to please you, then," said Vladimir, taking the sandwich.

At the same moment the door flew open; the nurse whom Peter Ilych had addressed as "Désirée" and "Antonina" appeared. She beckoned to Vladimir Davidov, crying "Come! It is the end! He asked for you!"

For a moment Vladimir stood like one turned to stone; then he dashed from the room. He let the sandwich fall in the corridor.

When he reached the sickroom he found the nurse already leaning over the bed; she had been quicker than he. As the young man stood in the middle of the room, the nurse turned to him: "It is too late," she said.

Vladimir took two strides to the bed but did not dare to look Peter Ilych in the face; he turned away and staggered to the wall.

In the meantime Modest, at the bedside, collapsed and filled the air with a shrill scream. "Pierre! Answer me! Pierre! Answer me!"

In the open door stood Nikolay and the doctors; behind them pressed the servants and the young people, some of them still chewing; Buxhövden, with his proud, handsome head, bright eyes, and gleaming hair, overtopped the others.

Young Bob had leaned his face against the wall. This room had not yet been papered; the whitewashed wall was very rough and cold. Bob realized suddenly that he was freezing cold. He could not help coughing. His body was shaken both by coughing and weeping.

When will he dare to turn round and look on the austere, transfigured, waxen face of the great friend who had so greatly loved him? When will young Vladimir, with his convulsively heaving shoulders, come away from the wall against which he is leaning, in an attitude of sorrow, as if he wished to be turned into a stone figure of "The Mourning Youth"? What will happen to Vladimir now? Can this slight, sobbing boy prove himself worthy of the great trust and hopes that have been reposed in him? Will he remain steadfast? Without the loving encouragement to which he has been accustomed, will he not be helpless? Will he not stumble?

As he leaves the room, he staggers. In order to steady himself he presses his shaking body against the stone wall as if to embrace it, and he lays his wide-open, moist mouth against the rough wall as if he would give expression to a tenderness which he had too long withheld.